W9-ARZ-144

The Ocean of Air

THE OCEAN OF AIR

DAVID I. BLUMENSTOCK

RUTGERS UNIVERSITY PRESS
New Brunswick *New Jersey*
1959

Library of Congress Catalogue Card Number: 59–7509

Manufactured in the United States of America
by Quinn & Boden Company, Inc., Rahway, New Jersey

Designed by Leonard W. Blizard

For Nancy

Preface

When I started this book, it never occurred to me that it would occupy a sizable portion of my time and energies for more than a decade. What happened was that as this work progressed, I was led to the study of more and more materials on a variety of subjects related to the atmosphere and to its climates, its weathers, and its significance to man. Toward the end of my task I sometimes wondered whether it might not have been imprudent to attempt to write a book touching on so many different fields of knowledge. At such times my doubts were stilled only by the conviction that my major themes were worth expounding and that, even though these themes led me to the margins of fields as unfamiliar to me as archaeology, medicine, and nuclear physics, my presentation could not be in too great error if I studied relevant scientific literature as carefully as I could and if, as an essential corollary, I called upon qualified scientists to review my manuscript. This is the course I have followed.

The reader should be warned that though the facts presented here are widely accepted among scientists, the interpretations presented are not necessarily widely agreed upon. This is inevitable; more times than not, scientists disagree in their interpretation of the evidence. When, as often, I encountered conflicting views in those branches of climatology and meteorology in which I have worked, I decided which to follow through analyzing the problem myself. When I encountered conflicting views in fields in which I was a novice, I followed the scientists whose arguments seemed to me most logical or plausible, and then, afterward, I paid considerable heed to my reviewers, who in several instances convinced me that I had made the wrong choice.

In any event, I have not hesitated in this book to identify a theory, a hypothesis, or pure speculation as just that; and I have used the Notes at the back of the book to indicate some of the views that differ from my own. The Notes also identify the sources on which I have relied most heavily and give specific sources for quotations, for quantitative values that are not well known or generally agreed upon, and for discussions based on the work of scientists whose names are mentioned. The Notes are not intended, however, to be as exhaustive as they would be had I written this book exclusively for my scientific colleagues.

I owe much to the scientists who reviewed various parts of the manuscript, none of whom is responsible for the views or facts presented here. Without their help I would not have the courage to bring out this book. I acknowledge my debt to Professor Horace R. Byers, Chairman of the Department of Meteorology, University of Chicago, and formerly Scientific Director of the Thunderstorm Project, who reviewed the section "Rain, Snow, and Hail" (Chapter 7); to Professor Carleton S. Coon, Curator of Ethnology, University of Pennsylvania Museum, who reviewed the section "The Dry World" (Chapter 8); to Professor Marston Bates of the Department of Zoology, University of Michigan, Professor James J. Parsons of the Department of Geography, University of California, and Dr. F. R. Fosberg, Chairman of the Unesco Committee on the Humid Tropics and Director of the Pacific Vegetation Project, U.S. Geological Survey, all of whom reviewed the section on "The Amazon Basin" (Chapter 8); to Walter B. Langbein, Research Engineer, Water Resources Division, U.S. Geological Survey, who reviewed the section on "Floods" (Chapter 9); to Professor James R. Westman, Chairman, Department of Wildlife Conservation, Rutgers University, who reviewed the section on "The Complexities of Water Management and Supply" (Chapter 9); to Brigadier General Ben G. Holzman, U.S. Air Force, Commander, Office of Scientific Research, who reviewed an early version of Chapter 12 in detail and who read and made a few general comments on Chapter 18; to Dr. Harry Wexler, Director, Office of Scientific Research, U.S. Weather Bureau, and Chief Scientist, U.S. IGY Antarctic Program, who reviewed Chapters 13 and 14; to Dr. H. K. Douglas Lee, then of The Johns Hopkins University and now Chief, Research Branch, Office of the Quartermaster General, U.S. Army, and also to Professor Thomas Goreau, Department of Physiology, College of Medicine, University College of the West Indies, both of whom reviewed Chapter 15; to J. C. Ellickson, Bureau of Agricultural Economics, U.S. Department of Agriculture, who reviewed Chapter 16; to Dr. Ralph E. Lapp, nuclear physicist, who reviewed Chapter 19, and to Professor Curt Stern, Department of Zoology, University of California, who reviewed that section of Chapter 19 which deals with genetics; and to Professor Ralph E. Turner of the Department of History, Yale University, Professor F. Clark Howell, Department of Anthropology, University of Chicago, and Professor Erhard Rostlund, Department of Geography, University of California, all of whom reviewed Chapter 20. I am also indebted to reviewers in the U.S. Weather Bureau who commented on Chapters 18 and 19, and to two reviewers in the U.S. Bureau of Land Reclamation who commented on the section on "Irrigation" (Chapter 9). I wish also to thank Professor George S. Benton, Department of Civil Engineering, The Johns Hopkins University, who read parts of the manuscript here and there and whose comments saved me from committing at least one major error. Finally, I am most greatly indebted to Professor F. Kenneth Hare and his associates in the Department of Geography, McGill University, who reviewed the introductory chapter and all of Chapters 1–9, 11, 12, and 14–16.

Beyond these acknowledgments, still others are properly due. I regret that I cannot list here all the colleagues, in universities where I have taught and in government agencies and industrial companies where I have worked, who have patiently explained to me some scientific point that I did not understand. I must, however, list those who acted as researchers during periods when I was not within reach of a large library. These were A. V. Carlin, Virginia Turner, and Everett Jones. And, more fundamentally, I must mention those teachers and professional associates whose knowledge, perception, and enthusiasm helped to mold the thoughts and ideas presented here. Among these I especially remember Professors Kurt Laves, Alfred S. Romer, J. Harlen Bretz, and Wellington D. Jones at the University of Chicago; Professors A. L. Kroeber, John B. Leighly, and Carl O. Sauer at the University of California; and such associates as C. W. Thornthwaite, Ben G. Holzman, Otto E. Guthe, Charles Stiefelmeyer, Woodrow C. Jacobs, Harry Wexler, John E. Brush, James R. Westman, and B. L. Smith.

Editorially and morale-wise, this book could never have been completed without the continued help and encouragement throughout the years of William Sloane or without the day-to-day help and encouragement of my wife, Nancy. As for James Fergus McRee, who joined this undertaking in its later stages, his fresh eye and skilled editorial ability added much to the final result, as did also the art work of Paul Rockwood.

In closing, I wish to thank the editors of the *Scientific American* for permission to reproduce in Chapters 10 and 11 parts of my articles on "Upper Atmosphere Research," which appeared in January, 1949, and "Weather Instruments," in December, 1951.

DAVID I. BLUMENSTOCK

Honolulu, Hawaii
Summer, 1959

Contents

Part Three

MAN AND THE OCEAN OF AIR

Illustrations

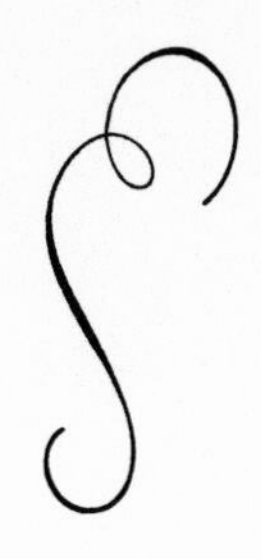

The Ocean of Air

Introduction: The Earth and Its Atmosphere

Man lives within the planet earth, not upon it. For earth, the planet, embraces not only rock and water but also air and all other substances that through gravity are held tightly together and compelled to form a globe. And this earth globe is a single heavenly body, moving detached and separate around the sun.

It is not easy to think of the earth in this way. To look downward is to see grass and pavements, rocks and soil, water and ice, each of which appears as a tangible, visible thing. To look upward is to see not air, but only the sun of daytime or the moon and stars of night; and if a cloud intervenes to screen this distant view, the cloud is perceived as but a momentary obstruction drawn across the window of the sky.

Yet two thousand years ago Plato perceived the earth as a whole, "the pure earth." "For we are dwelling in a hollow of the earth, and fancy that we are on the surface . . . But the fact is, that owing to our feebleness and sluggishness we are prevented from reaching the surface of the air." Plato imagined the earth, viewed from above, as appearing "streaked like one of those balls which have leather coverings in twelve pieces, and is decked with various colours."

When in the future man journeys millions of miles into outer space, he will see that earth shines, much as Mars and Venus are seen to shine on a night when the skies are clear. Approaching to within a few hundred thousand miles of the earth, he will be able to distinguish its different kinds of surfaces. The continents will appear as masses splotched with browns and reds where the dry lands are and with greens where the forests lie. These darker hues upon the continents will contrast strongly with the regions of white that mark the snow-covered lands. The seas will be grayish white. The cloud tops, far down beneath the surface of the ocean of air, will appear as streaks of white. The upper regions of the air ocean will be invisible because the feeble rays of light from these outer regions will be lost to view among the strong light rays reflected from the continents and seas and clouds. To know the nature of the outer regions of earth, the regions near the surface of the air ocean, the space traveler will have to descend through the atmosphere, making observations as he moves downward.

The uppermost part of the ocean of air is 18,000 miles or more above the solid-liquid surface of the earth. This is a strange, unreal place. Here the atmosphere is so thin that if all the air particles within a cubic space ten miles on a side were herded together and pulled down to solid earth, they would not fill a space the size of a pinhead. In this almost perfect vacuum, the fast-moving air particles, energized by the sun's rays, dart along paths hundreds of miles long before smashing into other particles and so bouncing back or sidewise. The moon is so bright that a few seconds of looking at it make the eyes ache. The earth below is brighter still. To gaze at the sun is to go blind. Yet despite the light from the moon and earth and sun, this is a place of utter darkness because there are so few air particles to catch the light and so to illumine space. Unseen in the darkness, millions of meteors race past, earthward bound.

At fifty miles a second a meteor speeds toward earth. It rushes through 17,000 miles of upper ocean regions, where the air, though slowly thickening, is still extremely rare. It passes the upper ionosphere, where particles pouring inward from the sun swarm toward the magnetic poles and cause the charged air there to glow with auroral lights. As the meteor plunges through the wind-swept regions of the lower ionosphere, it starts to burn through friction with the denser air. By the time it reaches the cold lower stratosphere, where the incoming cosmic rays break up and shower their particles downward, the meteor has burned away. The floor of the air ocean lies twenty miles below.

Five billion million tons of air, all but 1 per cent of the total atmosphere, are squeezed into the lowest twenty miles of the air ocean. The particles are packed more and more tightly as the earth is approached.

In the densest atmosphere, along the floor of the air ocean, live the air-breathing organisms of the earth. Here the overlying air presses down with a force of fifteen pounds to the square inch. Man, like the other organisms of the ocean floor, is adapted by nature to withstand this mighty force. Nor can he move far from the dense air region without taking with him the pressurized air essential to his existence. He is designed to remain a bottom-crawling creature.

The Spaniards who in the sixteenth century invaded the lands of the Incas, in the region of the Peruvian Andes, came all too well to know and to respect the effects produced by the thinness of the air at high elevations. The Spanish chronicles and letters of the period refer repeatedly to the *soroche*, the "sickness of the Andes," which is well described by Father José de Acosta in his *Natural and Moral History* (1590):

> There is in Peru a high mountain which they call Pariacaca. . . . When I came to mount the stairs, as they call them, which is the top of this mountain, I was suddenly surprised with so mortal and strange a pang that I was ready to fall from my beast to the ground. . . . I was surprised with such pangs of straining and casting as I thought to cast up my soul too: for having cast up meat, phlegm, and choler [bile], both yellow and green, in the end I cast up blood, with the straining of my stomach. . . . I persuade myself, that the element of the air is there so subtle and delicate, as it is not proportionable with the breathing of man, which requires a more gross and temperate air, and I believe it is the cause that doth so much alter the stomach and trouble all the disposition.

The Troposphere

Even where the land twists upward into towering mountain peaks, it remains surrounded by the shallow, lowest portion of the ocean of air, the troposphere. The tropospheric layer, about five miles deep at the poles and ten at the equator, is the scene of weather, as man knows it, in all its manifestations.

There are countless things to be seen in the ever-changing weather: fleecy puffball clouds that shine pure white against a background of blue sky; black, swirling thunderstorm clouds, pierced through with jagged lightning; fog that hugs the ground and stifles sight; rainbow-colored rings around the moon; walls of dust that sweep across the land; twisting waterspouts; ice fog of the night that makes the flashlight's beam a dazzling pathway filled with billions of twirling icy mirrors; falling snow; and sometimes, as the sun sets along the far horizon, the last upturned needle of light is seen to flash a brilliant green.

There are countless things to be heard: the incessant drumming of downward-spilling rain; the crisp-sounding crackle of lightning; the crash of thunder near at hand and the cannonading rumble of thunder from afar; the rattle of sleet; the roaring of the tornado; the screeching wind; and, barely audible along the surface of deep snow, one can sometimes hear the cracking, popping sound of collapsing ice crystals.

The changing weather even brings different odors. Such is the acrid scent of the thunderstorm and the whole range of smells carried on the winds, whether choking dry or filled with moisture. And the weather is borne in upon the sense of feel, which perceives the wetness of rain and snow, the overpowering weight of violent winds, the delicate touch of small breezes, the stabbing cold of frigid air, and the stifling heat of air from the desert.

In all its aspects the weather of the troposphere is a changing thing. Cloud patterns shift and alter in endless succession across the sky. Winds build up to furious strength, then slacken and give way to air so still that the falling leaf glides unhurriedly to the ground. Cold air races in, putting an end to mild weather. Sometimes things happen so swiftly that in less than an hour the countenance of the weather alters completely. Sometimes weather of the same general kind persists for weeks, as when a drought is upon the land. Then each returning day brings heat and wind and dust, and each returning night is like the day except that the heat and wind and dust are less extreme. And though there may be scattered clouds, there is no rain, either by day or night. For want of water, the land suffers, and with it the men who live on it.

Weather Rhythms

Though its pace be slow or speedy, the changing weather is sharply influenced by two underlying rhythms: one is the rhythm of night and day; the other, that of the changing seasons.

Solar radiation is emitted in a constant stream, lighting and warming that half of the earth and atmosphere which faces the sun. Every instant a new segment of air, moving with the twirling earth beneath, turns into the sunlit hemisphere, and some other segment turns from the light into the hemisphere of darkness. In the sunlit hemisphere the air is charged with warmth that speeds the pulse of the changing weather. Winds are brisker than by night. Air boils up and new clouds form above the sun-heated lands. In the nighttime hemisphere the weather must feed on the solar energy that was stored by day in the earth and atmosphere. Air cools along the ground and slowly flows downhill. At the margins of the lands, there are offshore breezes far gentler than the gusty onshore winds that blow by day.

Outside the tropics the rhythm of night and day finds a counterpart in the more slowly paced rhythm of the changing seasons. In these high and middle latitudes, late spring and early summer are the daytime of the year—a time when the sun is highest in the sky and the days are longest. Over the polar lands and waters, the sun does not set for hundreds of hours on end, but circles the horizon along a tilted path from highest point of noon to lowest point of midnight and back again. In middle latitudes the sunrise follows close upon the sunset, so that the night becomes a minor interval caught between the long successive days.

The warmth of the sun gained by places outside the tropics during the spring and summer is paid for in the autumn and winter months when nights are long and the sun is low in the sky. In regions near the poles this is truly the nighttime of the year, for the sun does not rise for many days and the only sources of light are the stars, the flaring auroral lights, and, perhaps, the moon. In middle latitudes the slight warmth of the short daylight hours is small recompense for the long cold night.

Since the earliest time of man upon the earth, the turn of the seasons has been mirrored by seasonal changes in the mode of life of the peoples. Sometimes the response of men to the changing seasons remained almost uniform for many thousands of years, as in the planting and harvesting of crops or in the moving of sheep to upland meadows in the spring. Even where responses varied, the lives of all were bent in one manner or another to fit the seasonal rhythm.

Solar Heating and the Atmospheric Circulations

The sun warms air unequally from the equator to the poles. In and near the tropics, its rays fall steep and sheer. Densely packed, they pierce directly downward through the air, strongly heating the surface of the earth beneath and the air just above that surface. There is life-giving warmth at all seasons, for even in winter the sun is high in the sky and the days are many hours long. In and near the tropics lie the searing deserts of the world—the Sahara, the great Australian Desert, the Arabian Desert. Here too lie the humid, fecund jungles of the Amazon, the Congo, and Malaya.

In polar regions, the rays of the sun slant earthward at low angles, strike the ground obliquely, and scatter their energy over large areas. Even in summer the polar lands and waters are not strongly heated, while in the nighttime of winter the temperature falls lower and lower as the heat stored up in the summer pours outward into space. In the great interior plains of Siberia and northern Canada and in the icecap regions of Greenland and Antarctica, the bitter, choking cold of winter comes early and stays long over the sunless land. Even in summer the icecap regions of the world are cold. If summer weather comes at all, it comes in brief spells of a few days, a dozen hours, or even less. In many places there are furious summer blizzards.

It was still summer in Antarctica when Captain Robert Scott and his companions started their return journey from the South Pole. Then, just as summer ended, he and the remaining members of his party were trapped in still another storm.

> 78° S. Thursday, March 29. Since the 21st we have had a continuous gale from W.S.W. and S.W. We had fuel to make two cups of tea apiece and bare food for two days on the 20th. Every day we have been ready to start for our depot 11 miles away, but outside the door of the tent it remains a scene of whirling drift. I do not think we can hope for any better things now. We shall stick it out to the end, but we are getting weaker, of course, and the end cannot be far.

The brutal cold of Antarctica would be even more extreme were it not for the vigorous mixing of air on a global scale. Warm air flooding poleward from over the tropical oceans beats against the denser, colder air that lies across Antarctica and sends massive arms of warm air across the continent. Cold Antarctic air spins outward across the surrounding oceans to inundate the shores of South America, New Zealand, Australia, and even the shores of Africa, over 2,000 miles away. Through such interplay of cold and warm air, much of the warmth of the tropics is fed poleward into sun-poor regions and much of the cold of the polar regions is sent equatorward to rob the sun-rich regions of their warmth.

In the never-ending interchange of air that operates to equalize the temperature differences created by the sun, the ocean of air is kept in ceaseless churning motion. The movement of air is not a direct and simple thing. Air on the move follows curving paths across the spinning earth: it is trapped in the whirling eddies of storms that march half round the world; it funnels through mountain passes; it becomes a part of the sweeping trade winds or of the driving westerlies. Over a cold snow surface on a clear night it sinks and lies close and still along the ground; in the midst of a thunderstorm it bounces 50,000 feet upward in the air.

At noon on Monday, August 27, 1883, the ship *Sir Robert Sale*, in the eastern entrance to Sunda Strait, was trapped in a darkness denser than that which any natural nighttime would produce. The blackness was set off and magnified by contrast with the brilliant lightning flashes that now and again flared in the southwest sky above the island of Krakatoa. To Captain Woolridge on the bridge, it seemed as though each burst of lightning left behind a branching pattern of light that remained impressed upon the black sky for long minutes before slowly fading out. The men worked furiously to rid the ship of her burden of dust and cinders. For hours they had been shoveling dust from the deck and beating it from the sails and rigging; but still it came down. The land being fed into the sky by the volcano on Krakatoa was still returning to earth in a rain of dust and cinders.

The same evening, aboard *Prins Frederik*, bound for Europe across the Indian Ocean, some 700 miles west of Krakatoa, all hands watched as the sun set purple-red beneath a shiny copper sky. And that was not all, for shortly thereafter there began a rain of fine ashes which continued for many hours, so that by morning the spars and masts and rigging were coated with gray.

By Christmas reports of unusual sunrises and sunsets had come in from far and near, making a list so long and so varied that it resembled a gazeteer of the world. "From a most careful analysis of the records, it is clear that the ash and dust from Krakatoa spread over the entire world . . . and much of it remained in the atmosphere for several years."

Major and Minor Weather Patterns

Air often travels in gigantic masses that cover areas of thousands of square miles and extend upward to heights of 30,000 feet or more. The lower atmosphere is crowded with such air masses, each bearing the stamp of the region in which it was bred. Down from the snow-covered winter lands come cold, dry air masses, their forward-thrusting edges wrapped in blizzards, their middle regions brittle-cold and dry. Outward from the vast subtropical deserts pours hot, thirsty air that sucks up moisture from the land and sea. Up from the tropical oceans come moist, warm masses, spilling out rain as they move. Masses of cool, damp air roll from off the colder oceans, carrying with them patches of fog and layered clouds with here and there a cradled storm.

No air mass retains for long the initial character gained in its region of birth. Cold masses warm as they move equatorward. Warm masses cool over lands and oceans colder than those in which they were born. Moist masses dry out upon the continents. Yet though an air mass begins to be transformed the moment it leaves its breeding ground, it often retains its distinctiveness over distances of thousands of miles. A cold winter mass from Canada that brings sub-zero weather to the Dakotas and sub-freezing weather to Mexico may still be recognizable as a "norther" bringing temperatures of 50° to Honduras, 3,500 miles from the heartland of northwest Canada, where the air originated.

At any one moment there are fifty or more air masses in the lower atmosphere, some young and fresh, some old and vastly transformed. Some move several hundred miles a day; others are almost stationary. The masses move fastest of all where they throng together in the stream of westerly airflow in the middle latitudes. Cold air knifes into warm, tossing up the warmer, lighter air like snow before a plow, to create a turbulent zone of violent storm. Warm air climbs over colder air that is retreating eastward, and as it does so layered clouds form along the air-mass interface and snow or rain begins to fall. Fresh, cold air catches up with cool air and slices beneath it, while at the same time warm, moist air overrides them both, its level marked by high layered clouds from which falls steady rain punctuated by intermittent heavy showers.

There are also minor motifs more intimately related to the nature of the surface of the earth. Every mountain, hill, and mound; every sea, lake, and pond; every river and stream; every barren field or stretch of sandy beach; every grassy meadow or woodlot stand—all of these have some effect, great or small, upon the local weather, the microclimate.

There are local shallow winds, such as the sea breeze and the wind that blows upvalley by day. There are small regions of quiet air trapped in the midst of thick forests and tiny pockets of quiet air caught among the growing wheat. On a cold night the air is warmer near the edges of a lake, especially on the leeward side, where small patches of air that have been plucked by the wind from over the warmer waters of the lake are carried onto the colder land. There are lower mountain slopes that in the spring often play host to hot, dry downslope winds that in a dozen hours evaporate snows half a winter in the making.

The finer weather designs are superimposed upon the broader ones to produce changing weather patterns of never-ending variety. Giant events fix the broad course of the changing weather. Finer, local factors determine just how the over-all weather will be expressed. Even when the over-all weather is dominant, as when violent winds are loosed upon the land, there will be some places where it takes a gentler turn.

The Upper Ocean

The lower atmosphere is the scene of only a small part of the Gargantuan three-dimensional panorama of changing weather. The upper atmosphere is almost constantly in motion. One kind of air current, aptly called the jet stream, rushes eastward along a path only a few score miles wide in the upper troposphere of middle latitudes at speeds of 150 m.p.h. or more, as though propelled from a high-pressure nozzle. Other, broader currents hurry along at well over 50 m.p.h., while in some regions the air drifts so slowly as to be virtually stationary. All these currents fluctuate in speed and size, and all shift position, creating a continuum of changing wind patterns.

There is more to the weather of the upper atmosphere than winds.

Most clouds are of the lower atmosphere; but sometimes, when the air is abnormally clear, one can see the shiny, banded coloring of mother-of-pearl clouds, racing across the sky at heights of thirteen to eighteen miles. Sometimes, toward sunset, there appear in the west the still higher noctilucent clouds, which shine from the reflected light of the sun.

There are, too, the intermittent auroral lights that may reach heights of 400 miles and produce, in the night skies of high latitudes, curious designs that take the form of radiating fingers of light that stretch outward from a knotted, glowing center; of pulsating sheets of light that seem to originate nowhere, yet cover the sky; and of bands of light that merge with alternate bands of gray-black darkness.

The auroral lights are associated with electrical storms that rage in the upper atmosphere, creating electromagnetic disturbances that disrupt radio and wire communication. The upper atmosphere also experiences wide variations in temperature, especially from night to day, but also as the result of the upwelling or sinking of air of different temperatures over large areas and through heights of many miles. And in the very high atmosphere—many hundreds to thousands of miles above the solid surface of the earth—there are great ring-shaped regions that contain large numbers of electrons and other particles which give rise to intense radiation.

In the past few decades the high upper atmosphere has commanded more and more attention, not only from scientists who seek more knowledge of the physical nature of the universe, but also from weather forecasters and engineers. The weather forecaster has begun to see that the behavior of the lower and higher atmosphere is interconnected, and so he hopes through studying their interrelationships to improve the accuracy of his forecasts and, perhaps, even to be able to predict long, slow changes of climate, such as those that caused the glaciers to overspread the continents many millennia ago. The engineer also must come to know the weathers of all the atmosphere, for it is he who must design better and better satellites and guided ships to sail to the surface of the ocean of air and beyond.

Yet despite the fact that modern man is slowly conquering the ocean of air, his attention remains focused upon the weather of the lowest layers of the atmosphere—the weather from which man cannot escape so long as he remains an earth inhabitant.

Part One

The Ocean of Air: Its Physical Order

I am enabled to judge of the physical order of things, although ignorant of their final cause; because to be able to form such a judgement it is sufficient for me to compare the several parts of the visible universe with each other, to study their mutual occurrence, their reciprocal relations, and to observe the general result of the whole.

—Jean Jacques Rousseau

1 The Heat System of the Air Ocean

Of the nine planets of the solar system, only earth is of just the proper warmth to support man and other familiar forms of higher life. It is barely possible that Venus and Mars, the planets whose orbits are adjacent to those of earth, may have some kind of life. But Venus is so close to the sun that, quite aside from other considerations, its atmosphere is far too hot for the development of true men; and Mars is so far from the sun that its atmosphere is much too cold. It is virtually certain that there are planets in other solar systems, unimaginably far away, that are precisely at the proper distance from their own sun-stars to provide conditions of heat and cold tolerable to the existence of true men. Still, in our own solar system only earth provides these conditions.

What are the special conditions of heat and cold upon earth? For the entire world, temperatures measured within the air at a level of five feet above the solid-liquid surface cover a range of 260°, from 125° F. below zero in Antarctica to over 135° above on the Libyan Desert. To man this is a large temperature range. It is, however, small compared to that on some of the other planets. The most extreme of all is Mercury, which has a scanty atmosphere whose temperature near the surface of the planet apparently ranges from more than 400° below zero, within the dark regions that always face away from the sun, to over 600° above zero, within the regions of constant light on the sunlit side. For man on earth it is fortunate that even the most extreme temperatures along the floor of the ocean of air are tolerable, with fire to provide warmth in the coldest regions and shelter to provide shade in the hottest ones. It is equally fortunate that over most of the world the air temperatures never even approach the extremes of 125° below zero or 135° above.

Largely because of the influence of the ocean of air, there are many different regimes of heat and cold in different regions of the world. Throughout over one-sixth of all the land area of the world, temperatures neither exceed 100° nor fall below zero. In other land regions the temperature range is between 50° and 95°. In still others it is −60° to 100°. Diversities of these kinds help create a variety of climatic environments that throughout man's history have been highly significant in both a biologic and an economic sense. And these diversities have been determined as much by the nature and behavior of the ocean of air as by the astronomic fact that in low latitudes there is a maximum intake of solar radiation, whereas in high latitudes there is a minimum.

The ocean of air is a heat trap, a heat source, and a carrier of heat. It traps energy from the sun and from the sun-heated surfaces of the lands and seas. This energy warms the air and makes it a source of heat for plants, animals, human beings, and for the soils, rocks, and waters of the earth. Yet the heat acquired in a certain location by a particular parcel of air is never entirely dissipated in the same location. Instead, the air carries the heat to other regions of the ocean of air, sometimes thousands of miles away. There the air passes the heat on to the surface of the earth or else to outer space.

This heat system of the air ocean directly governs the changing temperatures that are a prominent aspect of weather. It fixes the location of areas of cold and warmth. It regulates the outbreak of cold waves and heat waves. By these and other means, the heat system largely determines the conditions of heat and cold under which man lives.

The Nature of Heat

Fifty thousand years ago, men consciously recognized the existence and importance of heat. They knew that a heated rock loses its warmth and becomes colder and colder. They knew, also, that heat once lost can be restored by fire. Yet as recently as 200 years ago the true nature of heat was still unknown. The discovery of its nature by Count Rumford was one of the great events in the history of science. It was the essential prelude to all that has since been learned about the heat system of the ocean of air.

In the year 1794, the American-born physicist Benjamin Thompson, Count Rumford—colonel of Loyalist dragoons in the Revolution, knighted by the British, Count of the Holy Roman Empire, special administrator of Bavaria—came to Munich to supervise the boring of the first cannon in the new foundry he had established there.

The brass barrel was placed in its iron cradle and a steel borer was screwed tightly against it with a force of 10,000 pounds. A large horizontal wheel, to which two powerful horses were harnessed, was connected by ropes to the gun barrel so that it would rotate.

As the boring progressed, questions arose in the Count's mind. Whence came the heat that was being produced in the barrel, the borer, and the brass chips? Could the accepted view be true that heat was an actual substance; that here it was being derived by actual subtraction from the substance of the barrel itself?

"The more I meditated on these phenomena," he wrote afterward, "the more they appeared to me to be curious and interesting. A thorough investigation of them seemed even to bid fair to give a further insight into the hidden nature of heat. . . ."

Count Rumford carried out experiments of many kinds. Repeatedly he weighed the gun barrel, the borer, and the brass chips produced by boring to determine whether any of them lost weight in the process of giving up heat. Repeatedly he determined that no weight was lost; but then, perhaps the air itself participated in the reaction and gave up some of its substance to produce heat.

To dispel all doubt, the Count conducted a final conclusive experiment. To seal them off from the air, he submerged the borer and the cannon barrel in a tank of water. The results were the same: there was no loss of weight, even though enough heat was produced to make the water boil. Since the effects of the air could thus be ruled out, what was the meaning of the production of so much heat? To Rumford the meaning was clear. Heat could not be a substance that flowed from one body to another, as the great scientists of the day believed. As he expressed it in a paper before the Royal Society:

> . . . in reasoning on this subject, we must not forget that most remarkable circumstance, that the source of the Heat generated by friction, in these Experiments appeared evidently to be *inexhaustible*.
>
> It is hardly necessary to add, that any thing which any *insulated* body . . . can continue to furnish *without limitation*, cannot possibly be a *material substance:* and it appears to me to be extremely difficult, if not quite impossible, to form any distinct idea of anything, capable of being excited and communicated [in this manner] except it be MOTION.

Motion was indeed the answer, and Rumford's epoch-making experiments opened the door to a whole new understanding of the nature of heat. He was, however, far ahead of his time. For over five decades, until 1850, the results of his experiments were widely questioned. But then came Clausius in Germany, Thomson in England, and a dozen others, proving and re-proving that heat must be motion and elaborating upon the kinds of motion that must be involved.

Today it is known that heat consists of molecular motion. The higher the temperature of any body, the faster the motion of the molecules that make up that body. Yet two different substances whose molecules are moving at the same speed, and which, therefore, are at the same temperature, often contain different amounts of heat because the heat energy of each is related not only to its temperature but also to its molecular structure. When a pound of water is cooled from 70° to 60°, ten times as much heat is given up as when a pound of iron is similarly cooled. The principle also applies in reverse, ten times as much heat being required to raise the temperature of water from 60° to 70° as to raise the temperature of the iron a like amount.

Heat is transferred from warmer places to cooler ones. Transfer may take place by radiation, as from a sun lamp or an open-faced electric heater. It is by radiation that energy travels from the sun to the earth. Transfer may take place through the mass transport of air or any other substance, as when a warming pan is placed in a cold bed or when warm air moves upward from the ground. It may also take place by conduction, as when one end of an iron poker is held in a fire and the opposite end is warmed through successive jostling of the many trillions of tightly packed iron molecules, a jostling that starts at the heated end and is passed along in relay fashion. Conduction accounts for a high percentage of the transfer of heat through thin air layers that cling to a soil surface, to rocks, to the leaves of plants, or to the skin of an individual.

Radiation, mass transport, and conduction are all direct mechanisms for heat transfer in the atmosphere. There is in addition an indirect mechanism that is especially important because it provides the energy to drive such great storm systems as the hurricanes that form over tropical seas and the storms that sweep across the middle latitudes in winter. This indirect mechanism is the transfer of heat in a latent form as water vapor.

Water vapor enters the air by evaporation from the water bodies of the earth. In the evaporation process heat is consumed, just as it is consumed in the rapid evaporation of water from a pan upon a stove. Later, when the water vapor condenses to form the droplets of water that produce fog or clouds in the air or dew upon the ground, the same amount of heat consumed initially to produce the evaporation is given up and so is returned to the air or the ground.

Air masses carrying great quantities of water vapor may travel hundreds or thousands of miles before the vapor condenses and so gives up its latent heat. Heat-giving air of this kind is not only an essential substance of hurricanes and other storm systems; it also provides for the transfer of vast quantities of heat from strongly warmed lower latitudes to poorly warmed high latitudes. In this way, as well as through radiation, mass transfer, and conduction, there is maintained within the atmosphere a heat cycle whereby the atmospheric air is heated by the sun; whereby the heat so gained is distributed in a variety of ways within the atmosphere, largely through the motions of the air itself; and whereby heat returns by radiation from the atmosphere to outer space.

The Heat Cycle of the Atmosphere

The warmth of the earth and its atmosphere is derived from the sun. Ninety-three million miles away, within the sun, billions of hydrogen atoms are transformed into helium in a millionth of a second. In this reaction, which is like that of a hydrogen bomb, prodigious amounts of energy are released. From the surface regions of the sun, the energy rushes outward in the form of a pulsing wave of radiation that travels away from the sun at a speed of 186,000 miles per second. Two hundred seconds later an almost insignificantly small segment of the outward-sweeping radiation is intercepted by the planet Mercury. One hundred and sixty seconds later Venus intercepts its tiny share. Then earth, Mars, Jupiter, and the other planets each capture a share in turn. Within 350 minutes after leaving the sun, the radiation has passed Pluto, the outermost of the known planets. Then, with its energy diminished by less than one hundred-thousandth of 1 per cent through planetary interception, the wave of radiant energy sweeps into space beyond the limits of the solar system.

The earth's atmosphere intercepts the sun's radiation eight minutes and twenty seconds after it has left the sun. As the wave of radiation rolls into the atmospheric ocean, its even-sweeping front is shattered. Microscopic segments, especially those composed of short-wave-length blue and ultraviolet radiation, bounce from air particle to air particle and so follow erratic darting paths downward through the atmosphere or back into outer space. Segments of the wave are snatched up and absorbed by the atmospheric gases. Oxygen particles seize bits of light of just the right shade of red. Nitrogen grasps a particular wave length of ultraviolet. The ozone of the stratosphere absorbs and so blocks out a whole mass of radiation in the very-short-wave-length ultraviolet range.

Only partly diminished through running the gantlet of the high upper atmosphere and the ozone layers of the stratosphere, the pulsing wave of sun radiation sweeps on earthward. In less than one-thousandth of a second it reaches the lowest atmosphere. Over London, where it is afternoon, the wave encounters cloud and is flipped back, as from a mirror. Over the ocean east of Bermuda, the wave strikes squarely into the water at the height of noon, lighting and warming the ocean to depths of many fathoms. Over New York, where noon has yet to arrive, most of the incoming rays are absorbed by objects on the ground; but the exact fate of each depends on the nature of the surface on which it falls. One bit of incoming light hits the shiny dome of a building and so bounds back skyward; another bit is absorbed and turned into warmth by a patch of soil in Central Park.

On the average, taking together all the clear days and cloudy days for all parts of the earth at all seasons of the year, about 50 per cent of the incoming solar radiation is absorbed at the earth's surface. About another 16 per cent is absorbed by the gases and clouds of the atmosphere. The remainder is scattered back or reflected back into space and so does nothing to heat the earth or its atmosphere.

But averages often mask the specific realities of nature. On a clear, bright summer day, when the sun is near the peak of the sky, the rocks and grass and trees of rural places and the buildings and pavements of town and city are strongly heated by the sun. Then over 70 per cent of the solar radiation that falls upon the atmosphere is absorbed at the earth's surface. Quite different is an overcast day, when less than 30 per cent of the radiation is absorbed by the earth.

The behavior of waves of solar radiation as they flow endlessly downward through the atmosphere is evidenced in many familiar ways. The sky appears to be blue because it is the blue-colored light that is scattered most strongly in the upper atmosphere and therefore filters downward from all directions, giving color to the entire sky canopy. The gold and red clouds of sunset also owe their origin to the scattering of light. When the sun is near the horizon, its rays must travel at a low, sloping angle over long paths through the atmospheric ocean, so that nearly all of the blue and much of the green light is scattered out, leaving the golds and reds to penetrate far downward to the levels where clouds occur. Rainbows—"bridges of the gods," the Norse called them—are formed when the sun is shining through a sheet of water droplets which, acting like prisms, bend the white light, breaking it up into its component colors along an arc that is centered about the rays from the sun. The precise position of a rainbow depends upon the location of the observer. Though fifty people see a rainbow at the same time, each is looking at his own, particular rainbow, visible only to him.

Incoming solar radiation is the initial source of all atmospheric heat. It is, however, the direct and immediate source of less than one-third of that heat, for the air of the lower atmosphere derives most of its heat secondhand from the surfaces of the earth that have absorbed incoming solar radiation. Such absorption is especially great on a clear, sunny day. On such a day the sand at the beach can be too hot to walk on barefooted. It may well be at a temperature of 140° or more. In the world of the lizard, a quarter-inch above the sand, the temperature is only slightly less—135°. The temperature of the air around the head and shoulders of a man sitting on the sand is much less—105°. When this same man stands up, his head moves into an air layer where the temperature is only 98°. Within the six-foot layer from the soles of a man's feet to the top of his head, the temperature range is 42°—a difference as great as that between the 60° average July temperature at Fairbanks, Alaska, and the 102° average July temperature at Greenland Ranch in Death Valley, at both of which places the official temperature readings are taken at the standard height of five feet above the ground. The enormous decrease in temperature upward from the hot sand to a height of a few feet demonstrates that the chief heat source for the warming of the lowest air layers is the ground. If the incoming sunlight was the chief heat source, the air at five feet would be at least as hot as the air near the ground.

A clue to one way in which heat is passed upward from the ground to the air above is provided by watching the road ahead as one drives along the highway through hilly country on a hot, bright afternoon. As the car moves downhill toward a dip in the road, one sees what at first appears to be a shimmering pool of water at the base of the dip. As the car approaches, the pool gradually disappears. The shimmering pool is caused by "heat waves"—by the bending of light as it passes through currents of hot air that are rising from above the strongly heated pavements. In a similar manner, warm air moves upward from above water, grass, and other surfaces, transferring heat en masse from the ground to higher levels.

The second major way in which heat is passed upward from the ground is by radiation. The earth, like all objects that are not at absolute zero, is constantly radiating energy outward. But because of its relatively low temperature, as compared to the sun, the earth radiates at long wave lengths that are invisible to the human eye. There is never a time when its surface does not glow with invisible infrared light.

If, through a genetic quirk, someone should be born with vision that permitted him to see only infrared light, there would be no darkness for him in the outdoors, not even on what ordinary people call pitch-black nights. Instead, on such nights every object would be visible in a faint light that at times might be as strong as bright moonlight and at other times as faint as starlight. Weirdly, there would be no shadows on the ground, because the ground itself would be the principal source of light.

Such a shadowless man would discover many interesting things about the variations in the intensity of earth radiation. If he ascended in a helicopter, the glowing earth beneath would become fainter and fainter because the infrared light that emanates from the earth is strongly absorbed and changed to heat by the water molecules in the lowest layers of the earth's atmosphere. If he kept a twenty-four-hour watch, he would note that as the earth cooled off, the intensity of infrared radiation decreased, so that the earth would be seen to glow most strongly in the afternoon and least of all just before the sunrise. If he traveled from hot desert regions to cold polar regions, he would see that the glow was strongest where the temperature was highest and weakest where it was lowest.

Because the earth radiates energy only at very long wave lengths, the water molecules of the lower air are enabled to catch much of the earth radiation and convert it into heat. Yet these same molecules are unable to catch more than a small fraction of the incoming short-wave-length energy from the sun. The water molecules are like earthward-facing stop signs; they permit the flow of radiation downward but not upward. As a result, the lower atmosphere acts as a blanket that holds the sun-gained heat close to the earth and permits it to escape back to space only gradually.

This blanketing effect is strongest when the water content of the air is high. It is not the moist and cloudy nights that the grape farmer fears. He knows from experience that on such nights the warmth achieved in the daytime hours will be largely retained by the lower air throughout the night, and that therefore there is no danger of a freeze even though daytime temperatures may have been in the forties. The nights he fears are those when the air above the vineyards is clear and dry. Then, even though the daytime temperatures have been in the sixties, there is a good chance that before the night is over the temperature will have dropped below the freezing mark.

Conduction, as well as radiation, is important in the heat transfer that influences the temperature of crops and of the ground. There is a thin layer of air adjacent to the plants and ground that is directly warmed or cooled by the earth through conduction. This is the laminar layer, which is defined as the film of air within which motion is only lateral, along thin air layers. The laminar flow contrasts strongly with turbulent flow, in which air particles move vertically as well as laterally, often twisting and turning about in eddies of marked amplitude.

All objects exposed to the atmosphere, either indoors or out, are surrounded by a laminar air layer. It is possible actually to see this layer. If cigarette smoke is blown gently across the top of a table, the smoke will be seen to cling to the table throughout a thin zone. Within this laminar zone, the smoke will flow slowly and evenly; above it, the smoke will twist and curl upward. If smoke is blown across a rougher object, such as a tweed jacket, the laminar zone will be seen to be thicker. Smooth ground, such as even, barren rock, is like the table top: above it the laminar layer is only a fraction of an inch thick. Rough ground, such as a grass-covered surface, is like the tweed jacket and so has a laminar layer many inches thick.

The exact thickness of this layer that is heated or cooled directly by the ground through conduction varies not only with roughness of surface but also with the strength of the over-all wind. When the wind is speeding along, it rips away the topside of the laminar layer. Therefore, if the laminar layer has lost its heat to the rapidly cooling ground on a clear night, an over-all wind may prevent a hard freeze through repeatedly scooping up the cold, sluggish air near the ground and replacing it with warmer air that will conduct heat to the ground. By this resupply of heat in repeated small amounts, the ground will be kept warmer than it would be otherwise.

On a broad scale the atmosphere loses heat not only to the ground but also directly to outer space. The air particles of the atmosphere radiate at long wave lengths in the infrared, just as does the ground. Part of this radiation passes downward to the ground; part, upward. If there is considerable water in the air, either in the form of gaseous vapor or of liquid droplets, as in clouds, much of the infrared radiation headed upward toward outer space is caught and retained as heat within the air. However, if the air is relatively dry, nearly all of the radiation escapes outward from the atmosphere. This is one of the principal reasons why the coldest winter realms on earth lie well inland, in the dry-air regions beyond the reach of frequent invasions of moist air from the oceans. And it is from these dry inland realms, both in the cold lands and hot deserts, that much of the heat acquired by the atmosphere is passed back into space.

By great heat losses from the dry-air regions and by lesser heat losses from regions where the air is moister, the lower air returns heat to outer space. In this manner, on a gross scale, the energy gained from the sun is returned in balanced measure to the outer realms of the solar system and to all of outer space. At the same time, on a finer scale, the absorption and transfer of heat within the lowest atmosphere and within the surface lands and waters create different climatic milieus of cold or warmth and distinctive weather episodes that bring spells of frigid or torrid weather.

2 Patterns of Heat and Cold

In the geography books of a generation ago, it was still common to refer to the torrid, temperate, and frigid zones. Sometimes this concept was illustrated in the books by a map of the world that showed a red-colored zone in low latitudes, a yellow-colored zone in middle latitudes, and a blue-colored zone in high latitudes, as if there was a perfectly uniform banding of temperature zones, by latitudes, from the torrid zone of the tropics through the mild middle latitudes to the frigid zones of the polar regions.

This ultrasimple notion, which dates back 2,500 years to the time of the ancient Greeks, is far from correct. Central Greenland, 1,000 miles from the Pole, is far colder than the North Pole itself. The mid-Sahara, 1,200 miles from the equator, is far hotter than any location on the equator. There are, in addition, many other radical departures from this simple zonal scheme; and, in addition, in most regions of the world there are at least occasional extreme weather episodes that bring unusually hot or cold weather which must be reckoned as part of the total climatic environment.

It will be helpful to view the earth, not in terms of the North and South Poles, the equator, and the intermediate latitudes, but of multiple poles of cold and heat. From such a viewpoint the primary cold poles become Antarctica, Greenland, Siberia-Russia, and northwest Canada; the primary heat poles, the Sahara, the Arabian Desert, and other low-latitude deserts of the world.

These are also the hearthlands of the coldest and hottest air masses that swing outward and travel far across more temperate lands.

They help shape the patterns of heat and cold across the earth because they generate the cold waves and heat waves that sweep outward to engulf Chicago, London, Miami, Buenos Aires, Stockholm, Cape Town, Shanghai, Santiago, and thousands of other places.

Yet all is not extremes of cold or heat. There are mild regions of the earth across which stream masses of air off the ocean, pleasantly warm in summer and cool in winter. There are the rainy tropics, which are never as hot as the truly hot deserts. And where there are hills and mountains there are varieties of local temperature environments too numerous to list, so great are their diversities. In considering the distribution of regions of heat and cold upon the earth, these smaller elements as well as the larger must be considered as part of the total pattern.

The Lands of Coldest Winters

The coldest winter lands of the earth lie well inland, at high latitudes upon the continents of Eurasia, North America, and Antarctica. In Eurasia the coldest lands are in northeastern Siberia. In North America, they are in Greenland and in northwest Canada. Antarctica has the coldest lands of all, in the interior, high upon the ice-covered plateau.

In all of these lands extremely low winter temperatures are favored not only by the dryness of the air and the high latitude, with its long winter nights, but also by the presence of a mantle of snow. On the icecaps of Greenland and Antarctica, there is always a snow mantle, winter and summer. In Siberia and northwest Canada, there is some snow upon the ground by October, and even though additional snowfalls are few and light the snow persists over most of the region until April or May.

In these cold winter lands there is seldom any wind to disturb the frigid air that lies above the snow-covered ground. As winter approaches, the temperature of the snow surface falls lower and lower as heat is radiated outward during the long nights. The sun, if it rises at all, appears only for a brief while, moving along a low arc above the horizon that lies equatorward; and most of its feeble rays are reflected from the mirrorlike snow and so do nothing to raise its temperature. As the lower air loses its little warmth to the snow beneath, its temperature descends from $-50°$ to $-60°$ and then, still lower, to −70° and −80°. In some places the temperature of the air five feet above the ground reaches 100° below or lower.

So far as is known, the icecap regions of Greenland and Antarctica have never been inhabited on a permanent, continuing basis. In contrast, both Siberia and northwest Canada are not only inhabited today by peoples of European origin, but have a long history of native habitation. The modes of living of these natives in earliest times, 3,500 or more years ago, can only be surmised, so scanty is the archaeological evidence. They seem to have possessed sleds and they doubtless lived chiefly through hunting and fishing. In Siberia, they may have had domesticated reindeer. Whatever their mode of life, they must have been resourceful to cope with the extreme conditions of winter; and they doubtless stored food for the winter, just as do the Eskimo and other present-day natives of these lands.

In Siberia, even the icy Arctic Ocean supplies air that in winter is less cold than that many hundred miles to the south over Siberia. Throughout the winter the zone of contact between these two kinds of air swings erratically back and forth. Sometimes the arctic air pushes inland over the coastal regions. Whenever air replaces the air from off the continent, the temperature rises from around −60° or −70° to −20° or −30°. These higher temperatures are usually harder to endure than the lower ones, for often they are accompanied by wind and dampness. Dry, still air at 60° below is a tolerable thing; but a pounding wind packed with snow makes even 10° below unbearable for long.

The natives of the north Siberian coast fear the coming of the wind from the north. They call it "the Chief," or "Old Man," and view it with respect. I. W. Shklovsky, a Russian who in the last century traveled widely in northern Siberia, tells vividly of experiencing the stormy north wind during the course of a winter visit with a Yakut tribe at Sukharnoe, at the mouth of the Kolyma River on the Arctic Ocean.

> After the first gust the wind kept up a continuous, monotonous scream, like the sound of escaping steam from a million engines, dreadful to hear, and the hut shook violently. The moss plugging the cracks in the log walls was cut out by the wind as though with a chisel, and its icy breath whistled through the hut. I wanted to know what it was like outside. "Don't go out," said my host, " 'the Chief' will not like it."

But, seeing that I was determined to go out, they fastened a long strap round my waist, holding the end firmly in their hands. Hardly had I opened the door when I was flung violently to the ground. The hard snow, congealed by sixty degrees of frost, was dug out by the fury of the wind, and the air was full of ice crystals, which whipped my face like molten metal, and in an instant my cheekbones were frozen. I was as one blind in the impenetrable darkness which surrounded me, and the only sound to be heard was the insistent howling of the wind, which dominated all else.

Where could I go? Where was the door? Had it not been for the strap held so firmly by my friends, it would have gone hard with me, for I could not possibly have found the door; but I managed to crawl on all fours to the threshold. "Well, friend, what did 'the Chief' say to you?" my hosts asked jestingly, when, half frozen, I crawled into the warmth of the hut.

That northernmost Siberia, along the Arctic Sea, is somewhat warmer in winter than the interior of the continent to the south illustrates the fact that temperature does not necessarily decrease with increasing latitude. A still more striking example is afforded by comparing the conditions at Tromsö, 400 miles above the Arctic Circle on the west coast of Norway, and at Kiev, Russia, which is well inland and over 1,200 miles farther south. The lowest temperature ever recorded at Tromsö is −1°; at Kiev, −22° has been recorded and temperatures of −1° are fairly common. In North America there are contrasts that are fully as great. Ketchikan, Alaska, at 55° N., has a record low of −8°. Omaha, Nebraska, 950 miles farther south, at 41° N., has a record of −32°.

Winter temperatures are relatively mild at Tromsö and Ketchikan because these localities are usually immersed in moist, mild air that moves in from the oceans to the west. Kiev and Omaha, however, often lie in the path of cold air masses that move downward from the north.

For the world as a whole, the sources of the coldest air masses of winter are northeastern Siberia, Greenland, northwest Canada, and Antarctica. Thus the influence of these coldest lands extends far beyond their strict regional boundaries. Through exporting vast quantities of cold air, these lands contribute to the character of the winter weather over all the continents and oceans, even as far equatorward as the tropics themselves.

Cold Air Invasions

If the continents were all leveled off at one elevation to form a series of low, even-topped plateaus, the winter temperature regimes in middle latitudes would be much simpler than they are. Maritime air, borne from west to east in the dominant flow of the westerlies, would penetrate far inland. In a United States without the barrier of the Sierra Nevadas, maritime air would dominate the weather as far eastward as Salt Lake City, making the climate there much milder than it is. Cold air masses would still be formed in Canada and would still travel outward, but they would more often go only eastward or southeastward. Only seldom would they head due south.

As it is, the topography of the continents has a pronounced effect upon the paths followed by cold air invasions. And since each continent is different topographically and also is unique in outline and latitudinal location, each has its own arrangement of cold air passageways and of regions that lie shielded by mountain barriers from the invasions of cold air.

There are three principal channelways down which cold air spills southward out of northwest Canada. Occasionally it pours south and west through the low-lying passes of the Canadian Rockies in the Peace River area, then southward across the broad orchard lands of the Okanogan Valley, and southward farther still past Portland, Oregon, and the Central Valley of California, following the natural corridor that is rimmed to the east by the high Sierra Nevada and Cascade mountains and that has as its western border the low and scattered coastal ranges and the warm Pacific Ocean. When a cold air mass pushes strongly down this channelway, the smudgepots are lighted in the southern California orange orchards to ward off the impending freeze.

It is not common for cold Canadian air to move far south along the West Coast across the domain usually reserved for more temperate air from the Pacific Ocean. More often, the main body of air travels southward along the middle trough between the Rockies and the Sierra-Cascades. This great intermontane channel is itself a land of mountains. Cold polar air masses flowing southward spill across the Blue Mountains of Oregon, the Silver Mountains of Idaho, the Santa Rosas of Nevada, the Delanos of Utah, and dozens of other

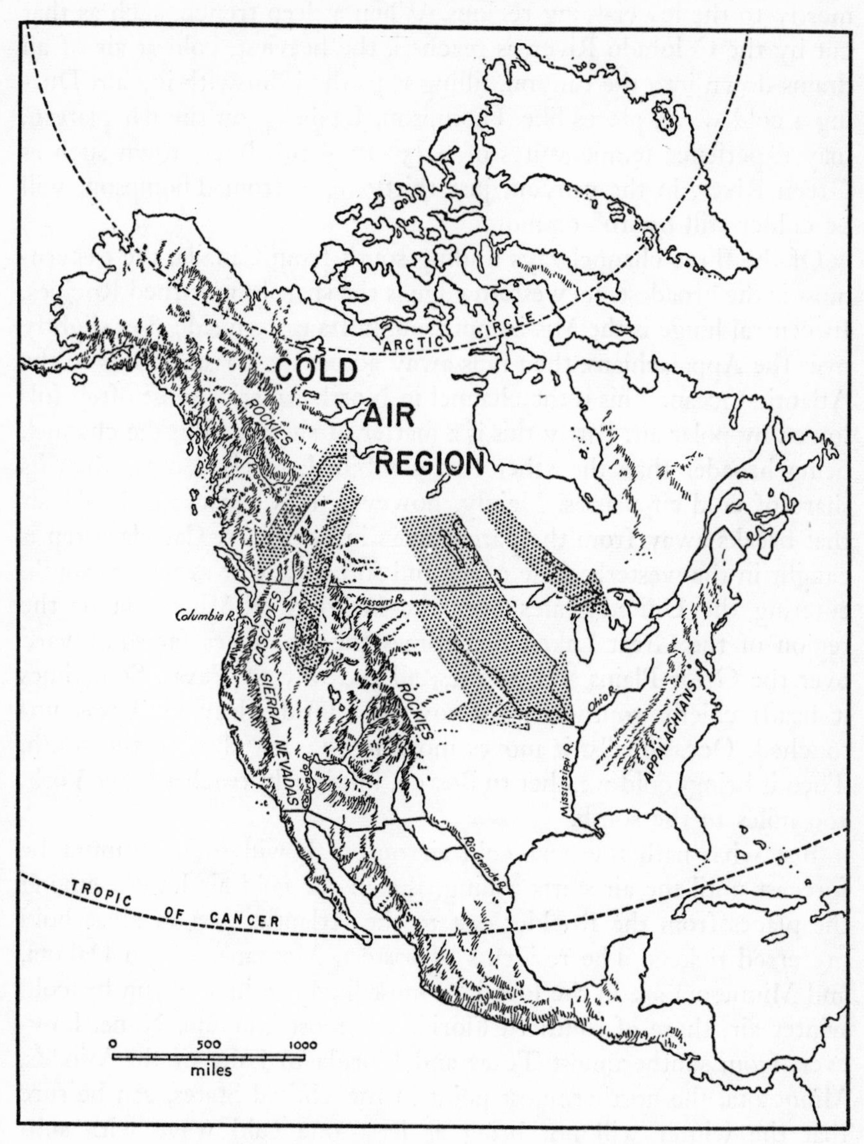

THE COLD AIR CHANNELWAYS OF NORTH AMERICA

ranges large and small; but the air in its coldest basal part clings mostly to the lower-lying regions. When a deep trench, such as that cut by the Colorado River, is reached, the heaviest, coldest air of all drains down into the canyon, filling it to the brim with icy air. During a cold wave, places like Thompson, Utah, up on the flat plateau, may experience temperatures of $-15°$ to $-20°$, but a town such as Green River, in the canyon, just thirty miles from Thompson, will be colder still by 10° or more.

Of the three channelways leading south from Canada, the easternmost is the broadest. Its western edge is the sharply upturned Rockies. Its central hinge is the Mississippi trough. Its eastern side rises slightly over the Appalachians, then falls away across the coastal plains to the Atlantic Ocean. This is the channel in North America most often followed by polar air. Partly this is a matter of sheer width; the channel, being broader than the other two combined, receives more than its share of cold air masses. Mainly, however, it is because the cold air that breaks away from the parent mass in northwest Canada often is caught in the westerly flow of air and so moves east as well as south, entering the United States over the Dakotas or Minnesota or the region of the Great Lakes. Sometimes the air moves far southward over the Great Plains and prairies, all the way to Texas. Sometimes it heads chiefly southeastward toward Florida, leaving Texas untouched. Occasionally it moves more to the east than to the south. Then it brings cold weather to Boston, but barely reaches New York, 100 miles to the south.

Just what path the next cold air outbreak will follow cannot be forecast until the air starts rolling. But in the cold air lottery among the places from the Rockies east to the Atlantic, certain areas hold preferred tickets. The residents of eastern Montana, North Dakota, and Minnesota are in the locations most likely to be overrun by cold winter air; those of southern Florida are most immune. None, however, from southernmost Texas and Florida to Lake of the Woods, Minnesota, the northernmost point in the United States, can be sure that the winter will not bring at least one cold wave with subfreezing temperatures. As the Texans say, often it feels as if the only thing between Texas and the North Pole is a barbed-wire fence.

When a widespread cold wave hits one part of the country, the chances are good that large portions of the remainder of the country will be unseasonably warm. This relationship is summed up in a jingle:

Cold in the East, warm in the West—
There's only one place the cold can rest.
Cold in the West, warm in the East—
For many days, say five at least.

It is no coincidence that there tends to be such temperature compensation over wide areas. The regions that nurture cold winter air masses cannot continue for long to export billions of tons of air into lower latitudes without a return flow to make up the loss. For the most part this return flow occurs over the relatively warm oceans. However, when cold air bursts equatorward in unusually large amounts, with cold air outbreaks following one upon the other so that half the country is caught in a prolonged cold wave, the return flow to polar lands must be so great that broad currents of warm air are pulled up not only over the oceans but also across those regions of the continent that are free of polar air.

The juxtaposition of cold spells and warm spells in the United States during winter is illustrated by the weather situation of January 7–12, 1937, which was about as extreme as any for which there are comprehensive records. In the East, the weather was springlike in its mildness; in the West, it was the coldest weather experienced in many years. On January 9, in San Diego, sixteen miles from the Mexican border, the temperature was ten degrees lower than at Boston; and San Diego was the warmest spot in California, according to official temperature readings. At San Diego, the temperature range was 36° to 53°; at Boston, 43° to 64°. The cold wave enveloped the entire United States west of the Rockies and lasted three to five days. The unseasonable heat wave extended from Maine to South Carolina and lasted two to four days. The two unusual temperature conditions were simultaneous on two days, January 8 and 9. They gave rise to curiously contrasting events in the East and the West.

In New York City, on January 9, Central Park was thronged with Saturday crowds out to enjoy the 64° weather. At Johnstown, Pennsylvania, passers-by eyed uneasily the rising water of the Conemaugh, fed by the melting snow in the 70° heat. Down in New Bern, North Carolina, it was the warmest January 9 on record. The day had started out with temperatures in the middle fifties, but by afternoon the temperature was 79° and the estuary was crowded with sailboats.

In San Francisco, children who had never seen snow before pulled their wagons up Market Street to the foot of Twin Peaks, packed the wagons full of snow, and returned home to throw snowballs at the children next door. At Bend, Oregon, the Fire Department rescued the city's ducks and swans, trapped in the frozen surface of Mirror Pond, with the temperature standing at −21°. Snow fell in Death Valley. Not far away, in the Kern River country, forty-nine deer were found frozen to death.

The extremes of January 7–12, 1937, were followed by lesser cold and heat waves in the West and East. Thus the same general circulation pattern seemed to persist throughout much of the month. The general rule of compensatory flow was strikingly illustrated: cold air spilling southward in the West was compensated for by warm air pulled northward across the Atlantic seaboard and adjacent inland regions.

North America is unique among the northern continents in that there is not a single major mountain barrier to block the passage of cold air southward toward the tropics. Europe has its wall of alpine mountains stretching across in almost unbroken line from the Atlantic Ocean to the Caspian Sea. This mountain rampart fends off the cold winter air that comes from European Russia and Siberia. Spain is guarded by the western anchor of the line: the Cantabrians and Pyrenees. Behind the Caucasus at the eastern end lies the only subtropical region of the U.S.S.R., the only area where citrus fruits are raised. Near the center of the wall are the towered Alps that shield the mild Riviera coast. In between, filling out the wall, other mountain ranges stand shoulder to shoulder, making a sheltered place of the Mediterranean lands to the south.

Asia, too, has its mountain wall, the highest in the world. Though frigid Siberian air beats at their northern flanks, the great Himalayas, the Hindu Kush, the knotted Pamirs, and other massive ranges effectively protect the southern regions of Asia. Because of this protection, the residents of Delhi, India, have never been exposed to below-freezing temperatures. In contrast, residents of Eagle Pass, Texas, which is farther south than Delhi, have felt cold waves during which the temperature fell to 7°.

In the Southern Hemisphere, it is Antarctica that supplies the coldest winter air. The air is flung outward across the southern oceans, and because it picks up moisture from the sea its winds are edged with dampness and so are doubly felt. The man on the deck of a ship that sails the southernmost seas in winter knows the cruelest

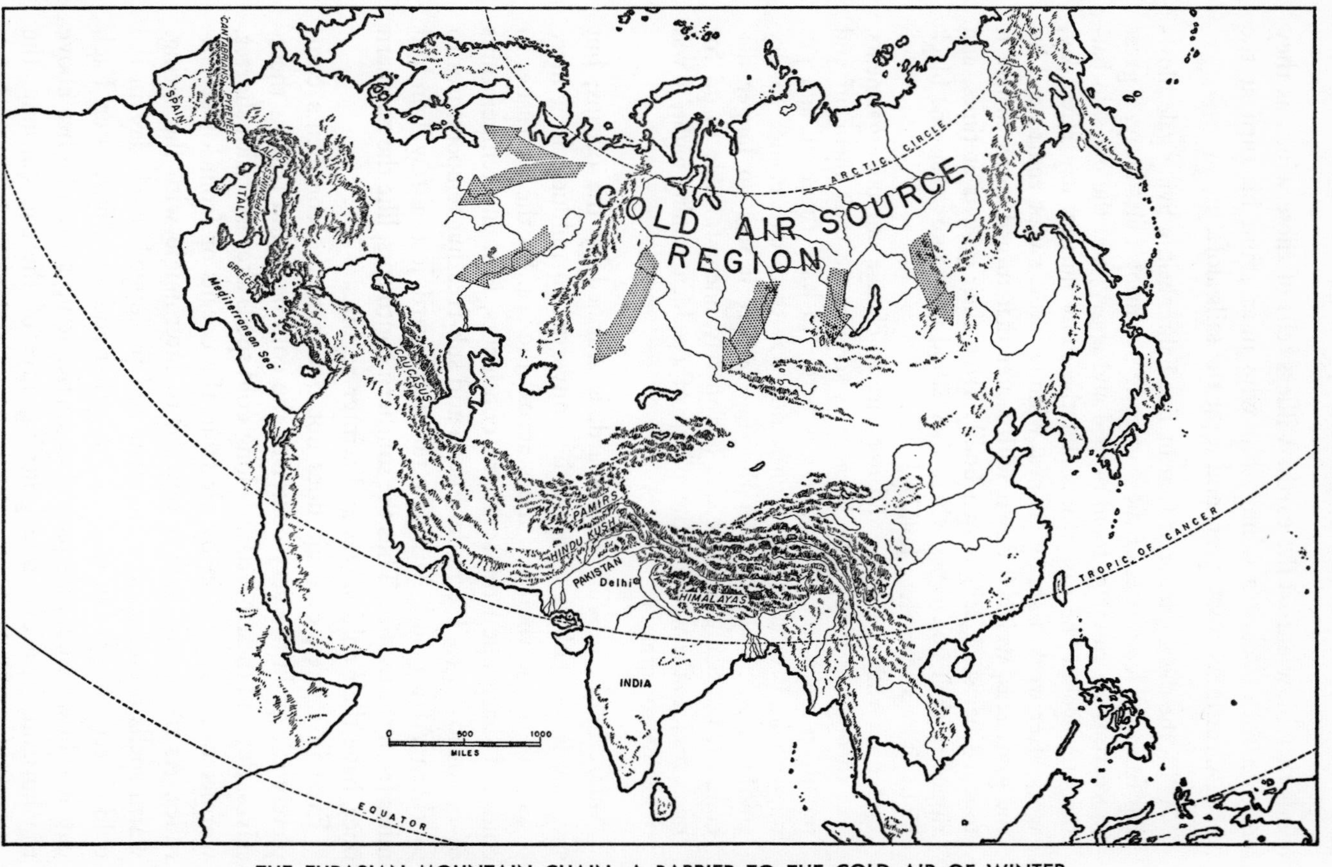

THE EURASIAN MOUNTAIN CHAIN: A BARRIER TO THE COLD AIR OF WINTER

winds that blow across the earth. Villiers tells of these winds as they feel to a man aboard a sailing ship who must stand his turn at the wheel, wrestle with icy gear, and fight the sails aloft.

> With the thermometer at four or five Fahrenheit, a living gale blowing from the ice-wastes of the Antarctic not many miles away, a great murderous sea running, foam-topped and angry; and the old ship battling on against the east winds and the snow flurries, day after day, week after week, fighting always, winning little, swept end to end by the great seas, weighed down with water that turned to ice where it touched her steel, sails blown bodily from their gaskets at times, and ripped to their bolt-ropes where they stood upon more than one black night–it was scarcely a holiday! . . .
>
> One remembers that we did not care to change our undergarments, wet through as they were, because as soon as we took them off and put them down, they froze. It was better to leave them on, and put up with it. We had no dry ones, nor was there any chance to dry anything. . . . Cold reached the stage where it was no longer discomfort, but acute pain. It was not merely uncomfortable to go for one's trick to the wheel in the middle of a sodden, raining night; it was sickening torture.

Antarctic air, moving northward, is warmed by the oceans; but such air is too cold a thing to be converted to mildness in a mere passage of a few thousand miles across the sea. So the air rushes in cold and sharp upon the southern continents, bringing temperatures of 15° or lower to Tierra del Fuego and sub-freezing temperatures to southern Africa and Australia far northward just a few hundred miles from the tropics. Thus the southern continents, like the northern ones, have their cold waves and winter regimes.

Even in winter, cold air does not dominate the continents completely except in the very center of the cold heartland regions themselves. Beyond these heartlands long cold spells alternate with shorter, warmer ones brought in by air from the oceans or from lower latitudes. As the winter moves onward to intermingle with the spring, warm spells become more frequent and prolonged. Each day in the cold air regions the sun rises a little earlier and sets a little later. Each day it follows a curving path that carries it up a little higher above the horizon. The ever-strengthening rays of the sun consume the edges of the cold air, causing the heartland regions gradually to shrink in size.

By summertime the cold air regions of Siberia and Canada are no more. They will continue to supply air cooler than that from many other regions, but the snow that breeds low temperatures is gone, the frozen soil has turned to marshes swarming with mosquitoes, flowers have appeared on the floor of coniferous forests, and where there is birch or aspen the trees have turned green in the warmth of the long summer days. For several months no really cold air will be exported from these regions. Instead, the temperate air from the oceans and the hot air from the deserts and plateaus will dominate the weather of the continents.

Deserts and Heat Waves

The hottest air masses of all come from the great subtropical deserts: the Sahara, the Arabian Desert, the Thar in India, and the Great Australian Desert. Because they are in low latitudes, even in winter the days are relatively long and the strong sunlight raises the temperature of the desert floor and the air above it to 90° or much more. In summer other deserts participate in supplying the lands with hot, dry air: the Sonoran Desert of Mexico and its northward extension in the southwestern United States; the deserts of central Asia—the Kara Kum, the great Mongolian Desert, the Takla Makan; and the Patagonian and Atacama deserts in South America. Summer air almost as hot comes from the semiarid high plains and plateau regions of the continents, such as the Great Plains in the United States.

Of all the deserts of the world, the one that generates the broadest currents of hot, dry air is the Sahara, which occupies an area larger than the United States and stretches 3,000 miles across northern Africa from the Atlantic to the Red Sea. The desert reaches northward to the stony outliers of the Atlas Mountains in northwest Africa and in its eastern part northward all the way to the Mediterranean Sea. Southward the desert extends well into the tropics, where it merges with the moister grassland belt near Timbuktu, Lake Chad, and the central Sudan.

Neither the Sahara nor any other desert is as Hollywood depicts it: a seemingly endless tract of sand, mostly in the form of dunes that hide some outlaw band. Gautier, the famous French geographer, who came to know the Sahara even better than the Bedouins, estimated that less than 12 per cent of that desert is covered with sand in appreciable quantities. There are wide hammadas, plateau regions whose stony floors are polished to a shiny, glassy smoothness by the blasting wind armed with particles of dust and sand. In places, for miles without change, the desert floor consists of sun-baked clay, hard as rock and seamed with deep cracks. There are saucerlike basins a score of miles across that for millennia have been the collecting grounds for the runoff from occasional rains and are coated with salt crystals left

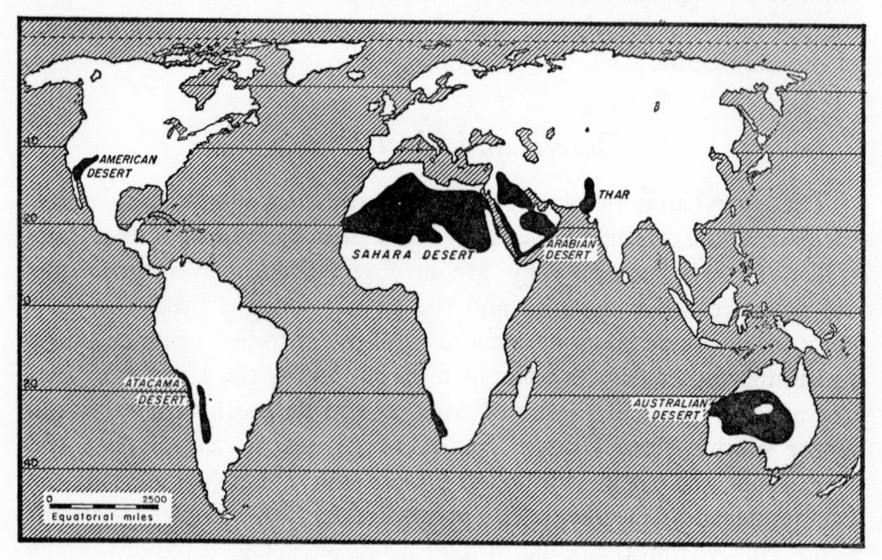

PRINCIPAL HOT DESERTS OF THE WORLD

behind when the water evaporated. And there are river beds, called wadis by the Bedouins, that cut through rocky hilly lands or fan outward onto the flat desert floor.

In summer particularly, the desert of daytime is a place of intense light. The sunlight floods downward through the dry, cloudless air. To a traveler upon the desert, the sunlight at first seems merely to be glaring and garish. But then it presses in upon the body, as though the light were a thing of substance and of weight. Still more, it reaches outward. It fills the entire sky, all that one can see. The light mingles with the heat, the heat with the silence, until that desert trinity of light and heat and silence engulfs the traveler.

Beneath the rays of the sun, the desert floor is heated to 150°, 170°, even to close to the boiling point of water. At a height of five feet, an early afternoon reading may be as high as 135°. Around the head of a man on a camel, the temperature is several degrees lower.

In the hottest parts of the desert, caravans shun the heat of midday and travel mainly in the latter part of night and in the early morning. By night the temperature may be in the fifties, where before it was over 130°; yet as soon as the sun returns, so does the heat.

> The nights are extraordinarily cold, compared with the great heat of the day, for the sand, light and porous, radiates its great warmth away directly the sun's rays are withdrawn from it. There is something rapier-like in the thin piercing cold of a desert night, matching in sharpness the steely glitter of the moonlight. Coats and rugs are flung on shoulders, while the hot coffee, invariable accompaniment in the desert to every halt or start, is got ready. The sleeping mats are rolled up, the tent struck and packed, the ponies saddled, the grunting, protesting camels loaded and corded, and in a few minutes the little caravan is winding in single file through the white drifts. . . .
>
> By and by we are watching the beginning of that tremendous spectacle, played for our sole benefit every morning—sunrise in the Sahara. As the moment approaches, the air darkens, as though for fuller effect of contrast, and the cold sharpens. There is a breath heard that comes from nowhere and dies away. It is the desert turning in its sleep, as they say. . . . Now a spark catches in the lower edge of a narrow cloud that lies along the horizon and runs along it like fire along paper. Next moment the sky is all ablaze. Two or three arrowy spokes of light dart to the zenith. The molten rim comes over the desert edge, and the first beam hits you full with marksmanlike precision as though you were a target.

Hot, dry air does not move in such distinct masses as does air of other types. Rather, it streams outward in broad or narrow currents and often, because of its great warmth and lightness of weight, flows up over colder, denser masses and so travels great distances without appearing at the ground at all. The fiercely hot Sahara air of summer creates, by its very nature, a situation that tends to inhibit the outward movement of large quantities of air along the ground. Not all at once, but here and there, in separate cells and segments, the air expands and rises, forming a general region of low pressure into which there edges cooler air from the Mediterranean, the Atlantic Ocean, and Equatorial Africa. The inward-moving air is in turn heated and converted to hot air that again rises, so that the process is maintained. In this process the Sahara acts like a stove in which the superhot desert floor is the burner ignited daily by the sun.

Despite the predominance of airflow inward into the Sahara in summer, there are times when hot Sahara air streams westward over the Atlantic Ocean or northward across the Mediterranean. The dry air snatches up moisture from the water so swiftly that even a few miles offshore the lower air is filled with water droplets that create a dense haze. To wartime fliers who ferried planes from South America to Africa, the great Sahara haze was seen to appear hundreds of miles out to sea. Yet, as Africa was reached, the haze abruptly vanished along a curving line that traced the outlines of the shore.

Spring is the season when Sahara air is most likely to move northward across the Mediterranean, to arrive on the shores of Europe as the hot and sticky sirocco wind. Despite the moisture in its lowest layers, the sirocco often withers the crops in the fields and causes the fruit on the trees to drop to the ground, shriveled and parched. It has brought temperatures of over 100° as far north as the Spanish border and of 120° to Palermo, which, lying as it does to the north of the Sicilian mountains, may receive sirocco winds that are doubly hot through having had added to them the heat from the moisture that was condensed in passing over the mountains.

The sirocco is a wind of many names: in Spain, leveche; in Egypt, khamsin; in Tripoli, gibbi. In Egypt, Tripoli, and other parts of Africa, the wind is fresh and hot and dry, straight from the desert. Often it carries with it choking dust storms. The temperature of the air is but little less than it was in the hottest Sahara. In Tunisia, temperatures as high as 136° have been recorded in such a wind.

In wintertime, Sahara air moves southward with the retreating sun. It is as though the desert had expanded southward, almost to the equator. From Liberia to the southernmost Sudan, the warm air pushes in, bringing a regime that is in marked contrast with the opposite season of the year when moist tropical air from the Atlantic brings ample rains to the land.

Deserts other than the Sahara are the source of hot, dry winds that invade the surrounding regions. No Australian can forget for long that the continent on which he lives is largely made up of hot desert. Whether he lives along the rainy Queensland coast or in the subhumid southwest near Perth, in the mild southeast near Melbourne or in

Darwin in the north, he sometimes feels the hot summer winds from the desert that bring temperatures of 100° or more.

India has the Thar Desert, whose winds wither the millet in the neighboring Rajasthan. China has the Mongolian Desert; Russia, the Kara Kum. In the United States, hot summer winds from the western deserts push eastward as far as central Texas, Oklahoma, and Kansas, and northward almost to the Canadian border. Occasionally the winds blow west to meet the cool sea air along the coast of southern California. Then the residents of Los Angeles are no better off than those of Phoenix, Arizona, 800 miles from the ocean.

The great heat of deserts, particularly in summer, is associated with the clearness of the sky. Because there is little or no cloud a high percentage of the time, a relatively small amount of the incoming solar radiation is reflected back into space; a relatively high amount is used to heat the ground and the lower air. But though week in and week out by far the hottest summer air is from the desert, there are times when other regions of the land manufacture air almost as hot because the sky remains relatively cloudless. Even comparatively cool air from the oceans can quickly become converted to hot air in moving across the land if conditions are such that it does not carry with it a cloud blanket to ward off the rays of the sun.

One of the worst heat waves that ever hit the central United States was of this nature. In early July, 1936, abnormally high temperatures persisted for from one to two weeks from the Rocky Mountains eastward to the Appalachians. In some places the temperatures reached 120°. One hundred degrees was commonplace. The state hardest hit by the heat was Michigan, where 679 people died as a result of the heat in the nine-day period July 7–16. In Detroit alone there were 285 such deaths. Michigan was not as hot as many states farther west, but the people of the state were far less prepared than the heat-hardened residents of the plains region to cope with 100°-plus temperatures that broke all records.

All of the things that happen when an abnormal, prolonged heat wave hits a modern industrial city happened in Detroit. Parks and beaches were crowded to overflowing as factories and offices dismissed their employees. At the Michigan Central Railroad yards, employees clamored for the chance to clean and polish the interior of the air-conditioned Mercury that had just rolled in from Chicago. Iceman

Charles Unser collapsed from the heat while carrying a cake of ice on his back. Soft-drink dealers sold out their stock in record time, then closed up and went home after learning the wholesalers also were drinkless. In an air-cooled restaurant on Shelby Street a man came in for breakfast and stayed all day. On Michigan Avenue a young woman stood balanced on one shoe while she yanked at the other, which was stuck in the asphalt pavement. Finally, on July 16, cooler air came in from the north, bringing with it cloud and rain that broke the heat wave.

The heat wave of 1936 was produced by the warming of air fed inland from the Atlantic Ocean and the Gulf of Mexico. For almost two weeks the air streamed westward across Georgia and Florida, then swung northwest and then north, fanning out across the broad, flat regions of the Mississippi Valley. Though the flow of air waxed and waned, it continued to follow the same broad path across the land; and because it carried few clouds beyond the margins of the Gulf itself, the land grew hotter and hotter with each succeeding day, and each day heated the slowly moving air to higher and higher temperatures. The heat wave ended when the flow of air became so weak that cooler air could push in from the north.

The Warm Tropical Lands

Within the rainy regions of the tropics, away from the great deserts that overlap the tropic zone, the temperature at all seasons of the year is dominated by air from the warm oceans. The air, sticky with moisture, surges in across the land. In areas such as the lower Amazon Basin, the southern Malabar Coast in India, tropical islands such as the New Hebrides or northern New Guinea, and the African Gold Coast or the Congo Basin, there are no really marked seasons so far as temperature is concerned. Anyone can make a temperature forecast ten years in advance for any one of these regions for any time of the year and not be off by more than a few degrees. Such a forecast would read: "Maximum temperature 87° at 3 P.M., minimum temperature 76° at 6 A.M." There would be days when the maximum might go close to 98°, and the minimum sink to 69° or even a few degrees lower. But at least in the lowlands it would never be cool, nor would it be nearly as hot as at locations outside the rainy tropics. At Tulagi in the Solomons the official temperature, taken at the standard five-foot height in the shade, has never exceeded 97°. At Belém, Brazil, at the mouth of the Amazon and on the equator, it has never exceeded 95°; but at Fort Yukon, on the Arctic Circle, the temperature has reached 100°.

To some persons unaccustomed to it, the heat of the wet tropics is intolerable not because of the temperature, which is not nearly so high as at many other places, but because of the all-pervading dampness and the insufferable monotony of hot, moist weather day and night, week after week, month after month. The air seems so heavy with wetness that the visitor prays for rain to clear the atmosphere. Then, when rain has been flooding downward for what seem to be endless days, it is as though there were no air but only water, filling the spaces among the crowded trees and undergrowth, until he curses the rain and the ceaseless drumming noise it makes and everything about it.

And all the time, rain or not, the heat continues. Clothes rot. Shoes mildew in the damp heat. A person goes to sleep on wet sheets, pulling over the bedposts a damp, musty-smelling mosquito net. He turns and twists, seeking what cannot be found: a spot slightly less damp on which to rest his head. As he tries to sleep, he struggles against the feeling that the air in all its hot stickiness is choking him with malevolent intent. When morning comes, he awakes exhausted in a bed sopping wet with perspiration. Ahead lies a day like yesterday and the day before yesterday and the day before that.

Within the tropics, only the lowland regions near the equator are hot and wet throughout the year. Toward the margins of the tropics, as in central India, northern Venezuela, and the southern Belgian Congo and Tanganyika in Africa, there are pronounced seasonal variations both in temperature and in precipitation. For the most part this is open country in marked contrast with the dense jungle of the rainy tropics. It is the natural habitat of herbivores like the elephant, giraffe, deer, and antelope; and of large carnivores such as the lion and tiger.

In the tropics as elsewhere, elevation is a major factor in its influence upon temperature conditions. Custom, rather than climate, is the principal reason for the early afternoon siesta that the native Ecuadorians take in their capital city of Quito. Even though Quito is only sixteen miles from the equator, because of its elevation, 9,350 feet above sea level, daytime temperatures are slightly cool to pleasantly warm, in the sixties or seventies. At night it is well to have a blanket handy, since the temperature is apt to drop to 50° or even 40°. The weather is quite different at Esmeraldas, less than 100 miles away. In this swampy malarial town, standing with its back to the jungle at the point where the Esmeraldas River enters the Pacific, there is no relief from the oppressive heat at any time of day or night, or any season.

In hot country everywhere, elevation is a highly valued factor, since at higher locations it is possible to escape from the heat of the lowlands. Such summer capitals and hill stations as Darjeeling, India, and Bandung, Java, show the importance that a foreign people, unaccustomed to the tropics, once placed in keeping reasonably cool at least part of the time. Nor are such favored mountain spots restricted to the tropics. Summer resorts such as Asheville, North Carolina, and White Sulphur Springs, Virginia, owe their popularity chiefly to their elevation with its accompanying cooler weather.

Elevation is but one of several factors that may strongly influence local temperature conditions. Among the other locally important factors are the size and arrangement of hills and valleys, the nature of the vegetation, and the slope of the land. The influence of land features of these kinds often creates distinct temperature conditions.

Land Features and Local Temperatures

In the free air of the troposphere, away from the influence of mountains, the temperature decreases upward at the average rate of 3.3° for every thousand feet of altitude. A propeller-driven Stratocruiser flying at 18,000 feet will be surrounded by air at sub-freezing temperature even though the temperature at the ground is 90°, as will a jet transport flying at 28,000 feet. At any particular time and place, the exact manner in which temperature changes with increasing height depends on the nature of the air mass that is present. In moist air, conditions are usually close to average. But in hot, dry air, such as that from the Sahara, the temperature decrease may be as much as five degrees with each thousand feet of ascent; and in cold, dry polar air, such as that from Siberia, there may actually be an inversion, with the temperature increasing upward for the first few thousand feet before starting to decrease again. During winter the mountaintops are often the warmest places in northeast Siberia. True, the temperature there may be −30°, but in the lowlands it is colder still.

Temperature changes in the free air, high above the frictional drag effects and the immediate temperature effects of the lands, are less from day to night and from season to season than they are near the ground. Also, at height there is a greater lag in the time of occurrence of maximum and minimum temperatures than there is near the ground.

These effects are evidenced even at small elevations, such as the Eiffel Tower in Paris. In July, on top of the tower, the warmest time of the day is 4 P.M., when the temperature averages 67°. For the Parisians 1,000 feet below, the warmest time is 2 P.M., with an average of 73°. At night, average July temperatures atop the tower reach a minimum of 57° at 5 A.M.; at the ground, a minimum of 56° at 4:15 A.M.

The effects observable on the Eiffel Tower are magnified many times on high, isolated mountain peaks. There the temperature is close to that of the surrounding free air because the amount of solid earth jutting upward is too small to influence the air temperature greatly. On a plateau, however, where there is an extensive ground surface, the heating and cooling of the land profoundly affect the air temperature, so that there are wide daily and seasonal swings despite the elevation. On very high plateaus, such as that in Tibet, the heating may be even more pronounced than in low-lying plains regions because of the rarity of the atmosphere, which admits a high percentage of the incoming sunlight.

Sometimes the great heating temporarily produces a hot lower layer of air, often filled with dust, that lies below higher, much cooler layers, a situation favorable to the development of mirages. Sven Hedin describes these effects as he observed them in 1906 on the western edge of the Tibetan plateau, just beyond the great Karakoram Range:

> The height at Camp IX is 4,914 [16,122 ft.], or a fall of only 2 m. since Camp VIII. The ground of the plain may, therefore, be regarded as practically level. The day was like a summer day, without clouds and wind. Still the air is not absolutely clear, though it is difficult to tell why. Because of the strong and intense insolation [solar radiation received] the ground becomes rather hot and above it one sees the fine vibrations of the air like those above a heated broiler. The hot air has a tendency to rise, and perhaps these vertical currents take some of the finest and lightest particles of dust with them. If this be the case the dust, however, does not reach very high into colder layers of the atmosphere, for it is easy to see that the upper parts of the mountains

are sharper and clearer in outlines and colour than those near the base. Layers of air of different temperature may also cause the very common mirage. Very often the mountains seem to be reflected as from the surface of a quiet lake, where no lake exists. Parts of the caravan marching at a distance appear double, as if they were marching on the shore of a reflecting lake. The same seems to be the case with kyangs and antelopes, which now are more common. The whole country appears in light, aerial tones.

Elevation is not the only local factor that influences temperature conditions. The nature of the land cover, whether forest or grass or barren rock, and the actual shape of the land are also highly important. The forest provides its own protective canopy against the sun's rays, and so the quiet air among the trees is cooler on a warm day than the air beyond the forest's edge. The canopy also suppresses heat loss, so that the forest is warmer on a cold night than surrounding open fields. The air above a field of grass or above cropland is, in turn, more moderate in temperature than that above bare rock or fallow soil.

The shape of the land significantly influences local temperatures in several ways. Valleys, pockets, and other depressions are the collecting ground for cold, heavy air that drains downslope. In mountainous areas special winds may be created, like the cold mistral that sweeps down from the Alps during winter in the neighborhood of the Rhone Valley. Because of their frictional effects upon moving air, mountainous regions sometimes cause eddies to form and move along a front between two air masses that meet near the mountain's edge, so that places in the foothills undergo ultrarapid changes in temperature as first one kind of air and then another overlies the regions.

The temperature effects produced by eddies moving along a stationary front are strikingly illustrated by the curious weather along the slopes of the Black Hills in South Dakota on January 22, 1943. At 6 A.M. in Rapid City the temperature was −4°. By 9 A.M. it had risen slowly to 6° above. Then began some amazing fluctuations: 9:20 A.M., temperature 54°; 10:30, 12°; 11, 55°; 11:30, 10°; 11:45, 35°; 12:30 P.M., 16°; from 12:45 to 4 P.M., a steady 56°. By 5 P.M., the temperature had dropped to 8°, and it remained low for several days thereafter.

While the temperature was thus zigging and zagging, the residents of Rapid City were finding it difficult to adjust to the changing conditions. A dentist, leaving home to walk to his office about 9:30 in the morning, stepped out into the warm air, turned back and handed his overcoat to his wife, then started coatless down the street, rejoicing in the warm weather. By the time he was three blocks from home, the air was freezing cold with the temperature still going down. He returned for his overcoat and completed his trip, only to find shortly after reaching his office that the temperature once more was in the fifties. In houses and offices, windows went up and down with the thermometer. Janitors banked the fires in their furnaces, then piled on more coal, then frantically banked the fires again.

The spectacular occurrences at Rapid City were caused by the presence of a shallow wedge of cold air that lay along the edges of the hills, with unusually warm air on top of the cold. As the cold air pushed southward, it brushed against the hills so that small eddies or waves were formed. When the wavelike motion caused the cold air to withdraw from over Rapid City, the warm air descended to the surface. When another wave came along, the cold air again swung in over the city and the warm air was again forced up aloft. The repetition of this process produced several rapid fluctuations in temperature until finally the cold air pushed in strongly and deeply enough to force the warm air far upward, where it remained.

While the temperature variations at Rapid City were extreme compared to most temperature effects produced by local conditions, they illustrate that broad-scale influences, such as the movement of large air masses of different characteristics or the length of day as related to latitude, do not wholly determine the temperature conditions at any particular place. Both broad-scale and local factors are important.

On whatever scale it is viewed, the heat system of the atmosphere is fundamental to the production of weather. This is true not only because in its workings the heat system determines the temperature conditions, but also because temperature differences are closely related to the generation of winds. At the same time, without wind there would be no horizontal transport of heat either by large air masses or by small parcels of air. Thus heat and cold are fundamental to the dynamics of the ocean of air, just as those dynamics help create temperature changes and differences. This mutual interrelationship between temperature and wind is a primary factor in the physical order that governs the behavior of the ocean of air.

3 The Nature of Winds

Winds spring up and die out. They blow hot and cold, weakly and with ferocity. The dust they carry, the leaves they roll along the ground, the trees they bend to the snapping point—all these are visible. Yet the winds themselves are not. For "The wind bloweth where it listeth, and thou hearest the sound thereof, but canst not tell whence it cometh, and whither it goeth."

Primitive peoples and even the learned ancients did not possess the knowledge that would permit them to fathom the nature of the wind. The ancient Babylonians spoke of Amon and Amannet, the Hidden Ones, the gods of the wind. The wind was personified, as among the Central Eskimo, who lashed it with long whips to make it cease. Sometimes it was sold by magicians, who kept it tied in knotted cloths and could release it knot by knot until at the last untying the wind reached hurricane force.

These peoples of primitive cultures or of early civilizations could not know the nature of the wind because they did not know that the seemingly empty spaces among the waves of the sea and among the hills and trees and man-made objects of the landscape were not really empty at all but were filled with that thing of substance which is the air. For wind is air in motion and, by definition, the speedier the movement of the air, the speedier the wind.

Land and Sea Winds

The winds of the lands and those of the seas are different in character. Over the land the underbelly of the moving air scrapes the uneven ground and so is twisted and distorted. Land winds slap against the sides of mountains, come skimming down long slopes, race across the plains, become slowed and tangled in their lower portions over great forest regions, and bound along the building-lined corridors of the cities. Over the great water realm that is the oceans, the winds rip free across the unobstructed surface of the sea.

In the long history of man upon the seas, winds play a vital part. Prehistoric men in sailless rafts and canoes were driven far off course by squall and wind, and so came to settle strange islands or remote and unknown sections of the mainland coasts. The ancient Roman sailors outward bound for Cornwall watched and waited for the far-reaching winds that in summer sometimes blew northward from off Iberia all the way to Britain. When, in the sixteenth century, men took to the world-wide seas, the captains out of Europe soon learned that, after rounding the Cape of Good Hope bound for the Orient, it was best to stand northeast across the Indian Ocean to take advantage of the monsoon winds that blow all the way from Madagascar to India. Even in this modern day of engine-driven ships, the wise navigator watches the changing weather and capitalizes on favorable winds, while keeping clear of dangerous ones.

The very movements of the ocean waters are geared to the winds. Wind generates far-reaching currents. It creates waves and ocean swells that are high and closely spaced in the windy area where they are formed, then spread outward for hundreds of miles, all the time becoming flatter and flatter, with longer and longer distances between successive crests.

From a knowledge of the winds in mid-Atlantic it was possible to forecast the wave conditions that would exist three days later at the time of the Allied invasion of North Africa in World War II.

On November 5, 1942, a great convoy, ten days out of the British Isles, cleared the Straits of Gibraltar and headed eastward into the Mediterranean Sea. Two hundred miles away, beyond the bay that forms the funnel-shaped western end of the Gibraltar Straits, a second convoy out of the British Isles was headed eastward for the Mediterranean. West by southwest, 400 miles away, came the American convoy. Two weeks earlier it had assembled off the East Coast of the United States. Now it was headed landward, for Morocco.

In the North Atlantic, 1,500 miles away, the winds were whipping across the sea, following long, sweeping paths in circular fashion, counterclockwise around a storm center that lay to the west of the

British Isles. The rushing air pushed and scraped against the water, raising whitecapped waves; and as the turbulent air, filled with eddies, created partial vacuums in the troughs to leeward of the waves, the waves were sucked forward with increasing speed. Thus waves were created and grew and moved until, escaping from the wind-blown region of their birth, they became giant swells moving southeast toward North Africa at speeds of almost thirty knots, more than twice the speed of the convoys. Without interference the swells would arrive as mammoth waves upon the invasion coasts.

But there were other winds abroad in the Atlantic. By midnight, November 7, the twenty-foot swells, still moving southeast toward Africa, began to enter the zone of the trade winds, which throughout much of the year blow across the oceans in low middle latitudes. These cross winds flattened the swell crests and pushed water into the troughs behind the crests. All day long the waves from the north ran the gantlet of the trades until, by the morning of the 8th, the invasion date, the swell that arrived from the northwest was hardly strong enough to form small breakers on the beaches; while out in the open water, the invasion ships rode serene and almost still upon the barely ruffled surface of the sea.

All these events were reckoned in advance. All were timed and measured with the greatest possible accuracy. And the slide-rule calculations showed there would be a net effect of almost zero wave along the invasion shores.

The wave forecast for the North African invasion was the first of its kind; never before had there been an operational forecast that involved anything more than local wind and wave conditions. Special wave-forecasting techniques had been worked out for the North African invasion. These techniques and the forecast they made possible were the outward, practical manifestations of knowledge accumulated over many decades about the behavior of ocean waves and the nature and behavior of the winds that create them.

The Mechanics of Winds

Air is set in motion to produce wind where there are differences in air pressure from place to place. Without such differences there will be no wind. With them there must be wind. This holds true whether the wind is strong or gentle; whether it is far-ranging or only blows along a path so small as to be measured in feet or even inches.

The relations between wind and pressure are illustrated by considering in slightly simplified form the mechanics of the formation of air currents within a room. Such currents are miniature winds and, like their more full-bodied counterparts of the outdoors, they too arise from differences in air pressure.

If a room is closed up, the shades drawn, and if it is well insulated so that there is little or no flow of heat either in or out, all currents of air in the room will slacken, become imperceptible, disappear. Dust that has been kept aloft by the buffeting of small air currents will slowly settle downward to form a thin layer across the floor and on the furniture. The pressure of air upon the floor will everywhere become the same. If a weather map should be drawn in the same manner as if the floor was the surface of the earth, there would be no areas of HIGH or LOW pressure, no areas of wind, no areas of higher or lower temperatures. From wall to wall, beneath the furniture, and in the open places, the weather conditions would be the same.

Now suppose that on some cold night, when the air outdoors was still, one of the windows of the room was raised slowly and steadily so as not to disturb too greatly the quiet air within. Suppose, too, that the heat was turned on so that within the room, along the wall opposite the open window, the radiator became warmer and warmer. What effects would these changes have upon the weather within the room?

Becoming warmer, the air above the radiator would rise and expand. Soon the whole column of air above the radiator would consist of relatively light expanded air whose weight exerted downward on the floor would be distinctly less than the weight of air in other parts of the room. A LOW pressure area would develop along the floor in the region of the radiator. In adjacent portions of the room, the air near the floor, being squeezed downward by the greater weight of the cooler, denser air above, would move into the LOW, there to be heated and so to rise. At the top of the warm air column, along the ceiling, the air would move outward to descend in the region near the open window, where the cooling of air was most rapid because of heat loss to the outdoors.

The simple circulation would be completed by the flow of air along the floor from beneath the window to the radiator; for the colder, denser air by the window would press downward with great weight, forming a HIGH pressure area. Now, if a weather map was drawn to show the weather conditions along the floor, the winds would be seen to blow away from the HIGH and toward the LOW, and the temperature would increase as the radiator was approached and decrease as the window was approached.

In the free atmosphere, as in the air trapped within a room, there are winds whose immediate origin is thermal, which blow from cooler regions of high pressure toward regions where the air is strongly heated and so rises upward to create an area of low surface pressure. The small wind currents between shaded and sunny spots in a planted field are of immediate thermal origin. So also are the sea breezes that blow from the cool water to the heated land on a warm summer afternoon.

There are, however, other winds, including those that travel the greatest distances and blow with the greatest force, whose origin is thermal not in any simple immediate sense but only in the basic sense that they are driven by energy that was initially obtained from the sun. These are the winds associated with dynamic LOW and HIGH pressure systems, with cyclones and anticyclones. The discovery of the existence of these systems added greatly to the scientific understanding of the mechanics of the generation of winds.

Within a few years after 1643, the year of Torricelli's invention of the barometer, it became generally known that air pressure is not constant at any one place but varies markedly from time to time. By 1670, it was realized that over a period of many days there are more or less periodic swings in barometric pressure, with the pressure first rising, then falling, then rising again. These barometric changes, which are most marked in middle latitudes, appeared to be related to the weather conditions, with high pressure roughly correlated with fair conditions and low pressure with storms.

As barometric data accumulated, it became evident that there were geographic as well as temporal variations in air pressure. These geographic variations could not be understood, however, until the early nineteenth century, when Lamarck in France, Espy in the United States, and other scientists entered on maps weather observations that had been collected from all parts of the world. These were the first synoptic weather maps, their distinctive feature being that they showed the simultaneous weather conditions over wide areas.

Through the study of series of successive synoptic maps, it was learned that there are HIGH and LOW pressure areas that move across the earth. The moving LOWS were seen to be especially well marked, and it was noted that they often carried with them rain or snow and high winds. Later investigators demonstrated that these moving LOWS were dynamic systems, great whirls of air wholly similar to the eddies that are formed in rivers. They were, however, eddies that were often 500 miles across and they carried with them storms that were frequently of great intensity. These eddies came to be known as cyclones and included not only the storm systems of middle and high latitudes but also hurricanes, or tropical cyclones.

As for the HIGHS, they were found to be of two kinds. One was the moving HIGH associated with cold masses of air. This kind of HIGH was best developed over the continents in wintertime. Quite different were the HIGHS that lay across the subtropical oceans. These were warm HIGHS, being composed of warm maritime air. They owed their existence to the sinking of air aloft, which produced a piling up of air that yielded high pressures at the surface of the ocean. And unlike the smaller, more swiftly moving cold HIGHS, these warm ones tended to persist for many days or weeks and to shift position and alter shape only gradually.

While all this knowledge was being gained, much was being learned about the effects of the earth's rotation upon the winds. It was found that winds do not blow directly from place to place, but follow curving paths across the surface of the earth. This discovery provided the last important link that was required to explain the fundamental connection between wind and air pressure.

The Curve of the Winds

Any object traveling across the earth tends to swerve to the right in the Northern Hemisphere and to the left in the Southern Hemisphere. An artillery shell swerves in this fashion, and in the actual firing of a shell corrections are made for such deflection. The winds swerve too. The amount of their deflection is greatest at the poles, less at lower latitudes, and zero at the equator.

If the wind should be filled with smoke so that an observer hovering in outer space could view its motion, it would appear to him that it followed a straight-line course. What the observer would not see is that the earth rotates beneath the moving air, causing it to curve with reference to the earth's surface, though not with reference to the man suspended in space.

If the earth is likened to a merry-go-round and the space man is like a man watching the merry-go-round, the situation is precisely analogous. Should a boy on the inner, slow-moving edge of the merry-go-round throw a baseball outward, the man, outside the whirling system and concentrating only on the path followed by the ball, would see it move in a perfectly straight line. Yet the boy, watching the flight of the baseball with reference to the merry-go-round itself, would observe that the ball follows a curving path; for as it moves outward, the ball is left farther and farther behind by the movement of the merry-go-round, which speeds around at a faster and faster rate as its outer edge is approached. The reverse is also true. To throw a ball inward from the speedy outer edge is to cause it to curve because its initial rotational speed, in the hand of the thrower, is greater than the speed of the merry-go-round at points nearer the center.

Because of their deflection by the rotation of the earth, winds do not blow directly out of HIGHS or directly into LOWS. Instead, they edge outward from HIGH pressure areas and they edge into LOWS only very slowly. In these circulations, friction and centrifugal force also play a part; but essentially, the indirect nature of the airflow is related primarily to the deflection caused by the earth's rotation.

All winds are deflected by the earth's rotation. The deflection is, however, most evident in winds that blow strongly or over great distances, such as the speedy winds of the cyclonic LOWS or the long-distance trade winds that blow out of the warm HIGHS of the subtropics. Large-scale winds of these kinds are especially well developed, in relatively simple form, over the smooth surface of the ocean. These ocean winds sweep across such wide areas and play such a fundamental role in the circulation of air on a world-wide scale that they are properly considered to be the master winds of the earth.

4 Winds of the Sea and the Land-Sea Borders

The sea is the domain of many winds. On the equator side of the great subtropical HIGHS lie the trade winds, which are so well defined and blow across such vast distances that they must be listed as the foremost of all winds that blow. On the pole side of the subtropical HIGHS are the westerlies, which lack the constancy of the trades, yet often blow with three times their force. The westerlies ride across the continents as they do across the sea, but it is on the sea that they are best developed and most neatly defined; at least in their purest form, they are ocean winds.

Still other winds are primarily identified either with the sea or with the land-sea borders. Hurricanes form only over tropical seas; though they may sometimes bring their tremendous rains and vicious circling winds onto the land, nearly all of their life is spent at sea.

There are also the two wind systems that result from the juxtaposition of sea and land. One of these is the monsoon system, which carries large quantities of air from sea to land in the summertime and from land to sea in wintertime. The other is a comparatively tiny circulation system, which shunts air back and forth across the borders of the lands, the air moving first upon a sea breeze flowing landward in the warm afternoon, then upon a land breeze drifting seaward during the cool night.

Among them these winds of the sea and of the sea-land borders dominate the flow of air across 80 per cent of the surface of the earth. The heat and the moisture that they carry with them determine the weather regimes of wide reaches of the continents as well as of the world-wide sea itself.

The Trade Winds

The trade winds are the steadiest winds on earth. They dominate the weather over wide expanses of the oceanic realm in the subtropics and tropics. They give distinctive character to thousands of islands and to long segments of the continental coasts. No area of anything approaching like extent has such a uniform natural personality as has the 35 million square miles of sea and island regions encompassed by the trade wind realms of the earth.

Within the province of the trades, the very texture of the air is different. Its special quality is clearly and suddenly revealed to the traveler who, after a nonstop flight from the American mainland, alights from his plane at Honolulu. This trade wind air is warm and gentle, with a vibrant freshness, as though alive. The feel of it is quite different from that of the cool, moist air of coastal California or the brisk, damp air of Puget Sound.

To appreciate the full nature of trade wind air, the traveler should leave Honolulu, which lies against the leeward side of the coastal mountains of Oahu, and travel across the Pali and down to the eastern coast along the beach at Kailua or farther north where the tropical vegetation crowds down the gentle slope to the edge of the shore. Along this eastern coast the wind blows onshore almost without interruption from March till mid-October, and even during the period from November to February the trade winds blow more often than not.

Two thousand miles away to the northeast this air traveled southward a few hundred miles to sea off the western coast of the United States. It was cool air then, cool and damp like that which brings the summer fog to San Francisco. Then it started to enter upon the ocean at lower latitudes, where the sunlight falls at a steeper angle and strongly warms the water. It began to gain more warmth and to draw up more moisture from the sea. Always the air kept following a broadly curving path, edging outward away from the center of the HIGH pressure area that lay across the mid-Pacific. By the time it was 1,500 miles off Oahu it had become a steady northeast wind, moving equatorward at an angle, headed for the doldrums where the air was rising upward to create a zone of LOW air pressure, of small, whiffling breezes, of dead calms.

Here on the windward coast of Oahu, as on the coasts of Molokai and Maui and other rugged islands of the trade wind realm, the inward-moving air, thrusting up the mountain slopes, yields massive bands of towering clouds that first obscure the mountain peaks, then build downward toward the coastal plains. Beneath the clouds the land is drenched with rain as part of the water that was gathered over the ocean is returned to the surface of the earth. On the crests of the Koolau Range in eastern Oahu and on its upper slopes at elevations of 1,600 feet or more, the annual fall from trade wind air exceeds 200 inches in places. Mt. Waialeale, on Kauai, is a place of this kind, facing the moist incoming trade wind air. There the annual rainfall averages over 470 inches a year, the highest recorded anywhere.

On the trade wind islands, the natives of 500 years ago gathered the fruits nurtured by the bountiful rains and the warm winds. For the Caribs and other Indians of the trade wind islands of the West Indies, the staple foods were maize, guava, and the banana, which thrived in the mild, rainy clime. The natives of the Pacific raised taro, the root of which is a mealy substance that to this day is used for making poi. They also gathered the starchy fruit of the breadfruit tree, which provided not only food but also cloth from its fibrous inner bark, wood for canoes and furniture, and glue from its juice.

Above all, however, they cultivated the coconut palm, that tree of "erect and lofty bearing," which, as Melville said, "compares with other trees as man with inferior creatures." The blessings of this tree were incalculable to the natives. As Melville observed from firsthand observation:

> Year after year, the islander reposes beneath its shade, both eating and drinking of its fruit; he thatches his hut with its boughs, and weaves them into baskets to carry his food; he cools himself with a fan plaited from the young leaflets, and shields his head from the sun by a bonnet of the leaves; sometimes he clothes himself with the clothlike substance which wraps round the base of the stalks, whose elastic rods, strung with filberts, are used as a taper; the larger nuts, thinned and polished, furnish him with a beautiful goblet; the smaller ones, with bowls for his pipes; the dry husks kindle his fires; their fibres are twisted into fishing lines and cords for his canoes; he heals his wounds with a balsam compounded from the juice of the nut; and with the oil extracted from its meat embalms the bodies of the dead.

The diffusion of the coconut palm from its native habitat in Malaysia to the islands of the Pacific was doubtless aided by the trade winds and trade wind currents. Though the initial eastward spread, against the prevailing trades, must be credited to early navigators who carried the coconut to the major islands, that to lesser islands was almost certainly promoted by wind and current, which, hundreds of years ago just as today, must have borne floating coconuts long distances across the ocean. A single floating coconut, washed up on the shore of some remote atoll, would have been sufficient to populate the island with palms; and given sufficient time and the ever-steady trades, "accidents" of this kind were certain to occur.

Today the trade wind realms support a thriving commercial agriculture based chiefly on the raising of sugar cane. Over 60 per cent of the cane sugar that enters the world market comes from trade wind lands. In all of these areas, the sugar cane can be grown under natural conditions only along the rainy coasts against which the trade wind strikes. But the benefits of the trade wind rains are extended to drier areas of these islands through the use of ingenious systems of irrigation.

In the Hawaiian Islands, tunnels gather in rain water that has seeped into the ground along the rainy eastern slopes of the mountains, thus providing for dry leeward valleys. On one large sugar plantation the wells and gravity systems supply 200 million gallons of water a day—almost three times the amount used in San Francisco.

At first thought it appears curious that islands bathed almost continuously by moist trade wind air should be arid in places. Yet for mountainous islands this must be true because of the sequence of physical events that occurs in moist air as it passes over a mountain barrier.

As the moist air of the trades surges upslope on the windward side of the mountain, it expands, because for every foot of increased elevation there is one foot less of overlying atmosphere that pushes down upon the air and so constricts it through sheer weight. In expanding the air cools. With cooling, the moisture in the air is condensed to form rain-producing clouds. But condensation returns to the air the heat energy that was used initially, many miles away, to evaporate ocean water and add that water to the air; so once condensation starts, the rising air does not cool as rapidly as it did before.

When the air descends the leeward side of the mountain, the sequence of physical events unwinds in reverse order. The descending air is pressed more and more tightly together. Cloud particles swept across the mountain and carried downslope in the descending air evaporate quickly as the temperature rises. By the time the air reaches the foot of the mountain, its temperature is higher than when it started its ascent, for in its transmountain journey it has acquired new heat through condensation of moisture. Its absolute water content is lower than at the start, for it has lost much of its moisture as rainfall on the windward slope. It is hot, dry air. It is air that breeds a desert.

Desert areas, virtually small Saharas, lie along the leeward side of mountainous trade wind islands. If one tires of the ample rains and the lush tropical growth along the east coast of Oahu north of Kailua, he has only to drive thirty miles across the island to the coast northwest of Ewa, where cacti grow along the upper edges of the beach and are scattered along the otherwise barren slopes on the sides of steep arroyos carved from the neighboring hills by occasional desert rains. Or he can bask in the bright desert sun at Kona Inn, on the west coast of Hawaii, and watch the clouds that high in the east are crowding close upon the slopes of the mountains. Thus on scores of islands of the trade wind realm, there are deserts and humid regions side by side, with only a mountain between.

The Westerlies

An earth entirely covered by water would have no towering Himalayas to thwart the movement of the ambient air, no frigid polar lands to manufacture mountains of cold air almost as high as the Himalayas and covering twenty times the area. There would be no deep-trenched valleys to guide the wind downslope, no desert areas whose surfaces of rock and sand and clay, heated to the scorching point, would send the air aloft to great heights. Over such an earth of uniform surface the winds would blow without impediment and they would all be ocean winds.

The circulation of air would be relatively simple. There would be but two major wind belts in each of the hemispheres, northern and southern. The easterly trades would dominate the lower latitudes; the westerlies, the latitudes from 30° to the poles. There would be no seasonal winds like the monsoons that blow outward from Asia in the wintertime, and no polar easterlies like those found over the waters off the coast of Greenland.

On the earth as it really is, there are large ocean regions over which the movement of air is strongly influenced by the presence of the continents, even of continents that are hundreds of miles away. But the oceans are so vast, comprising as they do over 70 per cent of the surface area of the world, that the dominant winds remain the trades and the westerlies, just as they would on an earth without land. Indeed, despite innumerable fluctuations in wind direction, the broad currents of the westerlies extend across the lands themselves. So doing, they "carry the weather" with them. In middle latitudes the weather moves from west to east.

"If you don't like the weather . . . just wait a few minutes." Mark Twain's statement expresses the essence of the weather of the westerlies. Within their broad, massive current, which flows always eastward round and round the world, there are vast swirls of air and crosscurrents and upwellings from beneath.

Swirling cyclonic eddies caught in the flow of the westerlies bring a whole succession of weathers. To the observer in the path of such a cyclonic storm, first may come the warmer air that, in the Northern Hemisphere, has been drawn into the counterclockwise swirl. The wind is from a southerly direction. But as the cyclone moves on eastward, the cold air drawn into it from the north comes roaring through. The wind shifts suddenly, to northwest or to north. This is the west side of the cyclone. As the cold front comes through, it tosses above it, like snow tossed upward by a moving plow, the warmer, lighter air that lies ahead. Quick and violent storms are formed, with sudden rains or heavy snows or hail, and then the deep cold air, following behind the eddy, dominates the scene and cold, clear weather sets in.

The gentle and persistent rains of summer and the long and steady snows of winter that also characterize the weather of the zone of the westerlies come at the eastern or front side of the moving cyclones. The polar sides of these eddies are filled with cold air. The warm air from milder regions, riding poleward, climbs up the retreating cold-air mass that all the time is moving in an easterly direction. Thrusting steadily up the gently sloping surface of the cold-air mountain, the warm air cools and in so doing forms a canopy of clouds from which the rain comes down across a region twice the size of half a dozen states.

After the retreating cold-air mass has left the region, carrying with it the overlying clouds and rain, the winds go into the south and the weather turns balmy, with only scattered puffball clouds across the sky. This weather persists for a few hours or even a day or so until the back, west side of the eddy arrives, bringing with it the fresh cold air that once more yields a sharp and sudden storm.

With cyclones dominating the circulation in the realm of the westerlies, the winds are highly variable. Only the steady drift from west to east and the greater force of the west winds when they blow resolve the equation in favor of dominant westerly winds and so permit calling these zones the realms of westerly winds.

In sailing-ship days these zones were given names that have persisted to the present time. In the regions of 40°, 50°, and 60° north these winds were known as the "brave westerlies." The phrase carried with it the emphatic meaning of having to brave the gale-force winds and heavy storms that mark the ocean regions of these latitudes, especially in winter. In the Southern Hemisphere, where the westerlies are even more vigorous and the storms more violent, the west-wind belt was known as the "roaring forties." This phrase applied to all the winds that blow so furiously between the latitudes of 40° and 60° south.

Over the oceans, at the center of the westerly belts, the winds in some regions exceed 25 m.p.h. more than half of the time during the winter. The peak velocities, experienced when an intense cyclone comes through, may top 70 m.p.h. Except for hurricane winds, these are the fastest-blowing winds on all the oceans. They dig strongly into the water and so create tremendous waves that pound the coasts of islands and continents hundreds of miles distant. As for ships within the wind region, even the mightiest ocean liner rolls and wallows in the mountainous seas. In the roaring forties, waves that measure sixty feet from trough to crest have been observed. In the westerly realm of the Northern Hemisphere, there are wind-created waves of fifty feet.

The reputation of the westerlies for bad weather was in good measure responsible for the growth of Charleston, South Carolina, during the colonial period. In those days Dutch and English merchantmen out of Europe and slavers out of Africa most commonly sailed westward to America in low latitudes during the summer, with the strong easterly trade winds aft to speed the square-rigged ships along.

Their first port of call was the West Indies, where they dropped part of their cargo of merchandise or human cattle. After picking up rum and molasses, they would sail northwestward on a starboard tack. This would bring them into Charleston, which in those days of the early eighteenth century was a major port that quite compared with Boston or New York. Being by now three months or more out of their home ports, the ships would lay over in Charleston until spring, for they feared the raging winds and stormy waters of winter on the North Atlantic. Thus Charleston became not only a first port of call on the mainland coast but also a supply depot that thrived on the business brought by ships from across the sea.

Only in later times, when sailing ships became much larger and eventually schooner-rigged, did Charleston begin to lose out in importance to more northerly ports such as Baltimore and New York. Finally, in the nineteenth century, when steamships began to cross the oceans with or against the winds, the trade wind route to the Americas was generally abandoned as being the long way round. The city of Charleston became a minor port.

Hurricanes

Take two trillion tons of air. Spread it across a circular area 300 miles in radius. Start it spinning, with the air swirling round the center at 100 miles an hour. Fill the air with clouds. Dump down water from those clouds, fifteen inches of it in twenty-four hours. Start the whole swirling system moving at 12 m.p.h. Have the circling winds bite into the ocean waters. Have them pile the water onto the land. That will be a typical major hurricane, and its effect upon a populated coastal area can be disastrous.

The hurricane has many names. In the Southwest Pacific it is known as a typhoon; in the Bay of Bengal, as a cyclone; in Australia, as a willy-willy. Whatever its local name, the hurricane is a spinning eddy, like the cyclonic eddies in the zone of westerly winds. But though the eddies of the westerlies may generate tremendous winds, they do not pack the concentrated punch of the hurricane. The eddies of the westerlies originate in high or middle latitudes and carry with them both polar and tropical air. Hurricanes are born in low latitudes. Their substance is warm tropical air. The source of their strength is the sea, which feeds water vapor into the storm. The continuous conversion of the vapor into water droplets within the hurricane releases in a single hour more energy than is discharged by the explosion of 700 nuclear bombs of the Hiroshima type. This is the energy that drives the hurricane winds. It is a force to be coped with only by forewarning.

As summer approaches, bringing with it the hurricane season, weather reconnaissance planes of the U.S. Air Force are on the alert at airfields in the Philippines and Guam, in Florida and Bermuda. The planes from the Philippines patrol the regions of the China and Philippine Seas; those from Guam, the regions to the east of the Philippines. They fly crisscross routes high above the sea, searching for typhoons. Once a typhoon has been spotted, it will be trailed by planes in relay. Its growth will be observed, and its decay. Its wind speeds will be measured. Air pressure readings will be taken. Its course will be plotted constantly. All this information will be dispatched by radio to weather forecasting centers where the deadly serious business of anticipating the typhoon movements is in progress.

In the regions of the Gulf of Mexico and the Caribbean and in the Atlantic Ocean farther east, similar surveillance is maintained by aircraft based in Florida and Bermuda. To avert disaster, or at worst to soften it, a constant watch is kept. Yet so vast are the spaces of the ocean in the regions of hurricane birth that sometimes a hurricane may form and grow to full size and move perilously close to land before it is discovered.

If all hurricanes traveled the same kind of curving paths, forecasting would be greatly simplified. Unfortunately, many of them do erratic things. They start to turn in the usual way, then quickly reverse direction. They steer a zigzag path without any marked curving at all. They dip equatorward, then swing back. They curve twice. Sometimes they even loop around, like the hurricane of 1910 that on October 14, while moving northward, scored a direct hit on the town of San Juan y Martínez in western Cuba and on October 16, coming from the west, hit the town again.

To ships at sea no storm holds a greater threat than a well-developed hurricane. The violent winds and the confused, mountainous seas inflict a beating even upon large battleships and ocean liners. In December, 1944, Admiral William F. Halsey's Third Fleet was trapped in a fully grown typhoon, about 500 miles to the east of Luzon, in the Philippines. The Fleet Aerologist had known well in advance that a typhoon was somewhere in the area. So also had the aerologists in the Fleet Weather Central, 4,000 miles away at Pearl Harbor. Yet even at Pearl, where coded weather reports streamed inward from ships at sea, from aircraft in flight, and from American-held bases on scores of Pacific islands, it was uncertain just where the typhoon center lay.

Halsey's Third Fleet blundered into the typhoon. The fleet steamed right into it, so close to the center that conditions could not have been worse. Destroyers and cruisers, battleships and carriers, were tossed about like shavings on a stormy pond. "Proceed at will" was the order from the flagship. The fleet scattered before the wind and waves. Not a ship escaped heavy damage. Three of them, *Spence*, *Hull*, and *Monaghan*, went down, and only a few survivors were rescued.

Though a ship at sea is vulnerable when trapped in a typhoon, by careful navigation it can at least be kept clear of the innermost region of the storm, where wind and wave conditions are most extreme. Less fortunate are the inhabitants of an island that happens to lie in the path of such a storm. If it strikes the island head on, all that can be done is to seek what shelter exists and, if there is advance warning, to evacuate coastal areas. If the island is a low one, such as an atoll, even evacuation is impossible. The devastating effects of a typhoon upon an atoll are evident from the results of the typhoon that struck Jaluit atoll on January 7, 1958. Though the loss of life on Jaluit might have been minimized had there been advance warning of the storm, nothing could have been done to save the land, the food crops, and the houses and other native buildings. For the nature of an atoll is such that there is no protection from a direct typhoon strike.

An atoll is a ring of low-lying islets upon a flat-topped coral reef that partially or wholly encloses a lagoon. The lagoon may be one to fifty miles across. The islets themselves, at least the larger, inhabited ones, are typically several hundred yards wide and a few hundred yards to a few miles long. At their highest points they are seldom more than ten or twenty feet above the sea. The coral reef upon which the festooned islets are perched descends abruptly on the ocean side, falling off into deep water along a submarine cliff. On the lagoon side, the descent from the flat-topped reef into the water is far gentler. At their deepest points, atoll lagoons only rarely extend downward to more than 200 feet below sea level, and in the immediate vicinity of the islets the descent is usually gradual to a depth of twenty or thirty feet, at which steeper declines may occur.

Jaluit atoll, in the eastern Marshall Islands of the tropical Pacific Ocean, is in many respects typical of a large atoll. The Jaluit lagoon measures some fifteen by thirty miles. The islets rise to maximum heights of ten to fifteen feet above sea level.

The 1,200 natives of Jaluit were first warned of an approaching typhoon during the morning, when huge waves rolling in from the east began to bang against the outer reef on the eastern side of the atoll. At the time the tide was still extremely low, so that the eastern islets were not immediately awash. But as the tide rose and the fury of the waves increased, the water began to sweep farther and farther onto the reef flat and then onto the land itself. Meanwhile, a sudden strong wind set in from the northeast quadrant. Within an hour the winds had reached hurricane force and water was being swept clear across several of the eastern islets from the ocean into the lagoon.

By now it was afternoon. The tide had risen to nearly full height. The wind was piling the water across the land, and upon the water huge confused waves joined the wind, uprooting trees and carrying thousands of coral fragments, some weighing 100 pounds or more.

One man described the storm in this fashion: "There were four or five great waves from the east, then some from the west that made a big jumble of water. Trees were falling down everywhere and even flying through the air." Another said: "We half-swam, half-waded from one big tree to another, but since the trees were going down everywhere we weren't sure what was safe. I saw a whole family drown. They'd tied themselves to a huge tree, high above the water. Then the tree went over and they were swept away."

It is astonishing that only fourteen persons were killed during the storm. Two more died from exhaustion afterward. The low toll of life was owing to the World War II, foot-thick Japanese blockhouses, deeply sunk into the coral, and to the happy coincidence that the natives of Mejetto, one of the most seriously devastated islets, happened to be visiting another islet that was never completely awash.

Drastic changes were wrought upon Mejetto by the storm. Coral debris was spread across more than half of the islet, to depths of up to three feet. Throughout most of Mejetto over 90 per cent of the formerly densely spaced trees were either completely gone or else snapped off, only the roots and some ten to fifteen feet of their trunks remaining. Whole sections were scoured clean. On the lagoon side, there were outwash deposits in the shape of fans and deltas, as if small rivers had flowed across the narrow islet for many years. As for native huts and such food crops as coconut, pandanus, and breadfruit, virtually all were totally destroyed except at the northernmost tip of the island, where many of the trees were left standing.

Part of the rehabilitation of Jaluit is being carried out by the United States Trust Territory of the Pacific. The program includes replanting of coconut palms, breadfruit, pandanus, taro, and other food crops required for subsistence of the native Marshallese, as well as building new boats and houses. This part of the work is already largely accomplished. Yet nothing can hasten the fundamental rate of rehabilitation, which is determined by such natural processes as the conversion of coral debris to soil and the re-establishment of natural vegetation outside the small areas of replanting. If there is not another typhoon before that time, the atoll will return to something resembling its former tropical luxuriance by about 1975. But sooner or later another typhoon will come, devastation will again ensue, and lives will be lost. For nothing can intervene between the action of atmosphere and wind-driven seas upon these slight bits of land.

By far the greatest damage at Jaluit, and all of the loss of life, occurred on the eastern islets, where the water swept across the land. Similarly, when hurricanes strike coastal lands anywhere, the greatest danger is in zones where the winds are onshore and so will sweep the water onto the land in the form of a surge wave, sometimes called a "tidal wave," a term that is a misnomer since the wave is not produced by tidal forces. The effect of these surge waves may be devastating in densely populated coastal areas. This was illustrated by the New England hurricane of 1938 and by earlier and even more disastrous hurricanes at Galveston, Texas, and in the Ganges Delta in India.

In the New England hurricane of 1938, some 600 lives were lost and the damage exceeded a quarter of a billion dollars. Most of the losses were in eastern Long Island, eastern Connecticut, Rhode Island, and southeastern Massachusetts, all of which lay to the east of the center of the storm, so that as it moved inland, from south to north, these areas were exposed to a surge wave swept onto the land by the tremendous winds from the south. In contrast, westernmost Connecticut and other areas to the west of the center of the storm experienced northerly offshore winds and so suffered little or no inundation.

In the Galveston hurricane of 1900, 6,000 persons drowned in the ensuing surge wave.

The wave produced by a typhoon of 1864 in the Bay of Bengal took a toll of 50,000 lives in the low, flat ricelands of the densely populated region near Hooghly. In the very same area, on October 7, 1737, there had occurred one of the three or four greatest known natural catastrophes ever to strike at mankind. A typhoon created a forty-foot wave that rushed far inland, destroying thousands of small fishing craft and drowning at least 150,000 people.

Once upon the land, the hurricane begins to lose its power since it can no longer draw moisture directly from the sea. For two or three hundred miles inland it may still generate high winds that blow down power lines and disgorge heavy rains that produce local flooding, which in some communities may result in heavy damage. Yet the farther inland it moves, the weaker it becomes. Six hundred miles inland it almost resembles a storm of the more usual type. Eight hundred miles inland it has lost its distinctive punch and has become just another intense storm.

Winds of the Coasts

The continents intrude upon the world ocean, which presents a virtually level surface; the continents are comprised of many surfaces of differing slopes and elevations. Water in solid or liquid form is the one great substance of the ocean; the continents are a mosaic of forests and barren rock, water and arid sand, grasses and snow and soil and city pavements.

Where the land and the sea meet, the sharp contrast between their surfaces produces a zone that is the scene of many distinctive weather events. The zone is a narrow one, extending landward not more than a dozen miles and seaward an even lesser distance. Within it there is a gentle interplay of sea air and land air. Within it also are found some of the most violent winds of all the lands; for when an intense storm stands out to sea, it generates winds that comb the tangled edges of the land with furious power, yet cannot reach far inland because the increased friction with the ground beneath saps them of their strength.

Anyone who has ever walked along a headland toward the coast on a day when a storm is over the sea knows how the force of the wind increases as the sea-land border is approached. Perhaps this is an open headland covered only by grass and scattered shrubs with occasional clumps of trees. Three miles from the sea the shrubs are slightly bent before the wind. This is a stiff breeze. It comes in at a steep angle upon the land, so that the observer must face the wind. Yet except for occasional gusts, there is no need to maintain balance by leaning into the wind.

Another mile and the going is much more difficult. Now the gusts are violent enough to throw a man off stride. The grass is bent almost to the ground, and the shrubs are deeply bowed. The sea air has real freshness, laden with the smell of salt.

A mile from the sea, the battle with the wind, soon to be edged with spray, really begins. The walker bends far forward as if moving in battle across an open field toward enemy lines.

By the time the outer margin of the headland is reached, a dozen yards from the edge of the sea cliff, it is impossible to walk any farther, even crouching down. There are few shrubs here and no trees at all. The nearest tree, 300 yards inland, is bent so that its crown almost touches the ground. Back there the wind must be blowing at 50 m.p.h., but here its speed is 60 or more. Few trees could stand through many storms like this.

In the zone of the westerlies, along exposed and open coasts, wind speeds of 60 m.p.h. are not uncommon, especially in winter. No hurricane is needed to create such winds. The vigorous cyclonic storms typical of these latitudes are quite sufficient. Places such as these experience stronger winds than any other sites upon the land, if one excepts the winds of the high mountains and of the tornado. Along the coast of Cape Cod, at Land's End in southwest England, and at scores of other coastal sites, record wind speeds have exceeded 100 m.p.h. In each such instance, however, the winds have diminished markedly in speed away from the outer coast, so that the great damage was confined to a zone a few hundred yards wide fronting on the sea.

In coastal regions where winds are strong, no elaborate network of weather observing stations is needed to map the broad lines of flow of strongest winds across the land. Every tree or bush tells in its location and its habit of growth the strength and direction of the dominant winds. Thus, on the Marin Peninsula, north of San Francisco, the most exposed and windiest areas of all are free of trees except for those that stand to leeward of some boulder.

In areas of somewhat lesser winds, laurels stand in clumps as if for mutual protection. Their trunks are close together on the windward side and lean downwind in hunchbacked posture. Their crowns are intertwined and form a mass of foliage streaming out to leeward. The only other trees in these windy areas are low-lying scrub oaks, which press so closely to the ground that they resemble cushions. In areas of more moderate winds, the trees stand singly; but even so they bend downwind. Their foliage is unusually thick, possibly because the pruning action of the wind stimulates leaf growth.

There are still other signs of the nature of the wind. Where trees have been chopped down, the stumps reveal a bunching up of tree rings on the windy side and a spreading out of rings to leeward. In regions near the sea, the kinds of grasses found tell something of wind conditions, for certain species prefer the salty soils that mark the inward path of strong sea winds.

The character of vegetation along the coast reflects the nature of only the strongest winds. Such winds are frequent, but it is by no means true that they blow a high percentage of the time. More often the wind regime of coastal regions, particularly in spring and summer, is characterized by gentle breezes. On warm days and during the nights thereafter, there is a rhythm to these breezes. They blow onshore in late afternoon or early evening and weakly offshore during the later night. These are the land and sea breezes that create a zone of cooler summer weather along the coast and so help make the shore a favored place to seek relief from the far hotter weather inland.

On hot, clear summer days, the land a few miles from the sea is like a radiator. It strongly heats the overlying air, causing it to rise. Over the ocean the air is cool, for the sunlight falling on the water is partly reflected and that which does enter the water spends part of its energy for evaporation and part for warming not the surface water but water at depth. Even where the solar energy warms the surface water, it cannot bring it to a high temperature, for waves and currents keep replacing the surface water, which, in any event, requires far more heat to raise its temperature than does the land. By afternoon the temperature contrast between land and sea is often sufficiently great so that sea air starts moving inland to replace the rising air above the land. At first the sea breeze moves straight in. Then, as it strengthens, it slowly turns through being deflected by the spin of the earth. By early evening it is a moderate wind that blows obliquely inland over distances of several miles.

At night, with the sea preserving its lesser warmth and the land cooling rapidly, the circulation is reversed. The breeze is from land outward to the sea. Unlike the sea breeze of late afternoon, this land breeze is not shallow but extends to heights of many hundred feet. Often the air returning to the ocean moves so lazily as to be barely felt. Nonetheless large quantities of air move seaward; should the coast be curved, as along a large bay, the air from the land may crowd together as if the curving land were a lens and the wind were rays of light converging at a focal point. Then nocturnal thunderstorms may spring up over the sea.

Sea breezes create thunderstorms too, especially in the tropics. The air converges on the edges of the land. Billowy clouds build up to enormous heights. There is a sudden torrential downpour. Ten to twenty minutes later the storm is over, and the rain water brought to the land on a sea breeze has already begun to flow downslope and underground to join the sea once more.

The Monsoons

Sea breezes and land breezes are created by moderate temperature contrasts between the sea and the land. Their rhythm is diurnal, from day to night and back again to day. The areas of land and sea that participate in the exchange of air are small. Suppose the temperature contrasts were much greater, the rhythm seasonal, and the areas involved were reckoned in hundreds of thousands or even millions of square miles. One would then have the situation of the monsoon winds, those winds of vast extent that blow off the continents in winter and onto them in summer. These winds are particularly well developed in the Australasian region, where in day-to-day and week-to-week reliability they rival the trade winds in their constancy.

The monsoon circulation of the Australasian region produces a flow of air on a scale unmatched anywhere else in the world. This circulation dominates the weather throughout an area of 30 million square miles—an area ten times that of the United States, extending

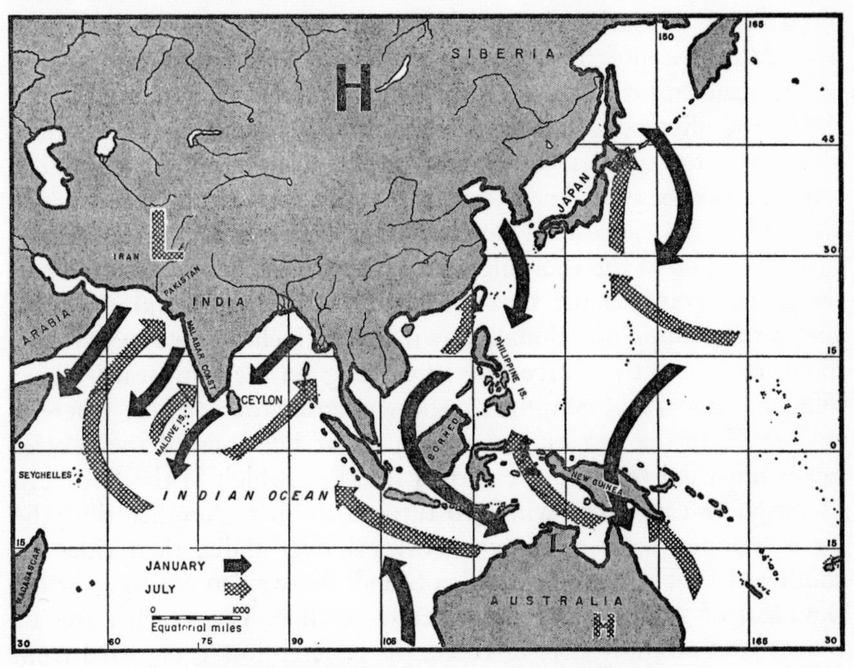

MONSOON WINDS OF ASIA AND AUSTRALIA

The arrows show the principal lines of wind flow. Though the wind speeds and directions vary from day to day, the general flow is remarkably constant and closely follows the flow lines indicated by the arrows. *H* and *L* mark the average location of the centers of the HIGH and LOW air-pressure systems over Asia and Australia. The shading of these letters indicates the month to which they apply.

from the Arctic Circle southward far beyond the equator into the middle of the Indian Ocean, and from Africa, Arabia, and Europe eastward beyond the margins of Australia, New Guinea, and Japan.

During winter the air overlying Asia, dense and heavy in its coldness, pushes down with added weight upon the plains, plateaus, and rugged mountains that stretch from the Himalayas northward to the Arctic Ocean. Thus there is created an enormous region of average HIGH pressure that reaches the width and breadth of the continent and is centered just south of Lake Baikal in northern Mongolia. In marked contrast, the surrounding oceans are usually covered with warmer, lighter air that produces an enveloping belt of lesser pressure.

Moving from higher to lower pressure, the air pours outward across the margins of the Asiatic continent at a rate that averages over 100 million tons of air for every second of the day and night. These enormous losses of air by the continent are made up by air returning over Asia high aloft to complete and maintain the circulation.

The exact distribution of HIGH and LOW pressure across Asia and the surrounding oceans changes constantly, to produce corresponding changes in the speed and direction of the airflow off the continent onto the oceans. One time the air is pumped most strongly southeastward from Siberia toward Japan, where it arrives foggy with moisture picked up in the 400-mile journey across the Sea of Japan. Then the air rides on over the Japanese islands, curves south and east back across the Philippines, dumps down fifteen inches of its new-found moisture among the native huts of Labang on the northward-facing hills of Borneo, and continues on down across the equator, where it swings off to the east onto Australia under influence of the reverse curve imparted to it by the earth's rotation, which in the Southern Hemisphere causes the winds to turn to the left. Another time the air is pumped most strongly southward over India, then rides on south and west across the Arabian Sea all the way to Madagascar off the coast of Africa, 1,000 miles below the line. Yet whether the air moves most strongly here or there, the general flow is outward from the continent, creating over the sea winds of amazing steadiness.

The winter monsoon begins to weaken by late February. By the middle of March there may be whole series of days when one or another part of the coast of Asia is free of offshore winds. By the middle of April the continent of Asia has lost its greatest coldness. This is the in-between season. Over the waters to the east of the continent the winds are light and variable. Over the tropical ocean to the south, the air hangs hot and still, day after day. These are the days of which Conrad wrote in describing the passage of the rusty steamer *Patna* westward across the Arabian Sea with its cargo of Mohammedan pilgrims, bound for their Holy Land.

> She held on straight for the Red Sea under a serene sky, under a sky scorching and unclouded, enveloped in a fulgor of sunshine that killed all thought, oppressed the heart, withered all impulses of strength and energy. And under the sinister splendour of that sky the sea, blue and

profound, remained still, without a stir, without a ripple, without a wrinkle—viscous, stagnant, dead. The *Patna*, with a slight hiss, passed over that plain luminous and smooth, unrolled a black ribbon of smoke across the sky, left behind her on the water a white ribbon of foam that vanished at once, like the phantom of a track drawn upon a lifeless sea by the phantom of a steamer.

. . . Such were the days, still, hot, heavy, disappearing one by one into the past, as if falling into an abyss for ever open in the wake of the ship; and the ship, lonely under a wisp of smoke, held on her steadfast way black and smouldering in a luminous immensity, as if scorched by a flame flicked at her from a heaven without pity.

The nights descended on her like a benediction.

On days like these in mid-April, the sun beats down also upon the plains of India and Pakistan, the black-soil cotton lands near Bombay, and the thorny brush and jungle lands of the Deccan from Rajputana southward to Madras. Everywhere the ground is drying out beneath the sun. The farmer in the field, sowing his crop of millet broadcast, driving his ox-pulled wooden plow, pauses in his labors to search the sky for the merest cloud that will tell of the turning of the monsoon, the onset of the southwest winds that bring the rain. If the monsoon is late, those dead of starvation may come to number in the millions, so great is the dependence of these 400 million peoples upon the annual bounty of the summer monsoon rains.

In the offices of the Indian Meteorological Service in Bombay, specialists examine the weather reports that stack up line upon line on the incoming teletype machine. Now, in mid-April, there should be telltale evidence whether the summer monsoon will be early or late. Closely they watch the temperature and pressure readings from northern India and from Iran and Arabia to the west. The higher the temperature rises in those regions, the greater will be the updraft of air and the lower the pressure will fall, creating a sort of semi-vacuum that will suck in air off the oceans. They watch, also, the pressure readings from ships at sea, 2,000 miles away in the Indian Ocean, between Africa and Australia. There, in the Southern Hemisphere, the pressure is building up and a strongly defined HIGH is forming that will shunt air northward toward the Asian coasts. Eventually, when the summer monsoon has set in, there will be a pulsing, swirling flow of air along an S-shaped curve from southward over the Indian Ocean up past the equator onto the Asian continent, where a well-marked LOW will exist. Now there are only the slightest signs of the turning of the winds.

A ship eastward bound for Colombo in Ceylon reports a light wind from the south. Another ship, headed northward for Karachi, reports calm. Three ships off the Malabar Coast all report southerly winds, and the pressure is falling lower over northern India. Meanwhile the HIGH over the Indian Ocean has strengthened measurably, and over the Seychelles Islands, where the vanilla plantations are, the wind is steady at ten knots from the southwest. Then a pulsing wind sets in over the Maldive Islands, pushes east and north across the Laccadives, and climbs up the Malabar Coast.

Rain falls on the Western Ghats, the first rain of the season, washing down the slopes where the cinnamon trees grow, flooding down the pinched-up valleyways beneath the passes. The rain, borne by the monsoon wind, spreads eastward, filling the open irrigation tanks of the farmers of Chitaldroog. Now it is the middle of May. The summer monsoons are on time. By June the winds and rains will have spread across the Indian Peninsula, everywhere except in the driest parts of the Thar Desert, where rain at any season is unexpected.

This same summer monsoon embraces much of Asia. When the summer circulation has been well established, the air moves inward not only onto India but also into Malaya, Thailand, China, Japan, and even Siberia. The air retraces the paths that it followed in winter. With the onshore winds come summer rains. By early September, or mid-September, or perhaps October, depending on the character of the year, the summer monsoon will die out. Once more will come a lull. Then, faintly, erratically at first, but always more and more strongly and with increasing constancy, the winter monsoon will once again set in.

5 Winds of the Land

Land winds are distinctive in character. On the land there are great extremes of heat and cold; they produce thermal winds that are far intenser than any winds of similar origin upon the sea. The ground and its vegetation form a far rougher surface than does water; and this promotes greater turbulence in the moving air, even in such flat and treeless regions as the plains and tundras. And on a far larger scale, the topographic roughness of mountains, hills, and valleys so disrupts the flow of air as to create in many areas whole assemblages of local winds whose helter-skelter character defies generalization. The winds that accompanied the remarkable temperature fluctuations at Rapid City in the Black Hills (pp. 46–47) were of this local nature.

In other ways, too, winds of the land differ from those of the sea. Except when they are laden with volcanic dust or the debris from tests of nuclear weapons, the winds far at sea are clean. Their chief burden is salt particles derived from the sea itself. In contrast, land winds are dirty winds. They carry sand, dust, plant spores, bacteria, and all kinds of noxious chemicals acquired over modern industrial areas. For man, the clean sea winds are a blessing; the dirty land winds are a nuisance or even a curse, as when there are dust storms or smog. Nowhere is this better illustrated than in those dry lands where the sand has invaded the habitats of man.

Wind and Sand

In eastern Iran, beyond the dusty Dasht-i-Lut tableland, lies the region of Seistan. It is a place of desolation, its surface of rocks and sand, its hills bare of trees. Except most rarely, and then in wintertime or early spring, the very riverbeds are dry.

Not quite six centuries ago, Seistan was a populous region with vigorous trade connections and a thriving agriculture based on elaborate irrigation systems. Then Moguls, riding under the banner of Timur–Tamerlane, "the lame one"–devastated Seistan. Whole populations were obliterated. Buildings were leveled. Dams and weirs were destroyed. An entire culture that over the long centuries had fought and won a war against a dry land was wiped out in a month or less.

In places other than Seistan, destruction such as Tamerlane wrought, thorough though it was, seldom leads to virtual abandonment of an area for hundreds of years. Irrigation works can be repaired; houses can be rebuilt; a patient people, even though greatly reduced in numbers, can with resolution regain its wealth. But in Seistan it was the sand that marched inward upon the villages. It marched in swiftly, at an almost fabulous pace, driven by the *bad-i-sad-o-bist roz*, the "wind of 120 days."

The wind sets in toward the end of May. "It blows with appalling violence and with little or no cessation till about the end of September." Always it blows from a little west of north. At its speediest, with velocities in excess of 70 miles per hour, the wind "creates a pandemonium of noise, sand, and dust." The sand arrives in echelons. First come the lines of skirmishers in the form of traveling dunes. Steadily they roll forward. Where they encounter obstacles too large to bury, they wait for reinforcements. Then more arrive and climb the slopes of those ahead, building one massive towering dune that with ease can top an obstruction fifty feet high.

Colonel Sir Henry McMahon, who led a party that surveyed the Baluchistan-Afghan-Persian border in the region of Seistan, reports that in a single season the village of Kila-i-Nau was buried by sand, although it lay to leeward of a sizable ridge. In far less than a season, a large pond was transformed into a hill ten feet high.

The wind piles up the sand and also excavates. Within a month, old ruins buried for centuries are exposed through wind scour. Even in clayey material, huge depressions are formed, some of them 200 feet deep. Scour and fill and marching dunes are the regime that the wind creates.

There is little doubt that in Seistan the strong, persistent summer winds have blown from the same direction with the greatest violence for seven centuries or more. The houses of sun-dried brick of the present day are built with a thick and solid wall, devoid of windows, facing in the direction from which the wind comes. Those of six centuries ago are similarly constructed and of similar orientation.

The most intriguing question raised by these findings is how, during the period of Seistan's greatness, before the coming of Tamerlane, the people managed to cope with the great summer winds and the encroaching sand dunes. Certainly they could not stop the wind or sand. Probably they waited out the sandstorms and then dug themselves out. Certainly it must have taken a spirited and united people to maintain a civilization in Seistan.

The summer winds of Seistan are the continental aspect of the monsoon circulation. Seistan is just to the west and north of the center of the LOW that develops over Asia in the summer monsoon season. Perhaps the counterclockwise circulation about this thermal LOW is sufficiently intense to create these steady summer winds. Probably, however, there are other contributing factors, such as the juxtaposition of mountains and basins and the effects of local heating. In any event, just as in the flow of monsoon air across the sea, when autumn arrives the winds begin to slacken. By wintertime other winds from other directions have replaced them.

The sand dune is the most impressive land form created by the wind. Dunes are formed wherever there is an abundant supply of sand and winds that blow from one dominant direction. The shore of the ocean or of a lake and certain preferred locations in the desert are the most common sites of extensive dune development. More rarely, dunes are found along the margins of large rivers, down on the flood plain where there are ample sediments deposited by the river in times of flood.

Dunes are of two main types. The usual transverse dune is simply a ridge of sand, slightly irregular in shape, which straddles the dominant direction of the wind. The barchan is shaped like a quarter moon, with long curving horns that trail off downwind, becoming lower and lower in height with increasing distance from its high mid-section. Powerful winds and a slight insufficiency of sand are required to yield the barchan form. If the wind was not powerful, the sand would not be swept around the sides; and if the sand was too plentiful, the dunes would be so densely spaced, one before another, that the wind would not have full play to curve back the corners of the dune. The dunes of Seistan are barchans. There are also many desert areas of barchan dunes, as in the Sahara and in its Hollywood counterpart, Death Valley. The majestic form and almost perfect symmetry of the barchan dune makes it a favorite photographic subject.

In detail as well as in broad feature, the form of the sand dune reveals the action of the wind. Dune slopes are long and relatively gentle on the windward side, where the sand grains are rolled upward. Their steeper side is to leeward, where the grains that have been rolled over the crest come to rest at the angle of repose. The larger the size of the grains, the steeper the leeward slope; for coarse grains can in repose maintain a steeper slope than fine ones. The constant movement of sand grains from the windward side across the crest causes the dune to migrate. This movement ceases only when grasses, scrub, and other vegetation have taken hold upon the dune surface.

In natural areas, uninfluenced by the activities of man, the dunes along a shore often stand row upon row inland from the coast. The newest, outermost dunes are almost free of vegetation and so press inland upon the ones to leeward. The next row is partly covered with vegetation and so moves more slowly. The third or fourth or fifth row is entirely claimed by vegetation. It has become stable. This zonation of vegetation and of dune movement is the product of a sort of balance among the natural forces of wind and sand supply, and the ability of various plants to take hold and maintain themselves upon dune surfaces of greater or lesser age. From the study of such areas it has been possible to develop control measures that have been applied in coastal areas to fasten down dunes that otherwise might threaten highways, houses, or other structures. Kudzu, a hardy, fast-growing vine, has been found to be especially effective in taking hold on fresh dune sand and pinning it down so that migration is suppressed.

Many years ago it was observed that the sand grains found in dunes along the shore were rounder than those along the beaches that supplied the dune sand. The reason for this contrast appeared to be obvious. Clearly, when the sand particles were swept across the beach and onto the dune slope, they became more rounded through having their corners rounded off. However, if sand is put in a barrel and the barrel is placed on a vibrating machine, the sand is mixed and churned in a manner that simulates the treatment that sand grains must undergo when they bump against other grains while being blown upslope by the wind. A microscopic examination of the grains before and after this treatment shows that there is no rounding of the grains.

What is the explanation for the rounder sand grains in the dunes? The true answer lies in the action of the wind, which picks up from the beach and rolls upslope chiefly those grains that are already rounded and so will move most easily.

Sand dunes are not the only products of the wind to be found in the landscape. In desert areas the wind removes fine sediments from basin floors and leaves behind only rocks, which form a pavement like a rough, irregular flagstone terrace. Where rock pedestals or cliff faces are composed of rocks of differing hardness, the wind, armed with sand particles as its cutting tools, cuts most deeply in the softer layers and so produces strangely chiseled forms of great complexity. Winds maintain the basins of desert regions through sweeping upslope the finer materials brought down onto the basin floor by flash floods produced by sudden mountain rains.

Even in humid climes the work of the wind is important. It transports dust over long distances and scoops up topsoil from the cultivated fields. Together with the running waters on the surface of the earth and the glaciers that in times long past extended far across the continents, the wind is a major force in the molding of the surface of the land.

Wind, Dust, and Drought

As it streams across the continents, the flow of air varies throughout its depth from level to level. Within the air 2,000 feet and more above the ground, there is a gradual shift in wind speed and direction from one level to the next. Below 2,000 feet the shift is more marked. In some places there are such abrupt changes that the winds near the ground are of utterly different character from those at height.

Except in rugged mountainous regions, the winds at height are seldom influenced by the terrain beneath. They are of the free air, the "winds aloft," whose paths are in balance with the pattern of air pressure across wide regions. These are the winds that blow in steady fashion clockwise round the HIGHS and counterclockwise round the LOWS of the Northern Hemisphere.

In contrast, the winds nearer the land surface often violate the pressure pattern. They are the earth-bound winds. Even smooth ground acts upon them like a brake, slowing them down through friction and changing their direction. Where the terrain is rough, these lower winds are inhibited further still by valleyways that close them in and by hilltops that turn them aside like water in a stream deflected by a boulder in its path.

Though often distinct in character, the winds above and those below may act strongly one upon the other. Powerful winds at height, through dragging along with them the air that lies beneath, make themselves felt at the surface of the land. The speedier the winds aloft, the greater their influence on surface winds; and where the ground beneath is flat and smooth, the winds within a few feet of the surface of the land may be almost as strong as those at height. It is chiefly for this reason that maximum wind speeds are much higher in a region such as the Great Plains or the Argentine Pampas than in a hilly region such as central Kentucky or the Brazilian highlands.

On the Great Plains of North America and in similar regions in Patagonia, Australia, Russia, and Africa, there is a coincidence of natural conditions that often produces dust storms wherever the land has been put to cultivation. These regions are as flat as any in the world. They are subhumid lands, too dry for the natural growth of trees, whose foliage would fend off the wind and so protect the soil beneath. Short grasses, often with bunched growth habit, comprise the natural vegetation. They, like the land itself, do little to weaken the force of the wind. Throughout wide reaches of these plains regions, the soils themselves are particularly susceptible to blowing, because upon drying out they form only tiny aggregates that are easily rolled along the ground before the wind and so can soon be broken down into fine grains that can be carried high aloft.

In these plains regions, under natural conditions the power of the wind to erode the soil is opposed by the strength of the grasses that hold the soil fast. The grasses are short and widely spaced, but their root systems are amazingly well developed. In its struggle to survive through gathering in what little moisture is available, each plant sends out extensive roots that may total a mile or more in length. In the uppermost twelve inches of the ground, it would be difficult to find one cubic inch of soil that lacked a root to bind it to the total soil mass.

In plains regions, cultivation and cattle are the allies of the wind. Both destroy the grass. On the crop lands and grazing lands, it may be possible to maintain for many years a precarious balance that favors the holding of the soil against the wind. But sooner or later, after two years, or five, or ten, the climatic fluctuations that are a normal part of the weather regime will cause a major drought.

On the grazing lands, the drought will destroy the living roots of grasses already impoverished by overgrazing. On the cultivated lands, the crops will wilt and die, leaving the soil exposed. Then even winds of modest force will easily erode the soil. The time will be at hand when once again dust storms will ravage the plains, as they did in Texas in 1956 or throughout the entire plains area of North America during the 1930's.

On the Great Plains and in adjacent portions of the prairies farther east, 1930 was a bad year for drought and dust. In 1931 the rains were far more plentiful, and it appeared possible that the land might recover soon. Then came three drought years in a row. By the spring of 1935, millions of acres of land between the Rocky Mountains and the Mississippi lay bare beneath the wind. Soil was being blown away at an alarming rate. Already thousands of Okies and Arkies, Texans and Kansans, had left the dust bowl. Among those who stayed on, most were on relief. All that kept them there was a sort of desperate, stubborn tenacity.

In the spring of 1935, Margaret Bourke-White, the photographer, visited the dust bowl. Reporting on her experience, she wrote:

> The dust storms have distinct personalities, rising in formation like rolling clouds, creeping up silently like formless fog, approaching violently like a tornado. Where has it come from? It provides topics of endless speculation. Red, it is the topsoil from Oklahoma; brown, it is the fertile earth of western Kansas; the good grazing land of Texas and New Mexico sweeps by as a murky yellow haze. Or, tracing it

locally, "My uncle will be along pretty soon," they say, "I just saw his farm go by."

There were those who said in the 1930's that the droughts of that time were unprecedented and that such severe droughts would not occur again. They were not unprecedented. The droughts of the 1890's were just as bad and so were occasional droughts of still earlier times. And they did occur again, in the middle 1950's, throughout much of the southern Great Plains, and on a scale that was fully as intense.

Indeed, on subhumid plains lands everywhere, there will always be occasional droughts; and with drought there will be wind and dust, as so many times before. By the time the drought arrives, man's actions will already have determined how effective the wind will be in creating a dusty wilderness where before there were rich farm and grazing lands. Where man has forced the land to the utmost, wresting from it in a few successive years the greatest possible money yield in crops, cattle, or sheep, the drought and wind will bring desolation. Where man has been prudent in his use of the land and content to maximize his economic gain over a period of decades through husbanding his land as a continuing source of wealth, drought and wind will still bring dust and crop failures, but on a far less intensive scale. Those who were careful will suffer heavy losses; but those who were improvident will suffer disaster.

Smog

As defined by California law, smog is a combination of fog and such impurities as "smoke, charred paper, dust, soot, grime, carbon, noxious acids, fumes, gases, odors, or particular matter or any combination thereof." To this list might be added other items such as ash, soil, tar, asphalt, paint from buildings, and rubber scraped off tires by friction. The list could be extended almost indefinitely if every solid substance present in the air should be included, for all that is required for a substance to be represented is that it break down into sufficiently small particles to be blown upward and to remain suspended in the air for a period of a few hours or more. In an industrial area, if all the solid impurities in the lower air were deposited in one location, the resulting dust pile would be fully as noxious as any refuse heap.

However, smog is worse than a mere refuse heap, widely dispersed through the lowest air. It is worse than the list of its constituents suggests, because these constituents change chemically as they enter and move with the air, and the change renders many of them far more harmful than before. An intensive study by Haagen-Smit and his coworkers at the California Institute of Technology involves the production of large quantities of ozone. Ozone is a powerful oxidizing agent—it forces oxygen atoms upon other chemical substances, including living organic tissues. And it is highly significant that in a smog situation, eye irritation increases as the oxidizing power of the air increases.

High ozone concentrations and the presence in the air of other harmful substances in abnormal quantities may be so extreme as to be poisonous. In the United States the classic example is the smog that in October, 1948, killed twenty persons in Donora, Pennsylvania, and brought illness to over 40 per cent of the population. Extremes of this kind have occurred elsewhere too, as in London, England.

No large industrial area is completely free of smog, nor is any free of temperature inversions that create the worst smog conditions. Usually temperatures decrease upward in the lower atmosphere. When nighttime cooling produces an ultra-cold layer of air near the ground, the usual condition is violated. A temperature inversion is formed, with colder air below and warmer air above. Such inversions suppress the vertical mixing of air because the colder, heavier air below cannot readily change places with the warmer, lighter air above. Whether they are produced by nighttime cooling or in other ways, temperature inversions favor the concentration of dust, smoke, and other impurities in the lowest layers of the atmosphere. They favor the formation of smog.

In Los Angeles, a common cause of intense smog is the movement onto the land of air in which there is a temperature inversion at heights of a few hundred feet. This inversion results from the sinking of air at great altitudes above the HIGH pressure region of the horse latitudes over the eastern Pacific Ocean. As the air descends, it gains heat and forms a deep warm layer that overlies the cooler sea air beneath. The inversion, imbedded in the air mass, moves over Los Angeles and other coastal regions of California in the general flow of air from west to east. In Chicago, winter is a season of frequent smog associated with the presence of cold, dry Canadian air that has been chilled most strongly in its lowest layers as the result of nighttime cooling of the ground. In the New York area, dense smog is especially favored during the autumn and early winter, when relatively mild ocean air may move onto the cold land and so be cooled in its lowest layers to form an inversion. It was this kind of situation that produced the period of severe smog during the autumn of 1953.

On the average, the air in New York City contains about half a ton of impurities per cubic mile. During the worst part of the smog that set in on November 17, 1953, and lasted for seven days, the concentration of impurities was over three and one-half tons per cubic mile. Throughout the smog period a weak LOW pressure area was slowly moving eastward toward New York. The counterclockwise circulation of air around the LOW gave the city gentle southerly to southeasterly winds that brought moist warm air in from the Atlantic Ocean. The cold land of late November lowered the temperature of the basal portions of the incoming air to the dew point; and as the air moved in to occupy the big and little spaces among the thousands of industrial plants that stretch from New Brunswick, New Jersey, on the south northward to Connecticut, the moisture condensed on the billions of solid and liquid particles poured forth in the acrid smoke from chemical plants, in the nauseous fumes from tanneries and oil refineries, and in the substances belched out by the disposal stacks of hundreds of other industries. Together with the exhausts of automobiles and the carbon produced by coal-burning furnaces, these fumes and smokes yielded a mixture of impurities which remained trapped in the lower air and increased the fog density.

The effects of the smog were many and were felt over a wide region in the general New York area. On November 20, schools were closed in Elizabeth, New Jersey, to permit parents to keep their children indoors. Airplane flights were canceled at La Guardia Field because of low visibility; two ferryboats collided in the harbor and the Yonkers ferry suspended service to avoid further accidents; there were a score of rear-end collisions on the Merritt Parkway. The hospitals were crowded with patients suffering from respiratory illnesses. Industrial plants shut down so as not to contaminate the air further. The smog was finally dissipated on November 23, when a light wind set in from the west, breaking the inversion.

In most large industrial areas, the air is sampled at frequent intervals to keep track of the nature of impurities that are present and of their concentration. At the Air Pollution Control Laboratory in New York City, the air is pumped in from the street, filtered, and bubbled up through various liquids to permit analysis of its contents. A different, more tedious, method that is sometimes used is to expose glass plates or small hollow dishes to the moving air and then to examine microscopically the particles that accumulate on them. This method is especially useful in identifying the kinds of bacteria carried by atmospheric dust. The glass plates or dishes are incubated at about 80° F. for several days so that colonies of bacteria that are readily identifiable are formed.

From such studies it has been learned that living bacteria can be carried hundreds of miles by the air and are even found at altitudes of 15,000 to 20,000 feet above the ground. These findings further corroborate the fact that, despite occasional temperature inversions that prohibit vertical mixing, over the land as well as over the sea, the dominant process is a great three-dimensional churning of the air. Dust from the drought lands, soot from the cities, and living organisms from forests, farmlands, and cities alike are all caught up in the moving air which is the one great stream that flows across all regions of the world.

Mountain Winds

The most complex and varied winds of all the earth are those of mountainous regions. Ocean winds follow long, smooth paths. Winds of the plains often ride far distances with little change in speed or in direction. Mountain winds defy generalization. Each valley and each mountain slope has its own peculiar wind regime. In one place the wind may blow downslope from the north; in another, upslope from the south. A side valley, deep-cut between two razorback ridges, may carry a strong, full wind out of the west. Simultaneously, in a closed basin 1,500 yards away, there may be no wind at all.

The wind pattern in mountainous regions is related to many factors. Deep valleys channel the flow of air so that if there is any wind at all it is either upvalley or downvalley. High ridges and mountain peaks deflect the moving air and create swirling eddies not unlike the whirls of water created by obstructions in a river. There are also the effects of unequal heating of the land from hour to hour throughout the day. As the sun moves from east to west across the sky, there is an ever-changing pattern of light and shadow upon the slopes of the land beneath. One slope will be heated only in late afternoon; another, in early morning; a third, near midday. Above the heated areas the air will rise and be replaced by cooler air from nearby shaded regions. Small winds will start and stop and reverse direction, all within a dozen hours or less.

All kinds of strange wind situations are encountered in the mountains. Among the most unusual is one that occurs in parts of the Apennines, in England, and in the coastal mountains of Ceylon. In these places, upon a land surface that is gently sloping, there is sometimes an astonishingly rapid transition from a zone of heavy rain and strong winds to a realm of clear and quiet air. This is not a transient condition. For hours on end, wind and rain may sweep one portion of the slope while simultaneously, a few yards away, the air may be clear and motionless.

The sharpness of the transition and the magnitude of the change are well described by Sir Samuel Baker with reference to the situation in Ceylon:

> From June to November, the southwest monsoon brings wind and mist across the Newera Ellia Mountains. Clouds of white fog boil up from Dimboola Valley, like the steam from a huge cauldron, and invade the Newera Ellia plain through the gaps in the mountains to the westward. The wind howls over the high ridges, cutting the jungle with its keen edge, so that it remains as stunted brushwood, and the opaque screen of driving fog and drizzling rain is so dense that one feels convinced there is no sun visible within at least 100 miles.
>
> There is a peculiar phenomenon, however, in this locality. . . . Dusty roads, a cloudless sky, and dazzling sunshine astonish the thoroughly soaked traveller, who rides out of the rain and mist into a genial climate as though he passed through a curtain. The wet weather terminates at a mountain called Hackgulla. . . . This bold rock, whose summit is 6,500 feet above the sea, breasts the driving wind, and seems to command the storm. The rushing clouds halt in their mad course upon its crest and curl in sudden impotence around the craggy summits. The deep ravine formed by an opposite mountain is filled with the vanquished mist, which sinks powerless in its dark gorge; and the bright sun, shining from the east, spreads a perpetual rainbow upon the gauze-like cloud of fog which settles in the deep hollow.

The transition from rain and wind to sun and virtual calm on the eastern slopes of Hackgulla marks the boundary between two distinct local circulation systems. On the western side of the boundary, the rain-bearing wind sweeps downslope, then rises sharply and suddenly. On the clear eastern side the dry, sun-warmed air drifts slowly upslope and then it also rises. There is a carry-over of moisture across the interface between the two walls of air, and this creates a mist that slowly settles downward through the slow, upward-moving current of dry air. Distinctly separate circulations, one next to the other, are quite common in the mountains; but typically the two circulations occupy adjacent valleys or are situated on slopes that face in different directions. The Hackgulla situation is unusual because the circulations occupy two portions of one broad sloping surface.

As every mountain climber knows, the most violent mountain winds are found atop isolated peaks and on barren slopes just below the summit. When a storm is raging, the air at elevations of many thousands of feet moves at tremendous speeds unchecked by friction with the lower mountain slopes far beneath. Where a mountain peak looms upward athwart its path, the oncoming air hurls itself upon the intruding mountain. To the mountain climber the sheer force of the wind is a grave hazard. Where he descends the face of a cliff on a piton-anchored rope, a sudden ultra-powerful gust of wind may dash him against the rock. Where, cautiously and slowly, he traverses the steeply sloping surface of a glacier, a sudden pulsing blast of wind may knock him down and send him sliding. Then his rope had better be well anchored by his ice ax.

The force of the wind is not the only danger. Filled with the snow it has swept from the mountain slopes, the wind creates a blizzard that blots out the sun and envelops each climber in a swirling shroud of gray. The wind produces frost that quickly accumulates to form caked chunks of ice on exposed portions of the climber's face. The frost covers his snow glasses, making him blind. When he removes the glasses, ice needles quickly form around his eyelashes; when he blinks his eyes, the lashes above and below suddenly freeze together. When he wipes his eyes with his glove, it is like pulling a jagged, ice-cold file across them. When he pulls his hand out of his glove, the better to wipe his eyes, ice forms upon his hand.

A mountain need not be especially high to carry winds of great force. The strongest wind ever measured officially was that recorded at the Weather Observatory on top of Mount Washington on the afternoon of April 12, 1934. Mount Washington is the highest of several prominent peaks along the crest of the White Mountains in northern New Hampshire. Its top is 6,288 feet above sea level. To the west the descent is not particularly steep, but to the east of the peak there is an almost sheer drop down the headwall of a deep circular basin formerly occupied by a glacier. Thus winds from easterly directions abruptly strike the summit of the mountain without having been slowed down by the slopes beneath.

During the forty-eight hours preceding the time of maximum wind, unusual weather prevailed. On the afternoon of April 10, there was a "singular period of strange near calm." Then light winds set in from the southeast. High, thin cirrus clouds appeared. The wind continued to blow from the southeast and to strengthen slowly and steadily. The next morning, inside the observatory the pen of the wind recorder was swinging up and down to form an N-shaped hump once each minute. A mile of wind in a minute meant a speed of 60 m.p.h., a modest value for Mount Washington.

That afternoon the wind increased to over 100 m.p.h. and stayed there, still from the southeast, throughout the night. It reached an average of 188 m.p.h. between 12:25 and 12:30 P.M. By now rough frost had formed to a thickness of three feet on the outer surface of the observatory building, on the sides of the weather shelter, and on other exposed objects. The men in the observatory were using a stop watch to time the intervals between successive humps formed by the wind-recorder pen. At 1:21 P.M. the maximum gust was timed at 231 m.p.h., the highest wind speed ever measured officially.

Tornadoes

Tornado winds cannot be measured. They destroy every wind-measuring equipment that has ever been devised. From their effects it has been estimated that they sometimes reach speeds of 500 m.p.h. Whatever the exact value, they are without doubt the strongest winds within the entire troposphere.

There is a special flavor about tornado weather. The air is damp, and the weather unsettled. Often the sky is overcast to the west and poleward. Sometimes the clouds assume a strange, unreal aspect, with huge cloud masses bulging downward as though the cloud were a quilt fastened to the sky by hundreds of invisible pins between which the quilt droops downward in loose, sharply curved folds. From out of such a sky or from a sky of jumbled cloud, the tornado descends. Few persons have tarried to observe an oncoming tornado closely. Among those who have, and who lived to relate what he saw, was Will Keller, a farmer living near Greensburg, Kansas. Except for the fact that tornadoes often occur singly rather than in twos or threes and that they sometimes do not contain lightning, his account is descriptive of a typical tornado:

> On the afternoon of June 22, 1928, between three and four o'clock, I noticed an umbrella-shaped cloud in the west and southwest and from its appearance suspected there was a tornado in it. The air had that peculiar oppressiveness which nearly always precedes the coming of a tornado.
>
> I saw at once my suspicions were correct. Hanging from the greenish black base of the cloud were three tornadoes. One was perilously near and apparently headed directly for my place. . . .
>
> Two of the tornadoes were some distance away and looked like great ropes dangling from the parent cloud, but the one nearest was shaped more like a funnel, with ragged clouds surrounding it. It appeared larger than the others and occupied the central position, with great cumulus clouds over it.
>
> Steadily the cloud came on, the end gradually rising above the ground. I probably stood there only a few seconds, but was so impressed with the sight it seemed like a long time. At last the great shaggy end of the funnel hung directly overhead. Everything was still as death. There was a strong, gassy odor, and it seemed as though I could not breathe. There was a screaming, hissing sound coming directly from the end of the funnel. I looked up, and to my astonishment I saw right into the heart of the tornado. There was a circular opening in the center of the funnel, about fifty to one hundred feet in diameter and extending straight upward for a distance of at least half a mile, as best I could judge under the circumstances. The walls of this opening were rotating clouds and the whole was brilliantly lighted with constant flashes of lightning which zig-zagged from side to side. . . .
>
> Around the rim of the great vortex small tornadoes were constantly forming and breaking away. These looked like tails as they writhed their way around the funnel. It was these that made the hissing sound. I noticed the rotation of the great whirl was anticlockwise, but some of the small twisters rotated clockwise. . . . The tornado was not

traveling at a great speed. I had plenty of time to get a good view of the whole thing, inside and out.

The funnel-shaped tornado cloud moves forward steadily in its upper part at a speed of from 5 to 60 m.p.h. But below, the cloud weaves back and forth, a cone-shaped monster of destruction that swings from side to side along a winding path. Sometimes the whirling cloud withdraws upward so that it touches the ground only along a path a few yards wide. Sometimes it burrows downward to cut a twisting swath a thousand yards or more in width. Or else it may bob along the ground, touching the earth just long enough to pulverize a farmhouse, skipping across a barn twenty yards away, hitting a chicken house ten yards beyond. Where the tornado crosses an open field, it may rip the grass from the ground, yank out fence posts, and pluck out occasional trees, roots and all. Where it crosses a stream or lake, it sucks up water. Where it crosses a snowfield, it suddenly turns pure white.

The giant hurricane causes greater destruction; but acre for acre and square yard for square yard, no natural agent of destruction can match the tornado. The scene of its most awesome devastation is the city, whose terrain, densely packed with houses and other buildings, is sure to yield a terrible harvest wherever the tornado strikes. Statistics for a few cases tell part of the story: 317 killed in the Natchez tornado of 1840; $12 million damage and 306 dead in St. Louis in 1896; on May 26, 1917, 101 dead in Mattoon, Illinois; almost 2,000 injured and 689 killed in the worst tornado on record in the United States, the tristate tornado that hit several towns in Missouri, Illinois, and Indiana on the 18th of March, 1925; and much more recently, in 1959, the tornado that killed 21 and injured 300 in St. Louis. When deaths are calculated on a square-mile basis, the power of the tornado becomes even more evident. The path of the St. Louis tornado of 1896 covered less than two square miles. The death toll was almost 200 per square mile.

The aftermath of the tornado is a hodgepodge of broken houses and houses without a blemish, of stacks of jagged debris and of areas free even of minor rubble. Fire, earthquake, volcanoes, and flood all decimate large, continuous areas. The tornado is so erratic in its effects that if the areas of destruction are entered in black ink on a large map representing a few square blocks of a city, the resulting pattern makes it appear that the ink was spattered on the map from a distance of several feet.

By the power of its wind, through the effects of its semivacuum, and because it often moves erratically to and fro as well as up and down, the tornado has caused many freak happenings. Even though they are authentic, some of these freaks are so unusual as to be virtually unbelievable. Tornadoes have been known to suck the blankets and mattress from a bed while leaving the occupant unharmed. One tornado removed an entire house, yet failed to move a bench that stood along an outside wall. Another lifted a baby from his crib and deposited him unhurt on the ground several hundred yards away. The tristate tornado of 1925 carried a grain binder one-quarter of a mile, a pair of trousers thirty-nine miles, and the lid of a compact forty miles. Tornadoes have driven straws into steel girders and have moved a crate of eggs 500 yards without cracking a single one.

Tornadoes are extremely difficult to forecast even though the general kind of weather that produces them is well known. They are especially likely to occur during spring and summer in situations when the lower air is very moist with drier air above, when a strong, narrow wind current is present at heights of between 10,000 and 20,000 feet, and when a sudden thrust of cold air produces a highly turbulent zone within which the tornado whirl, descending from above, can readily form.

The exact mode of formation of a tornado is not known, but a recent theory developed by meteorologists of the U.S. Weather Bureau is the most likely explanation developed so far and has already led to greatly improved forecasting techniques. Under this theory, when, for example, a mass of cold air sweeps eastward at a faster and faster speed across the southeastern United States, it acts like a piston and sets up a kind of shock wave that races ahead of the cold front. This shock wave cannot be felt, but its presence can be detected; for as the advance wave arrives, the air pressure jumps upward. At the same time warm, moist air surging northward from the Gulf of Mexico and held down by a lid of drier, warmer air above suddenly frees itself of its constraining lid and spurts outward like water from a restricting pipe, thus producing a second shock wave that thrusts on northward. The tornado forms where the two shock waves intersect; and since one wave continues northward and the other eastward, their intersection moves northeastward, carrying with it the tornado whirl.

In the general sense that tornadoes are caused by shock-wave intersections, this theory may well apply to tornadoes in all parts of the world. Certainly it would explain the general movement of tornadoes and the fact that they often occur in sequence from southwest to northeast in the United States. The theory should not be construed to mean that nuclear explosions produce tornadoes, for at distances of more than a few miles the shock wave from an explosion yields an infinitely smaller pressure jump than do the mechanisms described under the theory.

The center of the tornado area in the United States is eastern Kansas. Within this region and in adjacent portions of Nebraska, Iowa, Missouri, and Oklahoma, there have been over fifteen tornadoes reported during the thirty-year period from 1920–49 for each fifty square miles of area. As a crude estimate, the chances are even that in any one year a tornado will come within four miles of a person living in this region. Actually, thousands of people living in this area have never been that close to a tornado and never will be; yet thousands of others have been closer than four miles not once but several times, so that the figures average out. Even in eastern Kansas the possibility of any particular person being trapped within the path of a tornado is slight; for the chances are less than one in a thousand that a tornado that comes within a four-mile distance will strike a particular spot.

Tornadoes are moderately frequent in the Great Lakes-Ohio River region and in the southern United States. Their frequency is low in the northeastern United States, and they are virtually nonexistent from the Rocky Mountains westward to the Pacific Ocean. Yet every state has experienced at least one tornado. During the thirty-four-year period ending in 1949, Nevada was at the bottom of the list with one tornado reported, and California was next with only four. These figures, which are doubtless somewhat too low because of the lack of observations from sparsely settled areas, compare with a total of 587 for Kansas during the same period. In terms of topography, tornadoes are most common in the plains and most unusual over mountains.

Though tornadoes are tiny eddies compared to hurricanes or the cyclonic storms of middle latitudes, they are by no means the smallest eddies at the floor of the atmospheric ocean. Waterspouts are eddies; and though a few of them in coastal waters are produced by tornadoes and therefore have the same dimensions, most measure but a few feet across and extend no higher than fifteen feet. Dust whirls are also eddies. Sometimes they are several yards across; far more often, they measure but a few inches.

Tornadoes, waterspouts, and dust whirls move. There are other eddies that are stationary, their position being fixed by some obstruction about which the moving air curls to produce a circular eddy flow. On a miniature scale, standing eddies of this kind are formed about the legs and edges of a bed within a room. They act to pick up dust from the moving air and to shunt it backward into the quiet air region beneath the bed, where the dust settles out and so accumulates.

The presence in the atmosphere of many different kinds of eddies of vastly differing sizes demonstrates that the flow of air across the lands and seas is not a wholly mannered, orderly phenomenon. Rather, there are major currents of various natures and origins, each broad current carrying with it a multitude of lesser currents and eddies. The broader currents and larger eddies that are the major winds of the world carry with them the principal aspects of the changing weather. The smaller eddies and minor currents that are more finely wrought give to each place an individuality whereby the weather is expressed in local terms that are unique.

Whatever the dimensions of the winds, they are the dynamic element of the weather. They transport heat from place to place and so strongly influence the temperature regime. They transport moisture from sea to land and so provide for the snow and rain without which there could be no life upon the continents. In the dynamics of the atmosphere, wind and weather are closely intertwined both on a scale so vast as to encompass half the world and in details so minute as to cover but a few square inches of the earth's surface.

6 Water

Water is a primary substance of the earth. It is the distinctive substance of a realm that reaches far beyond the oceans. This water realm embraces the area of living organisms, which itself reaches to heights of 20,000 feet within the atmosphere and to depths of 30,000 feet within the sea and thousands of feet beneath the surface of the land. Within this aqueous life-filled zone, water passes with relative ease across the boundaries that separate land, sea, and atmosphere. Water is the one truly ubiquitous substance of the earth.

Upon the lands, the character of the natural habitats of man is intimately related to the water regime. The kinds of plants, the nature of the soils, the character of the erosive forces that mold the lands, the animal life, and often the types of minerals within the earth depend in large measure upon the variations throughout the centuries in the quantity and quality of the waters in the air above the land and within the ground beneath it, as well as upon the land surface itself. Everywhere the countenance of the land expresses its water circumstance.

To man, water is a multitude of things. Water is fifty million cubic feet of terror ripping through a man-made levee. Water is ice from Maine, carried on sailing ships round the Horn to San Francisco to cool the drinks of the forty-niners. It is rain that nourishes the wheat upon the field. Water is energy. At Boulder Dam it sends electric power surging down high-tension lines. In Tibet it turns prayer wheels that send up to heaven an endless chain of thanks and supplications.

How water originated is an unsolved problem. The very ancient rocks reveal that the oceans have existed from the earliest geologic times. Yet none of the many theories of earth origin provide for water at the beginning. Instead, water must have been formed early in the history of the earth through the combining of hydrogen and oxygen. If the earth of earliest times was at high temperatures, this alone would have permitted such a chemical combination to form water. If the earth was cold at first, water must have been formed through some special chemical circumstance, such as the presence of a catalyst that would permit the combination of oxygen and hydrogen at low temperatures. Possibly the first water was within the earth and was released from lava that poured forth upon the crust. Whatever its origin, water made possible the seeming accident of earliest life. Somewhere in the world, perhaps in the warm mud along the margin of some tropical sea, life came into being. Ever since, throughout the long and changing eons of geologic time, water and life have always existed together.

The Nature of Water

In terms of molecular structure a glass of pure water is composed of trillions of particles racing in zigzag paths. Most particles are simple molecules with an oxygen atom in the middle and two hydrogen atoms, one on either side. But many others are double or triple molecule clusters. A few are molecule fragments—ions composed of a hydrogen atom or of single hydrogen and oxygen atoms joined together.

Most unusual of all are the occasional heavy molecules. These are the molecules that the chemist sorts out from all others to obtain heavy water, which is a source of the heavy hydrogen used in the manufacture of a hydrogen bomb. The sorting out is usually achieved by passing through the water a current of just the right strength so that the ordinary water will be decomposed while the heavy water, being more sluggish chemically, will remain behind. Even if this separation process was perfectly efficient, five gallons of ordinary water would yield a mere thimbleful of heavy water.

Water has an amazingly high capacity for heat. In a cooling system a pound of water lowers the temperature of a pound of steel by 10° while increasing its own temperature by only 1°. It is for this reason that water cooling is so effective in removing the heat generated by industrial machinery and engines.

One of the strangest and most important properties of water is that it expands upon freezing, a property unique among the common liquids. To appreciate the importance of this property of water, suppose that, instead of expanding 9 per cent upon freezing, as it does, water contracted just enough so that ice would sink to the bottom rather than float. In such a case, 75 to 80 per cent of the water presently in oceans and seas would be locked in an enormous mass of bottom ice formed in earliest geologic times and since sealed off from the overlying water by a lid of sediments accumulated over the last three billion years. From time to time, in one place or another, there would be great upheavals of the ocean floor as heat from a volcanic eruption or from pockets of radioactive rock beneath the ice caused it to melt and thus suddenly to expand with explosive violence. Afterward, over the centuries, the ice would slowly re-form and again become buried beneath new sediments.

Most of the time, however, the bottom ice would be quiescent and immobile. In July it would be possible to wade in hip boots from Alaska across the North Pole to Norway, assuming one waded fast enough to make the trip in a month. In January the same trip could be made by sled over the ice without encountering any open water. The tropical seas would be deep at all seasons; but much of the middle-latitude seas would freeze solid in the winter, especially near the shore. Ocean currents would be altered radically. The Gulf Stream, if it existed at all, would flow strongly only during summer and early autumn. In winter it would become a weak, shallow current transporting only small amounts of heat northward through the North Atlantic Drift to the waters off northwest Europe.

As a result of this factor and of the influence of surrounding ice-filled seas, winter temperatures in northwestern Europe would be 10° to 20° lower than they now are. Indeed, if ice was denser than water, the effects upon all marine life and most terrestrial life in times past would have been so profound that the whole chain of plant and animal evolution would have been radically altered.

Water has other distinctive properties. For one, it is highly transparent. For another, great quantities of heat are required to change it from a solid to a liquid or from a liquid to a gas. Above all, water is the supreme solvent, capable of dissolving and holding in solution enormous quantities of many different substances. A cubic foot of pure water weighs only a little over sixty pounds; but at ordinary temperatures it can hold within it in solution over twenty pounds of salt or over 125 pounds of sugar. This dissolving power is the principal property that accounts for the importance of water in nature and that makes all organisms from the amoeba to man dependent upon water for their existence. Indeed, water is a necessary constituent of the protoplasm that is the essential living portion of all cells. In man it comprises over 90 per cent of his substance.

Water occurs as a gas, a liquid, and a solid at temperatures that are commonplace at and near the surface of the earth, and it is transferred in all three forms from one location to another. It is carried in the atmosphere as gaseous vapor, liquid water droplets, and solid ice crystals. It is carried in the oceans not only in liquid form but also as floating ice. It is carried across the land chiefly in its flowing liquid state, but also, far more slowly, as solid ice, as in a glacier. Beneath the ground surface, it mostly moves as liquid water, but it also migrates slowly as a gas through porous rocks and soils.

Whatever its state, the majority of the water in the world is constantly on the move from one location to another. For mankind, as for all forms of life that inhabit the lands, this mobility is fortunate, for it permits a constant replenishment of the waters of the land, which otherwise would soon be exhausted. In this replenishment process, the oceans are the great water reservoirs, the atmosphere is the chief conduit for the flow of water, and the land surfaces are the transitory recipients of water that is quickly lost in one way or another. The rate of these losses from any piece of land, when measured against the rate of water gains, determines the local water economy that is all-important to man.

The Water Cycle

As A. A. Milne suggested in one of his early essays, the annual financial statement issued by a large corporation is a remarkable document. In it, credits and debits are neatly displayed by dozens of categories and subcategories. Grand totals, gross totals, net totals, and subtotals are presented in profusion. The reader can tell how much interest was paid on Series Y bonds maturing in 1981 and how much was paid on all bonds, including Series Y. Money entries are carried out to the penny. And even a person who is an old hand at studying financial reports cannot repress a slight thrill when he looks at the final entry, the one far down at the bottom of the last page: "Net Balance: $0,000,000.00." What magnificent precision!

The scientist wishes he could be anywhere near so precise in calculating the molecular balance in a chemical reaction or the heat balance in the oceans. For scientists are often specialized accountants, and as such they usually consider themselves fortunate if their accounts come out correct to within 10 per cent. A certified public accountant would at first be horrified by such a margin of error; but if he spent many months observing the indirect methods that must be applied to estimate a single credit or debit item on many scientific accounting sheets, he would be forced to conclude that the balance struck was surprisingly close.

Calculation of the water economy of the lands is one of the most difficult of all scientific accounting problems. The standard accounting form to be used in summarizing the water economy of any piece of land might well appear as follows:

TYPICAL WATER-BALANCE STATEMENT FOR THE KISSIMMEE DRAINAGE BASIN [1]

(Billions of U.S. gallons)

Credit

1. Stored on the surface in streams, lakes, and ponds, and in the ground in such situations as to be available for stream recharge	61.2	
2. Stored as soil moisture and other ground water available for evaporation and transpiration, but not available for stream recharge	600.0	
Total water on hand at beginning of year		661.2
Water added by precipitation during year		2,400.0
Total water credits for the year		3,061.2

[1] The Kissimmee River is in south-central Florida, rising in Lake Kissimmee to the east of Winter Haven and flowing into the north end of Lake Okeechobee. The area of the basin is 3,260 square miles. The river is about ninety miles long and twenty-five feet above sea level. The country through which it flows is flat, as is most of Florida, and produces cattle, fruits, and vegetables; it is also a hunting and fishing region.

SOURCE: Adapted in generalized form from W. B. Langbein, "Hydrologic Studies," *USGS Water Supply Paper 1255* (Washington, Government Printing Office, 1955), pp. 511–70.

Debit

Water lost by transpiration and evaporation during the year	2,580.0	
Water lost by surface runoff during the year	438.0	
Total water debits for the year		3,018.0
Credit minus debit		43.2
Increased water on hand during year (plus reserve)		43.2
Balance		00.0

A detailed water-balance statement would theoretically include a breakdown of the broad credit and debit entries listed above. On the credit side, distinctions would be made among water stored in streams, lakes, and ponds, and also in the soil, as against consolidated rock masses. Distinctions would also be made among water received as rain, snow, fog drip, and dew or frost. On the debit side, losses through evaporation from the ground would be distinguished from losses through the transpiration of plants, and runoff losses through sheet-flow (across the ground) would be distinguished from runoff in streams. In addition to these refined credit and debit entries, still other items might be added, such as water removed from lakes, streams, and ground by man and water returned by man, as in sewage disposal. In practice, however, the more refined credit and debit entries, and such factors as man's water use, can seldom all be evaluated.

Balancing the hydrologic accounts is a difficult feat even within a small drainage basin such as that of the Vermilion River in north central Illinois. The Vermilion first flows west some twenty miles, then northwest fifty miles to join the Illinois River at La Salle. In its upper and middle reaches the river is wide and shallow. It seems in places to lie on top of level ground, so poorly marked are the valley walls. In contrast, where it nears its juncture with the Illinois River, the Vermilion has cut a strong valleyway with steep bluffs on either side. At times of heavy and long-lasting rains, the Vermilion fills its lower channel from side to side. In maximum flood it pours a million cubic feet of water into the Illinois River in a minute's time. In its lowest stage, where it enters the Illinois, the Vermilion is a trickle of water three feet wide that meanders lazily across the wide valley floor.

The terrain of the Vermilion region is gently rolling, rich Mid-western cornbelt land. In this valley of 1,300 square miles, fully half the farmland is in corn. And this is an area in which over 70 per cent of the land is planted to crops each year.

Within this rich agricultural region, the towns are small and the motif is rural. Only two are of moderate size. Streator, with a population of 16,000, is known chiefly for its glass factories, which draw upon the supply of high-grade quartz sand from nearby quarries along the river. Pontiac, a town of 9,000, is the county seat.

The face of the land is constant in all its broader aspects. Here are no extensive forest, no irrigated lands, no barren wastes, no rugged mountain slopes. If any drainage basin of modest size should have a simple water economy, the Vermilion Basin should. Yet even in this almost uniform basin the economy is complex.

Consider what happens to the water added to the Vermilion Basin. During a single heavy August rain, the water quickly floods the streets in Pontiac, then runs swiftly along the gutters and cascades down through the storm drains into the Vermilion River below. The water will flow on down the river and out of the drainage basin. In a cornfield less than a mile away, the rain wets the leaves and stalks of the plants and forms shallow pools upon the ground beneath. The water on the plants will later evaporate and so return to the air; that on the ground will either evaporate or sink slowly into the soil. Where the rain falls along the river banks, most of it flows downslope to join the stream. Where it falls in the quarry near Streator, it is trapped to form a pond that for days afterward will supply water to the air above and to the fine sands beneath. Toward the top of a gently sloping hill, a cluster of trees holds most of the rain from the land; but only a few yards away the rain beats down on barren ground and a sheet of water sweeps unimpeded down the hill.

On each of the thousands of surfaces upon which the rain descends, differing proportions of the total fall are disposed of in different ways at different rates; and the complex equations of water disposition are rendered still more abstruse because the rainfall itself varies in amount, intensity, and duration from one place to another.

During the course of the year, one hundred storms or more distribute water across the Vermilion Basin. One hundred times there are complexities of water disposition, just as there are in a single August storm. Therefore, the annual water accounting must be highly generalized even when computed for the basin as a whole rather than for its multitudinous individual parts. Two measured quantities are fundamental in the accounting system.

Precipitation is measured by six rain gauges within the basin. These show an average annual fall of thirty-five inches. The amount of water flowing out of the basin through the Vermilion River is measured at the Lowell gauging station, a few miles above the point where the Vermilion enters the Illinois River. The Lowell records show an average runoff equivalent to nine inches of precipitation annually.

The remaining precipitation (26 inches) is returned to the air by transpiration and evaporation or else leaves the area as overground runoff or underground water flow. There is no practical way to measure these kinds of losses; but knowledge of the area, of the transpiration rates of different plants, of the influences of specific weather conditions upon evaporation, and of underground water conditions in the region permits the making of crude estimates. One-quarter of the annual precipitation leaves the basin through the Vermilion River. Somewhat more than a third is lost through transpiration, and somewhat less than a third evaporates. Virtually all of the remaining one-twelfth of the total is lost through underground flow that leaves the area.

In all drainage basins of humid lands, transpiration, evaporation, and stream runoff are almost equally important modes of water loss and account among them for practically all such losses. In contrast, in arid regions evaporation becomes the single dominant mode of water loss. Here the plants compete fiercely with one another for the slight amounts of available moisture and so are widely spaced across the desert floor. Further, these are thick-skinned plants designed to retain any precious moisture they can gather in. Thus, both by the nature of the plants and by reason of their relative scarcity, transpiration cannot account for a high percentage of water loss in desert lands. Nor can losses through stream flow be high; for typically streams run out onto the desert floor, there to disappear as the water sinks into the sediments or evaporates into the air. Most important of all, the clear skies, high temperatures, and dry air typical of the desert environment all favor extremely rapid evaporation. Often the water from a desert shower barely wets the ground before it is seized by the very air whence it came.

Although the individual drainage basin is the ideal unit for the study of water problems, actually there are no barriers that can inhibit the movement of water from one basin to another or from any one place to any other place. Part of the rain that falls upon London in a winter storm may come from the South Pacific. Part of the water that evaporates from a rooftop in Manhattan may later be deposited as dew in a garden in Hobart, Tasmania. There is a water accounting system on a world-wide scale. Under this system the waters move from the oceans to the lands and back again to the oceans in the water cycle.

It has been known since the time of the Greeks that there must be a continuous interchange of water between the oceans and the lands. However, the Greeks had a curious notion of the mechanisms of water transfer, and their influence upon early scientific thought of the Renaissance was so great that their ideas were still prevalent and accepted in the latter part of the seventeenth century.

In his *Mundus Subterraneus*, published in 1664, Father Kircher describes how ocean water plunges into the ground through great whirlpools and so comes to flow through subterranean passages that extend into the heartlands of the continents. From these passageways come springs that feed the streams and rivers of the lands, and these in turn carry the water back to the oceans. Father Kircher pointed out that his concept of the hydrologic cycle was in keeping with the prevalent theory that in all sciences there must be a similarity between phenomena in the large and analogous phenomena in the small, between the macrocosm and microcosm. Here the similarity was between the circulation of blood in the human body and of water upon the earth, the subterranean passageways being equivalent to the deep-seated arteries and the streams being equivalent to the surface veins that return the blood to the heart.

The Greek ideas propounded by Father Kircher were brilliantly refuted in 1674 by Pierre Perrault, a French scientist who, through observation and crude measurements of the water budget of the Seine River, demonstrated that rainfall alone was more than sufficient to explain the flow of that river and its tributaries. Perrault even calculated fairly accurately the percentage of total rainfall of the Seine Basin that was returned to the sea by the river system, although he was able only to surmise a few of the ways in which the remainder of the water was returned to the sea.

The modern view of the water cycle is more prosaic than Father Kircher's intriguing scheme. Through evaporation, ocean water enters the air, which carries the water over the land and there precipitates it. The return movement of water from land to ocean takes place through streams and rivers, through direct return in coastal regions by underground flow and by sheetwash, and through return in the air itself, which picks up moisture from the land and later precipitates this moisture over the oceans.

The moving air is the sole medium for transfer of water from oceans to continents and is also quantitatively the most important agent for return of water to the oceans. In this process different and distinctive roles are played by air masses of different kinds. The moist air masses from the oceans are the carriers of water from sea to land. They bring rain, and because they are already moist they deprive the lands of only small amounts of water. The dry air masses from off the continents are the carriers of water from land to sea. Because they are dry, they pick up great quantities of moisture from the lands. Thus the water cycle is closely geared to the flow and ebb of masses of air that move unbounded across the surfaces of the earth, across the seas and the lands alike.

7 Water in the Air

The amount of water in the air is trivial compared to that in the oceans, lakes, and ground. Yet this small amount of water is fully as important to life as all the other earth waters combined.

If the surface of the solid earth was perfectly smooth, without mountains, valleys, or ocean basins, and if all the water in the world then lay upon this surface, the enveloping ocean formed in this way would be about one and three-quarter miles deep. Nearly all of this vast liquid mass would be water from the oceans of today and from their adjacent seas. Water from other sources would be equivalent only to the uppermost 165 feet of this world-wide sea. Of these 165 feet, about 140 would represent the water presently bound up as ice in the great glaciers of the world, especially those of Antarctica and Greenland, and something like fifteen feet would represent all the free water within the ground beneath the land. All the water of the lakes, ponds, rivers, and other water bodies of the lands would account for another four to five inches. A mere one inch of water depth would be equivalent to all the water in the entire ocean of air.

A water depth of one inch is an insignificant amount compared with a total water depth of over one and one-half miles. Yet this is the most important one-inch segment of water in the entire world. As water vapor, it permeates the atmosphere to heights of many miles and acts as a deep blanket for the earth that holds the warmth obtained from the sun. As liquid droplets and as ice particles, it forms the clouds and fog that are strong determinants of the weather. As rain and snow descending to the earth, it brings the moisture that is essential to all terrestrial life.

Water in the air is distributed unequally from place to place, and it varies in amount from one time to another. In the vertical, the amount of water decreases upward through the atmosphere. On the average, half of it lies below a height of about 8,000 feet. Geographically, in the horizontal, the air that is richest in moisture is that above the tropical oceans, and the driest air is that which lies above the icecap of interior Antarctica. Yet even Antarctica occasionally receives relatively moist air, and even the tropical oceans are sometimes overlain with relatively dry air, as in the eastern Indian Ocean, to the west of the Australian Desert.

The form assumed by the water in the air also varies from one time to another. When cooling occurs, as when air rises, invisible water vapor changes to cloud or fog. With further cooling, and if other circumstances are propitious, rain or snow falls. Owing to these and other changes, the water in the air behaves differently at different times and so gives distinctive character to the changing weather and to man's environments.

Water Vapor

Many simple observations confirm the fact that the air contains invisible water vapor. On cloudless nights, dew often forms upon the ground. In some instances the water for dew formation is supplied from within the ground itself; but if a metal sheet, impervious to water, is placed upon the ground, it also will often collect dew, and the source of this dew can only be the water vapor in the air. If a pan of water is placed where the sunlight falls upon it, the water will soon disappear; and it is certain that the water can only have passed into the air as vapor since the only other possibility, absorption of the water by the pan itself, must be ruled out because if this occurred the pan would increase in weight. From observations of these kinds it has long been known that the air contains water vapor. Yet as recently as 200 years ago there was no simple method for measuring the humidity of the air.

Probably it was James Hutton, the Scottish geologist, who invented the wet-bulb thermometer, the first instrument for measuring humidity. Whether it was Hutton or not, the inventor may well have reasoned somewhat as follows. With relatively little moisture in the air, evaporation from an exposed water surface is rapid. With relatively large amounts of moisture in the air, evaporation is slow. Rapid evaporation strongly cools the evaporating surface; slow evaporation cools the evaporating surface only slightly. Therefore, if the bulb of a thermometer is wrapped in a wet cloth, evaporation from the cloth will lower the temperature shown by the thermometer and the greater the lowering, the less the humidity of the air. Thus the wet-bulb temperature, as compared with the temperature registered by an ordinary dry-bulb thermometer adjacent to it, can be used as an index of the amount of water vapor in the air.

Once the idea of the wet-bulb thermometer had been conceived, it was easy to devise an actual working psychrometer to measure humidity. Two mercury-in-glass thermometers were mounted vertically side by side upon a panel. The bulb of one of these was enclosed in a porous cloth that extended downward into a well of water, so that water was constantly drawn up into the cloth just as kerosene is drawn upward in the wick of a lamp. By the use of a fan to sweep air past the two thermometer bulbs, the stagnant air immediately surrounding the cloth wick was replaced by the fresh air whose humidity was to be determined. All that then remained was to read the two thermometers and to compute what the water content of the air must be to account for the observed lowering of the wet-bulb temperature.

The dry- and wet-bulb psychrometer is still the instrument most commonly used for measuring humidity. Now, however, air passage across the thermometers is usually achieved by whirling the thermometers around or by using instruments equipped with mechanically or electrically driven fans. And humidity values are no longer computed by the observer but are merely read from standard tables.

Comparative dry- and wet-bulb readings and measurements with other, more complex kinds of psychrometers have shown that from one mass of air to another there are great variations in moisture content. At five feet above the ground, air may contain as little as one-half of 1 per cent or as much as 5 per cent water per unit volume of air. Air that has traveled far across the ocean brings to the land a comparatively heavy water burden. Air that has long remained upon the land is only lightly burdened. The cool ocean air that brings January rains to coastal Alaska contains three times as much moisture as the continental air which a few hundred miles away lies upon the snow-covered lands of Northwest Canada. At the same time of year, air flowing from the tropical Atlantic into the Amazon Basin commonly contains twice as much moisture as the air entering Alaska.

There are many ways of expressing the humidity of the air. For most scientific purposes, it is convenient to specify how much moisture there is per unit of dry air, as, for example, grains of moisture per pound of dry air. More commonly, however, the wetness or dryness of the air is expressed in terms of relative humidity, which shows how close the air is to saturation. Air with a relative humidity of 50 per cent contains just half the moisture it is capable of holding in the form of vapor, while air with a relative humidity of 75 per cent contains three-fourths of the vapor it can hold.

Relative humidity depends upon the air temperature as well as upon the amount of moisture that the air contains. If there is no loss of moisture through precipitation or through condensation upon the ground, the relative humidity must increase as the temperature goes down. It is for this reason that the relative humidity is usually higher during the nighttime, when temperatures are low, than during the daytime, when the air has warmed up. This also explains why desert air with a relative humidity of 30 per cent may contain more moisture than extremely cold arctic air with a relative humidity of 100 per cent.

Relative humidity is a convenient expression in considering the relation between humidity and human comfort. With the temperature 85° in the shade and with the air fully saturated with water vapor so that the relative humidity is 100 per cent, the heat is decidedly more uncomfortable than when the temperature is 95° and the relative humidity is only 60 per cent. At low temperatures also, discomfort increases with high relative humidity. Experiments with human subjects have demonstrated that damp, chill air at 55° is far more unpleasant than dry, cold air at 45°. Sensible temperature is influenced by wind conditions as well as by the relative humidity. Wind lowers the sensible temperature. It makes hot, damp weather seem less hot, and cold weather seem colder still.

Under conditions of very low relative humidity, evaporation from the skin surface is so rapid that the effects are particularly unpleasant. An extreme situation of this kind took place at Karachi, India, in January, 1943, when for an entire week the relative humidity fell to below 5 per cent in the daytime hours. In the cooler nighttime the humidity rose only to 20 per cent.

Few of the thousands of American soldiers who during this period were quartered in the barracks near the airfield outside Karachi will forget that week. Men lined up for water not so much to drink it as to moisten their lips, which were dried out and cracked. There was a light wind which brought with it dust and sand that clung to the clothes and body. To take a shower was worse than to endure the arid grit. The showers were outdoors and even during the day, with the temperature over 65°, to step from the shower into the air made one bitterly cold, so swift was the evaporation. Shaving outside was impossible; if a man put lather on his face, it was dust-dry within ten seconds. One enlisted man worked out a scheme for shaving. He sneaked into the officers' quarters, which were indoors, steamed up the bathroom, and shaved in comfort in his man-created moist environment.

With extremely dry air at the surface, such as that at Karachi in January, 1943, there may nonetheless sometimes be clouds at height and there may even be rain, though in such an instance the rain will evaporate before reaching the ground. The presence of clouds aloft may indicate that the air above is from a different source than that at the surface and is therefore more moist in absolute terms; or it may be that the surface air, dry though it is, has been lifted to such great heights that it has cooled to the dew point, which is the temperature at which the relative humidity becomes 100 per cent.

Air at sea level with a temperature of 86° and a relative humidity of 5 per cent has a dew point of about 4° below zero. The air will be cooled to its dew point if it rises to slightly over 16,000 feet. It is not common for air to be lifted to such heights unless it is forced up the slopes of a high mountain; but occasionally, as over hot desert areas, convective updrafts carry the surface air to these heights and even higher. Then clouds are apt to form, especially if the air contains dust, salt, or other solid particles about which liquid water droplets or ice droplets can form. Cloud formation is, however, not assured; for often the air becomes supersaturated with water vapor without any condensation at all. It is in these situations of supersaturation that seeding of the air with dry ice will start a sudden, local "chain reaction" that will convert clear air to cloud with small streamers of snow or rain descending from the cloud toward the ground.

Whether the air is dry or moist, with a low or a high relative humidity, the water vapor it contains is always a potential source of cloud and precipitation. In the air within the troposphere, the situation is analogous to that in a closed metal chamber that has dry ice piled against one side of it and a heating coil beneath the bottom, the whole chamber being filled one-tenth full of water, the remainder being air. In such a chamber there will be ice, water, and water vapor all present at the same time; and if a fan is inserted into the system to stir up the air, billions upon billions of water molecules will change phase every second, from gas to liquid, gas to ice, liquid to ice, liquid to gas, and so on.

It is in this sense that water vapor plays its most significant role, as the transitory form of water that at first comes into being through evaporation from oceans, lakes, and other water bodies and then, in time and at a different place, condenses to yield clouds that precipitate water upon the oceans and the lands throughout the world. Invisible though it is, water vapor is an essential link in the water cycle.

Cloud and Fog

Cloud is the visible manifestation of water suspended in the air. The trillions of particles that give it visual substance may be either liquid water droplets or ice. These particles are kept aloft by the constant buffeting of air molecules in the same fashion that fine silt remains suspended in the waters of a lake through the buffeting of water molecules. Sometimes cloud droplets drift down to earth to produce a gentle drizzle. Usually, however, they are precipitated only by distinctive and often violent atmospheric events. Then they move steadily down as heavy drizzle, swirl down as snow, rush down as driving rain or sleet, or else spill down as pounding hail.

Nearly everyone has observed the inside of a cloud, for clouds often exist at or near the ground. Such clouds are referred to as fog, but there is no essential difference between the internal appearance of fog and that of most other clouds of the atmosphere. There are, however, differences in the roles played by fog and by other clouds in contributing water to the ground, restricting visibility, and modifying the thermal environment at the earth's surface. These differences are highly significant in the physical order of things within the ocean of air, and the differences are closely related to the varying forms of the fogs and clouds that are principal elements of the weather scene. To watch the weather scene with its cloud elements is to learn much about the structure and behavior of the atmosphere; and in the watching there is a bonus, for the sky holds scenes of splendor. Though cloudless air has its moods, "A sky without clouds is a meadow without flowers, a sea without sails."

The cumulus clouds make up one of the three cloud families. These are the billowy clouds that twenty-four centuries ago were to Aristophanes "the waving locks of the hundred-headed Typho," and that in the sunset hours "gathered the waves in golden vases," and bore them to the shore.

It is chiefly the low cumulus clouds, those at heights of several hundred to a few thousand feet, that take on individual forms. The altocumulus clouds, at heights of eight or ten thousand feet, are joined together to form a fluffy quilt of misshapen patches lined with blue. Sometimes cumulus clouds reach from the lowest levels to the very highest like wavy pillars. Where there are hundreds of these clouds all intertwined and all abutting one upon the other, they look like mountain masses. Nowhere on earth is there a more magnificent view of these reaching, crowding forms of clouds than over the tropical oceans, where almost without cessation the water escapes from the dense and liquid mass of the sea and becomes the rarefied, floating water particles that are the clouds. By daylight these clouds display all tones of color and shadow. As Tomlinson has said, they seem to be of solid substance.

> All round the horizon motionless and permanent storm clouds are banked. Their forms do not alter, but their colours change with the hours. They seem to encompass us in a circular lake, a range of precipitous and intricately piled Alps, high and massive. Cleaving those steeps of calamitous rock—for so they looked, and not in the least like vapour—are chasms full of night, and the upper slopes and summits are lucent in amber and pearl. In the south and east the ranges are indigo dark and threatening, and the water between us and that closed country is opaque and heavy as moulten lead. Across the peaks of the mountains rest horizontal strata of mist.

For a sheer wall of towering cumulus clouds, look to the doldrums. Here, where the trade winds of the two hemispheres edge inward together, lies the intertropical front. The clouds along the front extend to 50,000 feet. Two planes fly through the front. For one the going is smooth and rainless. The next one, twenty minutes later, is buffeted and smashed. In the intertropical front off New Guinea during the war, eight planes heading northward from Australia punched into that wall of cloud, a hundred miles across. Only two came out.

It is in the nature of towering cumulus clouds to contain regions of violent air turbulence. The clouds are formed and are maintained by rising air that often swirls rapidly upward. They also contain regions of downdraft, and often the ascending and descending currents are sharply adjacent, with violently turbulent air between. Towering cumulus may develop into thunderstorm clouds, with flat anvil tops. In this form they yield heavy showers, though such showers may also be produced if the cloud does not assume a thunderstorm shape.

Small, fluffy cumulus clouds, such as those so common within the trade winds, are different in physical character from towering cumulus. These are short-lived clouds that frequently exist for only a few minutes. Thus within the stream of air, clouds are constantly forming, growing, waning, and disappearing. During its brief existence a cloud may yield a shower, often one so light as to be barely perceptible at the ground. More commonly, no shower falls and the cloud merely appears and disappears as evidence of the delicate balance within the stream of air between conditions favoring condensation and those favoring evaporation.

The second cloud family, the cirrus, occurs at altitudes of 18,000 feet or more. Cirrus are unshadowed clouds. Their particles are ice crystals which are so widely spaced that the sunlight passes through the cloud with little diminution. Cirrus are frequently thinly streaked or wispy in appearance. As cirro-cumulus they show a cellular structure. In thin layers, they form a veil across the sky. In this form especially they often indicate the presence high aloft of a layer of air whose origin is different from that of the air at the ground and whose moisture content is distinctly higher than in the air immediately beneath the cloud.

Layered clouds belong to the stratus family. Stratus may occur at any altitude within the troposphere. Its layered character is evidence that the air has risen in a quite uniform manner to produce condensation at a nearly constant altitude. Warm air moving over a sloping mass of colder air often produces stratus, as does also air moving up a mountain slope. This is true also of air that rises upward to a height at which it meets a warmer air layer which is lighter than the rising air and so prohibits its rising farther still. It is this last kind of situation that produces extensive stratus off the coast of California. Since this stratus is frequently low, it is commonly referred to as stratus fog.

Except in the heart of the tropics, widespread stratus frequently prevails during the summertime along the west coasts of the continents. The stratus forms over the sea throughout an offshore zone that may be many hundred miles wide. Then if the winds are even slightly onshore, the cloud moves in upon the coast.

Intensive studies of summer stratus along the California coast reveal that the foggy days come in groups of three or four or five interrupted by shorter periods during which the coast remains fog-free. Within a foggy period the stratus tends to lower from day to day. On Monday, for example, the cloud height may be a thousand feet. "High fog," the Californians call it. On Tuesday, the fog will typically lower to 800 feet. By Friday, the last day of the period, the fog is upon the ground. Saturday and Sunday may then be clear, while on Monday another fog period may begin.

In California, Chile, Norway, and other regions of summer stratus, the fog seldom moves in upon the coast until late afternoon or early evening, when it is borne inland by the strengthening sea breeze. If the breeze is gentle, the fog seeps inward across the land. In a vigorous breeze the fog comes churning in. Where there are coastal mountains the fog funnels through the lower passes, cascades down the leeward slopes, and fans out across the lower-lying ground. In hilly cities along the stratus coasts, as in San Francisco and Capetown, fog-bearing winds are such that one locality within the city may average sixty days of fog for the summer while another locality less than a thousand yards away may average only twenty days. Such local variations in fog frequency are well known to real-estate agents; the locations that are relatively fog-free are in high demand as sites for homes.

Like other cloud, fog is produced by the cooling of air to the dew point. The difference between the air temperature and the dew point may be slight, as in air that has been long upon the oceans. The ocean air that moves onto the coast of southwestern England during the winter may be at a temperature of 38° with a dew point of 36°. Then little cooling will be needed for fog to form. The air of summertime in the Sahara may also have a dew point of 36°; but with daytime temperatures of 110° in the Sahara, an enormous drop in temperature would be required for fog or other cloud to form, so the skies remain clear. In every instance the critical factor is not the amount of moisture in the air, but rather the difference between the temperature and the dew point and how much cooling takes place.

To the farmer a dew point that is almost as high as the air temperature is insurance against a damaging freeze on many cool nights. With temperatures in the forties in the early evening, with a dew point of 20°, and with clear skies that permit the rapid loss of heat outward through radiation, the temperature is almost certain to go below freezing before sunrise. In the same situation, if the dew point is 39°, the temperature will fall swiftly only until the dew point is reached. Then moisture will condense not only on the ground but also upon the billions of microscopic particles of dust floating in the air, forming a mantle of fog that acts as a barrier against the further escape of heat by radiation from the ground and lower air. The temperature may still edge downward a few degrees, but a costly freeze will have been averted.

The cooling that yields fog may be brought about not only through nocturnal radiation but in many other ways. Coastal stratus is formed when air rises and cools through expansion. A similar kind of cooling takes place when air moves upslope. When a massive current of moist air from the Gulf of Mexico advances across the gently rising coastal plain, and pushes farther still up the slopes of the central prairie regions and northwest up onto the High Plains, fog may blanket simultaneously an area close to a quarter of a million square miles in size—an area that extends from Iowa on the north to Arkansas on the south and from the Mississippi westward almost to the Rocky Mountains. Moist air moving over cold ground or icy water frequently yields fog. The daytime fogs of winter and spring are often of this type.

More rare and more spectacular than any of these are two fog types found chiefly in polar regions. One is a fog that forms at temperatures far below zero and whose particles are ice crystals that during the brief sunlight hours sparkle like diamond chips and transform the air into a dazzling, luminous mass. The other forms where a cold, dry wind blows across an open sea or lake and mixes with the thin layer of moist, warm air that lies adjacent to the water. Then the surface of the lake throngs with fog streamers that come to life wherever the cold air eddies downward and disappear wherever a tiny eddy dies out. The lake resembles a steaming caldron.

There are many places where fogs are so frequent and so dense that they contribute appreciable quantities of water to the land. South of Bombay, India, beneath the crest of the mountains that face westward toward the Arabian Sea, there is a zone of dense jungle land that is overgrown with scrubby trees and matted, thorny brush. For eight months of the year, there is little or no rain in this jungle, yet always the soil is moist and on most days, even in the long rainless season, the trees and brush are dripping wet. This is a cloud forest, one that lies at just such an elevation along the mountain slopes that day after day, sometimes for weeks without cessation, the forest is immersed in cloud. Estimates are difficult to make, but it is likely that the moisture from these clouds contributes the equivalent of at least thirty inches of precipitation to this forest zone during the rainless period. Cloud forests of this kind are found along mountain slopes in many places toward the margins of the tropics. They are somewhat akin to the foggy desert areas of the world, like the Kalahari in South-West Africa, where the almost perpetual fog supports a scrubby growth of brush in an area where the total annual precipitation is less than five inches.

Calculations of fog drip have been made in the Hawaiian Islands, Tasmania, South Africa, and elsewhere. These measurements show that, at least in some preferred locations, fog contributes as much as ten or twenty inches of moisture per month to the land. In these favorable locations the fog clouds stream upslope across a forested area, and the leaves and branches of the trees gather the water from the fog with such efficiency that water not only flows downward from leaf to twig to branch to trunk and so to the ground but also, at times, drips directly to the ground from the sopping-wet leaf surfaces. In these locations there is frequently far more water received in a month from fog than from precipitation in the form of rain or snow.

For most parts of the world, however, rain and snow are the great bringers of water to the land, and it is as sources of such precipitation that clouds are of the greatest importance. Sometimes clouds appear and disappear without producing rain or snow. Often they travel hundreds of miles before doing so. When they yield precipitation, the event is one that contributes to the circulation of water on a world-wide scale. When and where they yield it is of great significance to man.

Rain, Snow, Hail

No one knows precisely why it rains. Air cools until it reaches the dew point, when the moisture in the air often condenses to form cloud droplets. So much is known. Yet what is it that causes the droplets to grow in size until they are so large that they can no longer be held in suspension in the air and so must fall?

There are a few clues that indicate some partial answers. In middle and high latitudes, heavy precipitation takes place only from clouds within which the temperature is below freezing. This suggests that the presence of ice nuclei may stimulate droplet growth to the point of precipitation. If moist air is placed in a closed chamber and the temperature of the air lowered to the dew point, water droplets will form on the dust particles in the air to produce a cloud. If the temperature is lowered further, to well below the freezing point, the droplets will be supercooled without changing to ice and without precipitation. Now if a single ice crystal is made to form in the chamber, suddenly the cloud turns white with snow, and after the snow has drifted to the bottom of the chamber it is seen that the cloud has completely disappeared. This fundamental physical effect, first discovered in the laboratory, is the basis of all techniques for the seeding of supercooled clouds to produce precipitation.

Many experiments have been conducted to determine how introduction of a single ice crystal can dissipate cloud throughout many tens of cubic feet of space. Evidently the ice crystal grows in size so rapidly in its saturated environment that it throws off microscopic ice splinters which in turn grow rapidly and throw off more ice splinters, and so on in succession until, for unknown reasons, the chain reaction ceases. Whatever the mechanism, it is certain that once ice forms within a cloud that holds supercooled water droplets surrounded by saturated air, precipitation takes place. Snow is produced within the cloud and this yields snow or rain at the ground depending upon whether the snowflakes melt during their descent. Even in summer, heavy rain in Chicago, Edinburgh, or other places outside the tropics means that, high overhead within the cloud, snow is falling.

Two fundamental questions remain. Without seeding, what causes ice crystals to form in supercooled clouds and so to trigger the precipitation? What explains the origin of drizzle in middle latitudes and of heavy rain in low latitudes, both of which may take place from clouds at temperatures above the freezing point? Much must be learned before either of these questions can be answered.

The broad-scale atmospheric events that lead to precipitation are well known, even though the details of the precipitation process are not. Moist air rises and so cools. Clouds form. Continued upward motion brings further cooling and with it rain or snow, sleet or hail. The necessary upward motion of the air may be brought about in several ways. Air thrusts upslope onto the flank of a mountain. Uplift of this kind brings five feet of snow in a single day to the ski slopes of the Andes Mountains, at El Volcán, near Santiago, Chile.

The upward motion may take place where moist warm air meets cooler air along a front. The steady, copious rains that in the spring may cover all of the upper Ohio Basin and bring record floods throughout the Valley are caused by the persistent upward flow of warm air over a cool air mass that for days on end lies almost motionless across New York, Pennsylvania, Ohio, and West Virginia. This is warm-front rain. In contrast, the showers that within an hour spill two, three, or even four inches of rain upon the land in Indiana or the Carolinas are often formed along a cold front, where cold air butts its way into warmer air, flipping it upward to yield sudden, violent storms. Precipitation may also come where there is an overturning of the air column either because the air above cools and plummets downward, forcing up the surface air, or because the air near the ground is strongly warmed and so rises. The nighttime thunderstorms so common in Iowa in the spring are caused sometimes by cooling of air aloft. The daytime thunderstorms of summer in Texas are caused by heating of the lower air by the warm ground beneath.

The situation that produces summer thunderstorms in Florida illustrates many of the processes that are often active to produce precipitation. No other place in the United States has as many summer thunderstorms as does north central Florida. The odds are better than two to one that at any given place in this area on any day between June 1 and August 31 there will be at least one thunderstorm. It is almost as likely that the daily storm will occur in the afternoon between 12 and 6 o'clock. It is during this time that the land surface reaches its highest temperature, causing the air above to boil upward, forming towering cumulus clouds.

Meanwhile, from off the Atlantic Ocean to the east, warm, moist air pours onto the land, carried in on a strong sea breeze. Simultaneously, the sea breeze on the Gulf Coast sweeps in moist air from the west. The two moist currents converge over the Florida peninsula and the air, crowded together, unable to escape sidewise, is forced to rise, thus reinforcing the updraft. The cumulus clouds grow larger and change to thunderstorm clouds with thick, black, angry-looking mid-sections and white, flat tops, spread outward like the top of a blacksmith's anvil. Then the breezes strengthen along the ground. The sky darkens, then suddenly is interlaced by pulsing welts of light. A cannonade of thunder ushers in the rain. The storm is on.

In the heart of the Florida thunderstorm belt is the town of Orlando. Nearby is Orlando Air Force Base. In the spring of 1946 there assembled at the base some 200 persons, brought there to participate in an elaborate study of thunderstorms. Army technicians arrived to operate the radar equipment that would track the weather balloons. Weather observers came to man the special rain gauges, thermometers, and wind-measuring devices. Pilots were there, young men in their teens and early twenties, back from the battlefronts in Europe and the Pacific. They were to fly the Northrop Black Widows that would pierce the storms and measure their violence. Sailplane pilots were there too, the glider men who fly unpowered aircraft; and many was the evening hour spent in debate at the Club arguing which was the safer craft in a thunderstorm, the powered plane that bucks its way through turbulent air or the sailplane that rides the currents up and down at a dizzy pace.

The design of the experiment had been worked out far in advance. General plans had been drawn by representatives of the Weather Bureau, Army, Navy, and the National Advisory Committee on Aeronautics, all of which were cosponsors of the project. Detailed plans had been worked out by a group of three—Professor Horace R. Byers, the Project Director; Commander R. H. Maynard of the Navy; and Colonel B. G. Holzman of the Army Air Forces.

On the ground were fifty-five weather observing stations spaced at intervals of one mile. Data from these stations would show the rainfall pattern yielded by each storm, the temperature variations from place to place, and the speed of the wind across the ground surface. Ten radar stations were established to track the weather balloons that would rise upward and travel on the winds like buoys upon the currents of the sea, thus tracing out the flow of air within the storm.

Black Widow planes, carrying elaborate weather recording instruments, were to fly through the storm at height intervals of 5,000 feet, up to a top altitude of five miles. To measure the updrafts and downdrafts, sailplanes were to be used. It was essential that all these observations be synchronized. Therefore, the aircraft were equipped with radar beacons so that each craft might be tracked in flight by radar on the ground. The thunderclouds themselves were also tracked, the large cloud droplets serving as targets for the radar beam and producing echoes that were displayed as masses of white upon the black radar screen. A master time system synchronized all aircraft, radar, and weather-instrument observations. Every measurement could be located in time and space with remarkable precision.

From the viewpoint of the participants in the thunderstorm project, the monotonous part consisted of setting up weather stations, installing equipment aboard the aircraft, checking the measuring devices, and assembling and analyzing the tens of thousands of observations that quickly accumulated once the study was under way. It was dull, too, awaiting the arrival of each thunderstorm; but once the alert sounded, monotony ended.

If you were a weather observer in charge of a dozen stations, you raced your jeep through rain and pounding hail from one station to another. At each station you leaped out, made certain all was well, then dashed back to the jeep and headed for the next station. If you were a radar man, you stood to one side, out of the way of the recording motion-picture camera, and peered at the radar screen to detect any target that threatened escape from the field of vision. When escape was imminent, you shouted instructions to the operator who sat at the wheels that controlled the tilt and angle of the disk-shaped antenna. If you piloted a Black Widow, you fought the controls clear through the storm, trying to keep the plane at a constant altitude. With downdrafts at 30 m.p.h. and updrafts twice that speed, with hail and wind and cloud and blinding lightning flashes, this took a little doing. Fortunately, it seldom required more than five minutes to fly on through the storm. As one pilot remarked, "You grab the wheel and, whammy, through you go!"

The glider pilots were amateur volunteers from the Soaring Society of America. They were towed aloft when a thunderstorm was starting to build. They hunted out the strongest updrafts that would send their craft bounding skyward through the cloud to the high snow-filled regions. Sometimes crosscurrents sharply flipped a glider over and sent it spinning toward the ground. Then the pilot would go into a dive and pull out and up until he found another ascending current to return him to the upper regions of the clouds.

Even before the Orlando study was carried out, much was known of the nature of thunderstorms—of the way they grow, of the violent turbulence within them, and of the tremendous rains and hail showers that they yield. Yet never before had observations of these and other aspects of the thunderstorm been studied synchronously on such a scale. The Orlando study and its sequel, a similar study carried out in Ohio a year later, led to a far better understanding of the anatomy and dynamics of the thunderstorm than had before been achieved.

The life span of a thunderstorm rarely exceeds an hour and a quarter. At birth it is a cumulus cloud a mile or so in diameter that reaches upward to the freezing level, some 15,000 feet above the ground. In the next ten minutes the cloud swells upward and outward at such a pace that its width may increase to five miles and its height to 25,000 feet. During this youthful stage the storm is fed by moist air sweeping inward at low levels. The body of the storm is a churning mass of upward-moving air, a single giant updraft that drags with it air from the surrounding spaces. In the last few minutes of this stage, there is thunder and lightning; but though within the cloud there may be snow and rain, none of it can reach the ground against the violent updraft.

The mature stage starts when somewhere in the cloud a mass of large and heavy raindrops breaks through the upward-moving air and reaches the ground. A downdraft forms and quickly is enlarged. Two minutes later there are several downdrafts interposed with regions in which the air shoots upward at speeds that may reach 70 m.p.h. At the ground, cooler air brought down from high aloft mingles sharply with warmer surface air. The winds are violent and gusty. Rain hammers downward for some fifteen minutes. All the time the cloud aloft is growing upward until it may extend to 50,000 feet.

The period of greatest violence, with all its hodgepodge of weather events, is over in twenty or thirty minutes. Then, as the vital updrafts of moist air die out, the storm enters old age. In a few minutes the air movement is downward everywhere. The magnificent thunderstorm cloud degenerates into broken stratus cloud with ragged edges. Within thirty minutes after its stage of greatest violence, the thunderstorm ceases to exist.

Modern commercial aircraft are designed to withstand the stresses to which they may be subjected upon flying through a thunderstorm. The principal threats of the storm are hail, which may cause structural damage; lightning, which may interrupt radio communications; and turbulence, induced by gustiness or by updrafts or downdrafts, which may produce structural failure if any portion of the airframe has already been weakened. These dangers are magnified for small planes. If a plane does not carry deicing equipment, the dangers of the thunderstorm are increased still further, because icing conditions may be severe in many regions of the storm.

The most distinctive characteristics of a well-developed thunderstorm are lightning, thunder, and hail. All three are related to the violent air currents within the storm. These currents rip apart the water droplets in the cloud, a process that sets up strong positive electric fields in the uppermost regions of the cloud and over wide regions in the lower cloud layers. In the middle cloud the charge is negative. The lightning produced by these charges is like the spark generated by a spark coil. Both sparks must burrow their way through air, which is a poor conductor of electricity. The lightning spark starts out as a tiny finger that thrusts forward a short distance. The main charge races after. A tiny spark jumps forward again. Again the main spark darts after it. So by successive jumps the main bolt swiftly chases the pioneer spark from one cloud to another or from cloud to ground. The whole thing happens so fast that the entire discharge over a distance of half a mile may occur in less than ten one-millionths of a second.

A single lightning bolt may develop 12 million horsepower. This blast of energy shatters the surrounding air molecules, causing them to glow as neon gas glows when a current passes through it within the tube of a display sign. Simultaneously, the air surrounding the lightning bolt expands explosively, creating the crashing sound of accompanying thunder. Where the sound waves are reflected and bent in different ways, the resulting thunder is heard as a reverberating sound that echoes and re-echoes.

During a lightning storm the safest place to be is inside a building. If lightning strikes the building, the electricity will be guided to earth through the walls. The worst place to be is by a lone tree, alongside an isolated building, in the water, on a hill, or in an area so flat that a person and the golf club that he carries become a conspicuous target for the lightning. If one cannot seek shelter during a violent lightning storm, he should sit it out in a hollow depression or, if the ground is perfectly flat, lie down. Persons traveling in a car or plane are quite safe; but those in a small boat may be in danger, especially if they are near the mast, which stands out conspicuously, like a lightning rod from the roof of a building. After the storm it is dangerous to touch metal surfaces that are not connected to the ground by a good conductor. Many persons have been electrocuted by touching fence wires that have become charged by lightning.

All thunderstorms produce lightning and thunder. Many, but not all, also yield hail. A hailstone is composed of alternate layers of ice and snow. The first event in its formation is that a downward-moving raindrop is caught in an updraft which flings it up above the freezing level where the cloud is filled with swirling snow. The drop freezes solid, then picks up a snow layer. Again it falls into warmer air. Again it rises. So the hailstone bounces back and forth across the freezing level, all the time growing in size until finally it becomes so heavy that it falls to earth even against the swift updraft. Unusually large hailstones, two inches in diameter, contain as many as ten pairs of ice and snow layers, indicating ten round trips between warmer and colder air.

The regions of hail beneath a thunderstorm are relatively small and irregularly shaped. Hail may break windows in the buildings on one city block and leave an adjacent block unscathed. Rainfall also is erratically distributed by the storm. To one farmer a thunderstorm brings moderate rain that replenishes the soil; to another, drenching rains that scour the crops from the field. Still a third farmer may receive no rain at all, even though all the surrounding farms are blessed or cursed with rain. This variety of effects within a small area, coupled with the lightning and thunder, give the thunderstorm its highly distinctive personality.

In many broad areas of the world, as in the southeastern United States, northern Brazil, and the monsoon lands of Southeast Asia, thunderstorms are common and in the aggregate deposit ten, twenty, thirty, or even more inches of rainfall upon the land in the average year. However, in most land areas thunderstorms are relatively rare and precipitation is chiefly from other kinds of storms. This is evident when one examines the daily weather maps that cover the entire Northern Hemisphere and are regularly prepared by the United States Weather Bureau. Any one such map, showing the weather conditions at one particular time for all of the area north of the equator, reveals that rain, snow, or hail is falling in scores of different places simultaneously, and that thunderstorms account for only a small percentage of the observed precipitation.

If the view afforded by a single daily weather map is multiplied by 365 to show the complex, shifting patterns of precipitation for an entire year, and if these in turn are multiplied by twenty to show the patterns for two decades, there begins to emerge a view of the geographic variations in precipitation on a world-wide scale. It is seen that there are wet lands and dry lands, and those that receive intermediate amounts of precipitation. It is seen, also, that even in the wettest lands the precipitation is not regularly recurring in fixed and certain amounts but varies episodically as rain events come and go. Nor are the driest lands completely devoid of precipitation. At times, if only occasionally and then only briefly, they receive abundant rain or snow.

This, then, is the significance of storms of all kinds. They bring moisture to the lands in the form of rain, snow, and hail. To some locations they bring copious amounts; to others, almost none. To all places they bring different amounts of water at different times, and so they yield not only a geographic pattern that in the average defines the wet lands, the semiwet lands, and the dry lands but a time pattern as well, so that droughts may visit the wettest lands and floods the driest ones. These variabilities, in space across the earth and in time throughout the years, produce the changing moisture environments of the sixty million square miles that are the lands of the earth.

8 Dry Lands, Wet Lands

The climatologist's view of the world embraces dry lands and wet lands, and lands where the water supply is sometimes abundant and sometimes not, depending on the season and the year. Others share this outlook, such as the hydrologist, the agriculturalist, the irrigation engineer, and the specialist who designs water-power installations.

The inventory of the water circumstances of the lands includes several different kinds of regions. There are the cold polar regions where, despite the low annual precipitation, water is always present, at least in the frozen subsoil, if not as snow and ice upon the ground. There are the monsoon areas, where summer is the season of superabundant rains and winter is a season of drought. The opposite regime holds in Mediterranean lands and along the west coasts of all the continents in middle latitudes. Here there are summer drought and winter rain; and where there are mountains, such as the Sierra Nevadas of California, there are deep winter snows which in melting pour constant streams of water into the riverways for many months after the snowfalls have ceased, so that in many places during the spring and early summer the land is nourished by water despite the lack of rain.

Different from all these regions are the desert and semidesert areas. There drought dominates all the seasons, even though there are occasional rains and occasional places where master rivers, such as the Nile, are never dry. Different also are the humid tropics, where water is plentiful at all seasons, though sometimes there may be no rain for a week or more. These two, the dry lands of the desert and semidesert and the wet lands of the humid tropics, are at opposite ends of the spectrum of water regions of the earth.

There are many dry regions in the world, but the greatest is that which extends from Mongolia in eastern Asia all the way to where the Sahara borders the Atlantic Ocean in North Africa. So large is this region that Russell and Kniffen have aptly called it the Dry World. At the other extreme, among the areas of the humid tropics, there is the Basin of the Amazon. Nowhere else, not even in the Congo, is there such a gigantic realm of warm, humid land.

The contrasting scenes within these two great regions illustrate the thesis that the water regime is a powerful determinant of the nature of the landscape and is strongly reflected in the activities of man.

The Dry World

For sheer size no other natural region upon the continents can match the Dry World. Its area is over twice that of the United States and three times that of all the other dry lands of the world combined. Within its borders lie a dozen deserts that in themselves are huge, such as the Gobi Desert of Mongolia, the Kara Kum of Turkestan, the Arabian Desert, and the Sahara.

The environment of the Dry World is harsh. Except near the margins of the area and in a few small scattered locations where wells or springs provide oases, or where there is some through-flowing river like the Nile or the Indus, water is everywhere so scarce that the raising of crops is impossible and even sedentary grazing, using the same rangelands year after year, cannot be practiced because the natural vegetation is too sparse. In such a land no commodity is more treasured than is water, and to give water to a stranger is an act of utmost charity, a fact that is reflected in the sacred writings of Judaism, Christianity, and Mohammedanism, all of which came into being within the Dry World.

The Dry World is comprised of three main topographic realms arranged in overlapping fashion, one above another from south to north. The southernmost, and by far the largest, is the Saharan-Arabian realm, which reaches from the Atlantic Ocean to the Persian Gulf. Here extensive low plateaus alternate with broad desert plains.

To the east and slightly offset to the north is the Persian-Afghan realm. Except in its easternmost portion, on the desert plains of Pakistan and India, this is a land of wide desert basins rimmed by mountain ranges that in many places rise to heights well above 10,000 feet. Toward its northern edge, the mountains press together to form a high and massive wall that only here and there contains gateways that grant ready access to the third realm of Inner Asia.

This northern land is quite unlike the other two. Its western segment is the low-lying desert region of Kara Kum. Its eastern segment is a series of great plateau surfaces bordered by gigantic mountains. The Tibetan Plateau, which itself is 14,000 to 16,000 feet high, is dwarfed by the lofty Himalayas on the south and the ragged-edged Kunluns on the north. To northward of the Kunluns is the low plateau of Sinkiang, within which are set the two enormous basin areas of Takla Makan and Dzungaria. Eastward from Sinkiang is the Mongolian Plateau, upon which rests the Gobi Desert. West of Sinkiang there rises upward a formidable mountain barrier that separates the eastern and western segments of the realm. The barrier is pierced by a single broad corridor, the Dzungarian Gate, which time and again in centuries long past has been the spillway for armies of Mongol horsemen, westward bound to conquer new lands.

Because water is precious everywhere throughout the Dry World, variations in precipitation from place to place and from year to year are of the greatest importance. Regions near the margins of the Dry World, where the annual precipitation often averages eight to twelve inches, are specially favored. So also are those mountain slopes in Persia, Afghanistan, and Inner Asia that receive eight to twenty inches of precipitation. At the other extreme are the basins and plains where there is less than one inch of rain in the average year, an amount not equal to that produced by a single heavy storm in the eastern United States. In these impoverished regions, as throughout the Dry World, problems of water supply are rendered even more critical because of the unreliability of the rainfall. In the driest places there may be two inches of rain in one year and not a drop for the next five years in a row. In places where the rainfall averages ten inches, the totals in five successive years might typically be six, fourteen, seven, three, and twenty inches.

Throughout the Dry World, water is the key to living. Population density, modes of life, social organization, and economic activi-

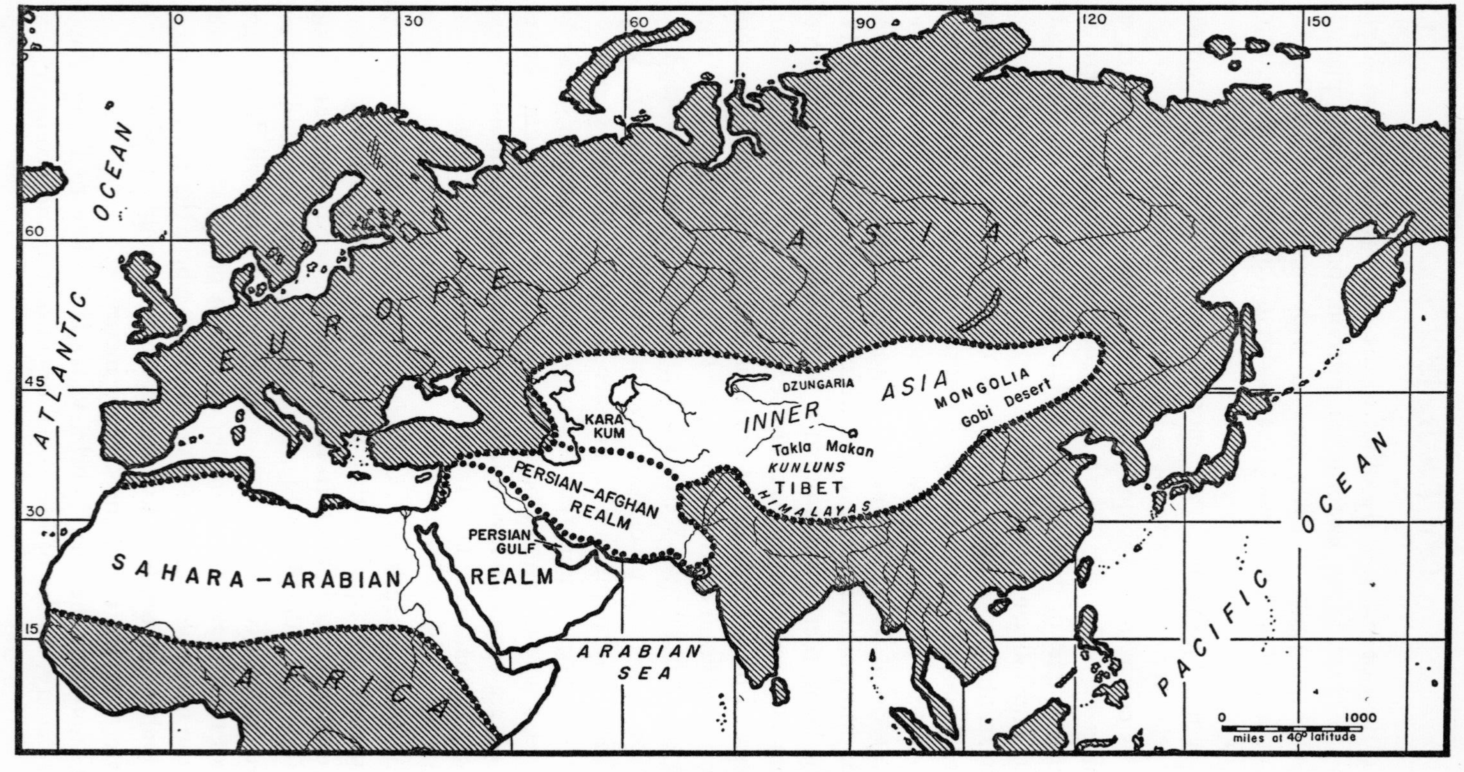

THE DRY WORLD

ties all sharply reflect the degree of water availability. The driest lands of all are uninhabited. If they are extensive, and a few are hundreds of miles across, these waterless regions are not even traversed by caravans. They are the dead lands. Even desert bandits seeking escape from their pursuers will not venture far into these sterile regions.

The areas of somewhat lesser dryness are the homelands of the pastoral nomads. The grazing animals that are the basis of the economic life of the nomads are the camel, horse, sheep, goat, cattle, ox, ass, and water buffalo. A tribe of nomads may have two or three kinds of grazing animals, but only one will be of prime importance. Which one depends almost wholly upon moisture availability, a factor that determines the conditions both for grazing and for watering the animals.

Villages whose economies rest both on the raising of crops and on animal husbandry can exist only in those limited areas where water is relatively abundant—in the somewhat rainier peripheral areas, in the foothills beneath well-watered mountain slopes, or in oases fed by wells or springs or some perennial stream. Where the water supply is just sufficient to sustain a village, that village is small and isolated. Where water is far more abundant, as in an oasis, the villages are large and closely spaced.

The really dense concentration of people in towns or cities requires the greatest amounts of water. Many factors, such as situation with reference to trade routes, determine the location of a town or city; but none can exist where the water supply is not reliable and superabundant. In the Dry World this means that towns and cities are found only where there are springs, wells, or perennial streams.

The Bedawin of central Arabia exemplify the significance of water in the lives of the Dry World peoples. These Bedawin are camel nomads. They own a few horses, which are chiefly used in combat and for display as a sign of position or wealth; but the camel is the center of their economy. Meat, milk, and hair are all provided by the camel, which also constitutes a "cash crop" to be sold in the towns so that grain, rifles, and other necessities can be bought for cash or acquired through barter. Sheep are barred from the Bedawin economy for two reasons. Unlike the camel, sheep cannot go for five days or more without water, and they cannot move swiftly, as can both the camel and the horse. Swift movement is essential both in warfare and to reach water quickly, before it has evaporated or sunk into the ground when a rainstorm is observed at a distance.

> The storms which bring the rain do not distribute it evenly. Watching a thundercloud and the flashes of distant lightning, the Bedawin will send scouts to locate the rainfall, and then race to reach it. If the only livestock in the camp are camels and horses, he will attain his goal. If encumbered with sheep, however, he might fail. . . .

Among the Bedawin the major social and political unit is the tribe. In summer—a season utterly devoid of rain—an entire tribe numbering many hundreds may camp along a major river, such as the Euphrates. To camp by a reliable source of water is essential at this season, "since the camels must be watered every day because of lack of moisture in the tinder-dry perennials which form their fodder and because of the heat." After the first rain, in October or November, the tribe breaks up into smaller camp groups, each with its leader. The several camps then move well out into the desert, and thereafter each camp moves as required from one grazing place to another. If the winter rains are poor, the individual camp groups are small and move quite often. If the rains are good, the groups are larger and more nearly sedentary, although they seldom remain at one camp site for more than a few weeks. By June the benefits of the winter rains will have been exhausted, and once more the tribe will assemble at some permanent water source.

The camel nomads constitute but one of the many types of socioeconomic units of the Dry World. There are also the horse nomads of Mongolia and the Kurds of Persia and Iraq, who in the spring drive their sheep long distances to mountain pastures and in the fall return to the milder valley regions that they consider home. There are villages of twelve households where the water resources barely permit the raising of a little wheat and the grazing of a few sheep and goats. There are villages of sixty households which are so favored that not only grains but also apricots, almonds, figs, dates, and even oranges are raised, while sheep, goats, horses, cattle, asses, and oxen are readily maintained. Add to these the villages of intermediate size and wealth, the other nomads and seminomads of several kinds, and the towns and cities in all their diversity, and the mosaic is complete.

Despite its water circumstance, or because of it, the Dry World claims a history that in point of time is longer than that of any other area of the earth. Three thousand years before the time of Christ, there were high civilizations in Egypt on the Nile River, in Babylonia on the Tigris-Euphrates, and—only slightly later—at Mohenjo-daro on the Indus River in northwest India. It is a curious matter, and one that surely cannot be laid to chance, that all three of these earliest civilizations arose along the banks of great perennial rivers surrounded by arid terrain. No one knows for certain how this came to be, but there are several factors that may well have operated to yield cultural ascendancy in these riverine locations. To see what these factors may have been, one must go back to an era that antedates the rise of civilization by many thousand years.

Eight thousand years ago the Dry World was far more sparsely settled than it is today. Many regions of the desert that now are the realm of the nomad were then uninhabited and even untraversed. The camel, horse, sheep, and other grazing animals had not yet been domesticated. Agriculture was unknown. The tribal groups that wandered on foot from place to place in search of fruits to gather and game to hunt were a tough folk, inured to the ways of the dry land and canny in their knowledge thereof. But even they were restricted in their movements; for if a man is to survive, his minimum water needs must be met, and there is a limit to the size of the water bag that he can carry. These wanderers were barred from the extensive heartlands of the desert.

In contrast, the strips of land along the permanent rivers were occupied by sedentary groups. With an everlasting supply of water immediately at hand, with fish in profusion, with fruit and game along the river edges, and with reeds and soft wood from which to fashion implements and boats and shelters, there was little need for these folk to wander. Upon occasion they sallied forth short distances away from the river in search of game, but always they returned. The river held them like a magnet, and more so because beyond, to east and west, was unattractive, hostile terrain. Indeed, in many places, as throughout nearly all of the middle and lower Nile Valley except in the delta, the desert to either side was waterless. It bound the people to the river and was their shield against invaders.

Certainly along the Nile, and probably also along the Tigris-Euphrates and the Indus, the sedentary tribes of 8,000 years ago possessed a high culture. They made baskets of exquisite, simple beauty. Their stone tools and weapons were finely wrought. Yet they were not civilized. Though their society was complex, it lacked the ornate structure—the classes and subclassses and the economic specialization—that characterizes the civilized community. They also lacked roads, buildings, an art divorced from handicrafts, and a calendar. Above all, they lacked that most distinctive attribute of civilization, a written language.

Meanwhile, close by the margins of the Dry World, at the edges of the forests in the more humid parts of Abyssinia, Turkey, and Afghanistan, plants had been domesticated and agriculture was being practiced. In time domesticated plants, such as wheat and flax and barley, were introduced to the riverine lands, probably through the borrowing of technical knowledge and the acquisition of seeds through trade. Certainly by 4800 B.C. in the Nile Valley, agriculture was being practiced. With water in abundance, with annual inundations of the river to renew the soil, with solar energy streaming inward unimpeded by clouds, agriculture prospered as it never had before in any clime.

Within five hundred years the agricultural resources were being utilized still more fully through irrigation. As techniques improved, the food supply increased; as the food increased, so did the population. Labor became more specialized. In resolving problems of special water rights and land tenure, additional classes and subclasses were formed. As boats became larger and capable of carrying heavier goods, the river became a major artery for transport and for trade. More than ever before, neighboring tribes jostled one another and wars were more frequent and intense. Tribes enlarged their domains. The soldier and the administrator joined the captured slave, the free farmer, craftsman, priest, and chief as members of the new and complex society.

All this required many centuries; but by 3000 B.C. on the Nile and the Tigris-Euphrates, and by 2600 B.C. on the Indus, there had come into being large concentrations of population with such diversification of labor specialties and special status that the arts and crafts, agriculture, military affairs, public buildings, formal religion, and writing all flourished. In some such manner and in these peculiarly congenial locations, civilization had been born.

The Amazon Basin

To people reared in middle-latitude lands, there is no region more crowded with unfamiliar elements than the Amazon Basin. The continual warmth, the copious rains and high humidity, the sheer fecundity of the tropical rain forest, and the myriad varieties of plants and animals present to the visitor from more rigorous climes a view that is foreign indeed.

The very strangeness of the Amazon Basin was an attraction to the great naturalists from western Europe a century and more ago; and when they came to know the area, many of them found it far more attractive than their bleak, familiar homelands. From 1799 to 1804, Alexander von Humboldt tramped the moist tropics of the Americas, and so became the first naturalist really to know wide regions of the Basin. After him came such men as the botanists Richard Spruce and Henry Walter Bates, each of whom spent many years exploring the vast rain forest. On his final leavetaking, from Pará near the mouth of the Amazon, Bates wrote:

> On the evening of the third of June 1859, I took a last view of the glorious forest for which I had so much love, and to explore which I spent so many years. . . . Recollections of English climate, scenery, and modes of life came to me with a vividness I had never before experienced during the eleven years of my absence. . . . To live again among these dull scenes I was quitting a country of perpetual summer, where my life had been spent like that of three-fourths of the people in gypsy fashion, on the endless streams or in the boundless forests. I was leaving the equator, where the well-balanced forces of Nature maintained a land-surface and climate that seemed to be typical of mundane order and beauty, to sail towards the North Pole, where lay my home under crepuscular skies somewhere about fifty-two degrees of latitude.

In many ways the basin of the Amazon is a remarkable region. The river drains an area two-thirds the size of the entire United States. It pours water into the ocean at a prodigious rate, a rate that exceeds that of the Congo and the Mississippi combined. In their lower courses nearly all large rivers are bordered by flood plains several miles wide. Many are fringed by lagoons and swamps. Some break up into smaller streams that branch out seaward across a delta, so that the water from the trunk stream enters the ocean through a score of different channels. A few even have more than one major channel a hundred miles or so above their deltas. All these characteristics apply to the Amazon, but on a scale at once so vast and so intensive that there is far more truth than falsehood in the saying that there are but two principal classes of rivers in the world: the Amazon and all others.

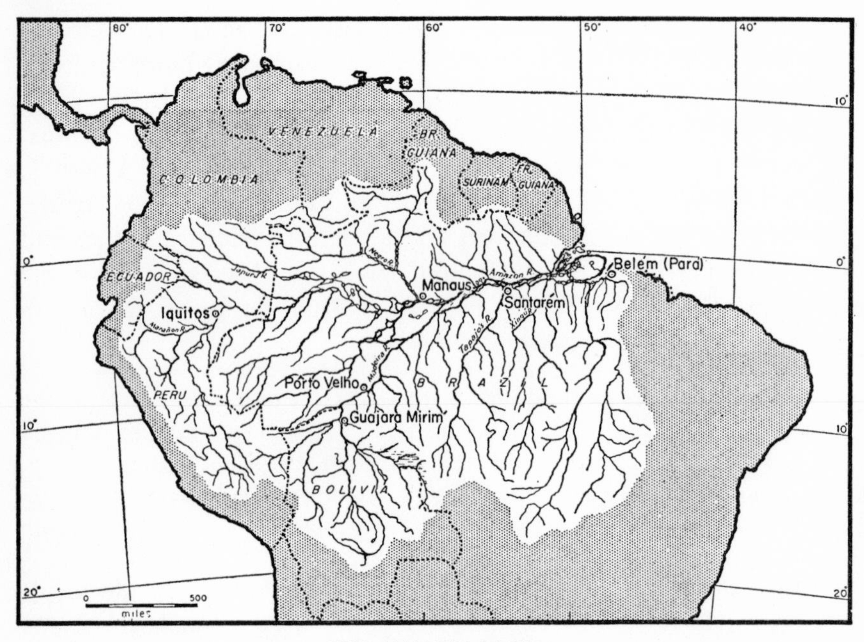

THE AMAZON BASIN

Throughout most of its length the Amazon is more like a spillway for tropical rains than a river. From Iquitos in Peru eastward across Brazil to the Atlantic Ocean, 1,500 miles away, the water flows through a winding belt thirty to fifty miles wide within which channelways, lagoons, and swamps are all intermingled. In a few places, as near Ilha Guaribas, the main channel is twenty miles wide. In its lower reaches, there is no single main channel, but rather two or three or even four. Here a strip of natural levee and swampland barely separates a channelway from a lagoon fifty miles long; there a whole series of lagoons are tied together by a narrow waterway that parallels the nearest main channel, forty miles away to southward.

Above Santarém for a distance of 200 miles there is such a profusion of channels and lagoons and feeder streams, of islands and of swamps, that even when the river is at low stage one often cannot tell where land begins and water ends. As if to achieve interblending of the river with the land, the waters swirling eastward through the channels may carry on their surface great rafts comprised of trees intertwined and matted with vegetative debris, as well as floating islands of grass torn from the lagoon margins along the river's edge. Other great rivers carry natural rafts, but floating islands are unique to the Amazon. Some of these liberated portions of grassy land are twenty to thirty feet thick and cover several acres. In the season of greatest flood, between April and September, they have been known to ensnare large river boats at anchor and to carry them bodily downstream.

As for the Amazonian rain forest, viewed from the river for mile after mile, it sometimes gives the appearance of a sheer wall of dark-green hue, formless and monotonous, imitating on an exaggerated scale each turn of the channel as smoothly and flawlessly as if a surveyor had determined the curving line that the forest's edge should follow. In other places along the river, the forest gives the impression of "a forest planted upon another forest," as Humboldt observed, the effect being produced by lofty palms rising far above a mass of lesser trees. In some localities, grasslands appear along the river's edge. Yet along the river, as inland from it, these grassland areas, or campos, are of insignificant size compared to the size of the forest. As Richard Spruce expressed it, "a greater gap would be made in the largest wood in England by cutting down a single oak than any one of these campos makes in the immense Amazonian forest."

He who travels upon the Amazon perceives the majesty of the rain forest. Yet he sees only that specialized edge of the forest which lies in a nontypical environment, where water is superabundant even for the rainy tropics and where sunlight can pour downward without impediment through the tree-lined reaches of the river to the bases of the trees and shrubs. To view a typical rain forest in detail, the explorer must leave the river and journey inland. On such a trip he may at first be forced to beat his way for several thousand yards around the margins of impenetrable bamboo thickets, to wade through reed-filled swamps, to skirt tangled masses of woody shrubs interlaced with vines, and to crawl beneath low-hanging lianas, some of which carry heavy spines bent backward like the barb of an arrow and fully as sharp.

After the spongy ground that fronts the river is left behind and there are no longer frequent pools of sunlight to violate the uniform pattern of sun-fleck and shade upon the forest floor, the going becomes easier. As for the lianas, to paraphrase Richard Spruce, like the shrouds and rigging of a sailing ship, they become hoisted high above the ground by the tall masts of the lofty trees; or, where they sag to lesser heights, they come to rest not upon the ground but on the crowns of smaller trees. The well-spaced trunks of the trees offer little obstruction. The floor itself is but sparsely populated by saplings and ferns. Though above him is a tangle of greenery so thick that it makes him a prisoner upon the forest floor, the explorer can readily traverse that floor with little inconvenience. The knife he carries is not so much for hacking away obstructing vegetation as for blazing a trail on which he can backtrack.

To the naturalist the most noteworthy characteristic of the rain forest is the great diversity of living species. The forests of western Europe and the United States commonly contain less than a dozen species of trees within a few acres, and not infrequently only one or two prevail, as in the pure stands of redwood in California or the pine-spruce forests of northern Europe. In the rich rain forest, counting only the larger trees, there are seldom less than forty different species and sometimes more than one hundred in an area of two and a half acres. The trees of the rain forest fall into several size groups, so that the forest is commonly said to have three or four stories of vegetation in the canopy.

The perpetually warm and moisture-rich environment that provides the conditions necessary to the development of the tropical rain forest also fosters ultrarapid plant growth. At certain stages in their growth cycle, trees may grow as much as fifteen feet in one year; bamboo, as much as nine inches in a single day. These extreme growth rates serve to convey some notion of the dynamism of tropical vegetation. The exuberance of the vegetation is evidenced by the manifest competition among the various plants. Biotic competition is the rule in all environments, everywhere on earth; but in the rainy tropics, it is more violently expressed than anywhere else. A macabre illustration of this theme is provided by Henry Walter Bates:

> There is one kind of parasitic tree, very common near Pará, which exhibits this feature in a very prominent manner. It is called Sipo Matador, or the Murderer Liana. . . . The base of its stem would be unable to bear the weight of the upper growth; it is obliged therefore to support itself on a tree of another species. In this it is not essentially different from other climbing trees and plants, but the way the Matador sets about it is peculiar, and produces certainly a disagreeable impression. It springs up close to the tree on which it intends to fix itself, and the wood of its stem grows by spreading itself like a plastic mould over one side of the trunk of its supporter. It then puts forth, from each side, an arm-like branch, which grows rapidly, and looks as though a stream of sap were flowing and hardening as it went. This adheres closely to the trunk of the victim, and the two arms meet on the opposite side and blend together . . . the victim, when its strangler is full grown, becomes clasped by a number of inflexible rings. These rings gradually grow larger as the Murderer flourishes, rearing its crown of foliage to the sky mingled with that of its neighbor, and in course of time they kill it by stopping the flow of its sap. The strange spectacle then remains of the selfish parasite clasping in its arms the lifeless and decaying body of its victim.

Climate of the Rain Forest

In general climatic terms, tropical rain forests are found in areas where the mean annual precipitation is in excess of eighty inches, where the rainfall is well enough distributed throughout the year so that there is no acute water shortage at any time, and where temperatures rarely exceed 95° or fall below 55° F. Uniformity of moisture and of warmth throughout the year is the primary characteristic. For this reason there is no one time of universal leaf fall or of flowering. Many trees do not lose their leaves at a certain season; rather, at any single moment a tree may be losing leaves from some branches and on others be carrying leaves at all stages of maturation, from buds to full-grown members. Thus the tropical rain forest is an evergreen forest, but with broad leaves rather than needle leaves.

As the margins of the forest are approached, where the climate begins to be a limiting factor, the rainfall becomes more and more seasonal in distribution and a distinct period of drought begins to appear. This is reflected in the character of the forest as new tree species begin to appear and old species drop out. Farther from the rainy equatorial regions, toward the margins of the tropics where the precipitation is largely limited to the summertime, the rain forest changes to a deciduous forest and then to savanna lands of scrub and thorn forest and of grass, as on the Deccan Plateau in India or the Mato Grosso of Brazil. Broadly considered, the transition from region to region is gradual and the types of vegetation continue to intermingle through a wide zone. As always, the immediate critical factor is not the total rainfall or its precise distribution but the availability of water to the plant, and this depends in part upon the conditions of drainage and soil.

Thus the rain forest extends as a narrow twisting band along the riverways far into drier country whose interfluves are in grasslands or scrub-thorn forest. So also, there are marginal regions where the dry season is sufficiently intense to eliminate the rain forest from sandy soils that can hold only small amounts of water, but not sufficiently intense to eliminate it from clay soils that can hold and store large quantities of water to tide the plants through the dry period. This is true in parts of New Guinea, where savanna on sandy soils alternates with rain forest on clays. In places the line between them is almost razor sharp.

Large-scale atmospheric events determine the gross character of the rain-forest climate, but the fine features of the climate are determined by the forest itself. There are, indeed, different climates at different levels within the mass of forest foliage; the most extreme differences are those between the climate among the crowns of the loftiest trees and that 125 feet below at the ground.

Soldiers and marines who crawled through the rain forests of New Guinea or the Solomons in World War II can describe all too well the climate of the air layer near the ground. The temperature is not high—68° to 80° two feet above the ground—but the air is dank and humid and there is not the slightest breeze to help remove the clinging perspiration. When the sun is shining, the ground is damp and gloomy. When a thunderstorm dumps water on the topmost trees, the raindrops are passed downward from leaf to leaf and layered canopy to layered canopy, and the rain arrives in streams and trickles.

From the viewpoint of comfort, it would be far better to be in the highest portion of the tallest tree. There, in bright sunny weather, the temperature may rise to 90°, or even 95°, but the relative humidity will then dip to 60 per cent or less. There may even be a stiff breeze. When a thunderstorm hits, the rain will slash downward without impediment, but it will feel cool in the gusty air. Most important of all to one reared in open, sunny regions, the brightness and light among the tall tops will be welcome after confinement in the shadowed reaches of the forest depths beneath.

The peoples who inhabit the tropical rain forests of the Amazon, the Congo Basin, the African Gold Coast, and other rainy equatorial regions live more with the forest than within it. They are so unobtrusive, their impact on the forest is so utterly slight, that they are almost to be considered as but another member of the complex biotic community. They may burn off or hack away a microscopic clearing to plant a few crops; but in three or four years, exhaustion of the soil and the pressure of the surrounding forest upon their small plot of land force them to move to another location, there again to clear the land and plant anew. Meanwhile the forest surges inward to obliterate all signs of their former habitation.

Even western man with his advanced technologies has made only minor inroads upon the forest. In a few marginal locations, he has cleared the forest and planted coconut palms or rubber trees or pasture grass or bananas. He has built a few roads, laid down a few airfields, and constructed a few towns along the ocean coasts or on the rivers. At tremendous cost he has felled a few trees of ebony and lignum vitae, of rosewood and mahogany, dragging them out single tree by single tree from among the profusion of trees of a hundred different species, floating the heavier logs downstream on lightweight rafts to buoy them up and keep them from sinking.

But overwhelmingly the forest has remained inviolate. It is still the one *Urwald*, the one primeval forest that for millions of years has remained essentially unaltered, not only unaffected by man but also changed comparatively little by the glaciations and climatic upheavals that in the not too distant past wrought striking changes in the vegetation of higher latitudes. Unfortunately, all this may change. There is reason to suppose that, with world population increasing at a rapid rate, man will in the future be forced to occupy wide reaches of the tropical rain forest. If this occurs on a world-wide scale and man succeeds in time in destroying the rain forest, the diversity of earth landscapes will be immeasurably diminished.

9 Water Behavior, Economics, and Management

There are two ways to consider water relations upon the land: on a broad, world-wide scale and on a detailed, local scale. One view, examined in the last chapter, leads to the concept of water realms, of dry lands and wet lands of contrasting character. The other leads to the study of water behavior, in specific places and at specific times, upon the lands and beneath them in the soils and rocks.

The detailed view that summons to mind visions of streams in flood, of rain water standing in ponds upon level plains, of snows melting in an early spring thaw, or of water filled with sediment clogging up an open irrigation flume is the most useful in gaining an understanding of the practical problems of water management. A flood is a physical event, even though one of great complexity; and in the practical business of flood control, as in all other aspects of water management, the purely physical relations are fundamental. Water management is inescapably linked to water behavior.

There is also the factor of economics. No country, state, or municipality can afford to guard absolutely against the extreme flood that occurs only once in a century. None can afford to invest a billion dollars for an irrigation works that returns only a million or so a year in agricultural benefits. And when it comes to considering the multiple, complicated problems of dispensing limited amounts of water to meet diverse, competing needs, economics is often the principal determinant.

That such is the nature of problems of water management is evident from the history of irrigation, from considering the nature of floods and the problems of their control, and from examining the problem of allocating water among many different would-be users. These three themes call attention to specific local conditions and requirements, and thereby serve to add important and practical details to the broader view that comprehends water relations on a worldwide scale.

Floods

Each river basin has its own unique flood characteristics. Each is of a certain size and shape. Each has its own arrangement of slopes, some steep, some gentle; of soils and rocks, some permeable, some not; and of vegetation that is more effective or less effective in holding back runoff from rain or melting snows. In addition, each river basin lies in a particular weather area that is not precisely duplicated anywhere else upon the earth. Though floods occur in all river basins, in each the behavior of the floods is unique.

Every flood is the product of a particular sequence of weather events acting upon a river basin of particular character. The two are dynamically joined by the behavior of the water in the narrow zone that includes the vegetation, the ground itself, and the upper few feet of the soil or rock. No understanding of flood phenomena is possible without a comprehension of the detailed events that take place in this zone, as Robert Horton, the well-known American hydrologist, realized.

Horton, during his long, productive life, had more to do with the construction of more major dams and spillways than any man before or since. His specialty was worrying about the amount of water that might come pounding down the streams and rivers, gathering mass and momentum until the dam was reached, when the water would surge against the new man-made obstruction. That dam had to hold; yet were it to be overbuilt, with too wide a margin of safety, millions of dollars would be wasted.

"Get out and see what precipitation does," he would say. "Study it. Observe it, not as water standing at the bottom of a rain gauge, but while it happens, while it's doing things. Look at the rivulets, the bits of soil in the sheetwash, the way the blades of grass get beaten flat and form a mat that covers the soil and skids the water off downslope.

"Did you ever see snow take in the rain like a sponge? And when the rain is warm and keeps on coming down, did you ever see that same snow turn to pockets of icy slush and then the whole thing into water, a whole mass of water, all in ten minutes' time? When that water comes banging downslope it really tears things up, and when it hits the streamways . . ."

He would talk in vivid detail about water behavior in the zone of interaction between river basin and atmosphere, stressing the emphatic importance of multitudinous small physical events.

In the aggregate, the little events yield floods. In dry lands they yield flash floods, where water comes ripping down steep slopes, its flow unchecked by dense vegetation. In humid lands they yield floods even with moderate rains, because the soil is already saturated from previous rains and so can accept no further infiltration and shunts the water downslope to the streams. In all areas there are many different situations that yield floods, even catastrophic ones, because of the character of the river basin, the nature of the weather situation, and the behavior of water in the critical flooding zone.

One sure recipe for a catastrophic flood can be stated quite simply. Take a hilly to mountainous region with plenty of steep slopes. Destroy the forest so that the trees cannot hold back the overland runoff. In wintertime spread snow across the area to depths of two to five feet. Let the snow melt sufficiently to fill its pore spaces with icy water. Otherwise, keep the temperature below freezing until the last minute. Everything is in readiness. Now suddenly push the temperature up to 50°. Simultaneously, spill down warm, heavy rains and let them continue for three or four days. You will then most surely have a hundred-year flood, a flood that would be of such magnitude that it would not be expected to occur more often than once in a century.

The recipe can be varied. One variant does not involve snow melt at all. It simply requires that the rains over a period of several weeks be well above average and that thereafter extremely heavy storm rains occur. The earlier rains will rob the land of its usual ability to hold back a high percentage of the storm rainfall from the streams and rivers. By the time the storm strikes, the soil will already be saturated, the hollows upon the surface of the land will be converted to ponds, the leaves of the trees will be wet, and the streams themselves will be at high stage. Now, when the storm lays tremendous rains upon the area, the land will swiftly shed its new water burden. Water will pour into the streams at a prodigious pace. A major flood will be inevitable. These were the conditions that led to the record-breaking floods of 1951 in Kansas and Missouri.

The state of Kansas lies west to east in the shape of a rectangle, but with a ragged piece taken out of the northeast corner, where the Missouri River forms a portion of the Kansas-Missouri boundary. A wavy line drawn on a map of Kansas, dividing the state into two almost equal parts, one to the north, the other to the south, would mark the approximate southern limit of the basin of the Kansas River. The river draws its water not only from the northern half of the state but also from southern Nebraska and from as far west as the foothills of the Rocky Mountains, near Boulder, Colorado. It flows eastward through the gently rolling country of northeast Kansas, past Manhattan, past the state capital of Topeka, to the twin cities of Kansas City in Kansas and Missouri, where, a strong-flowing stream a quarter-mile wide, it enters "Great Muddy," the Missouri River out of the north.

The Missouri itself swings eastward on the outskirts of Kansas City, Missouri, and continues on across the state along a broad, meandering course to enter the Mississippi River a few miles above St. Louis. It was in the region of the Kansas River and in the Missouri River region at Kansas City and to the east that the floods of 1951 were severest.

The rains of May, unseasonably heavy and frequent, had left the land dripping wet. Now the rivers were beginning to rise as the rains continued, not in steady, persistent fashion, but with downpours of a few hours' duration, with occasional longer-lasting storms, and with pelting thunderstorms that lasted an hour or less, yet added, each in its turn, an inch or more of water to the land.

By June 5, the hydrologist whose job it was to monitor and record the height of the Kansas River had begun to include in his work schedule each day a stop at the bridge at Lawrence, there to note and to enter on his official data sheet a figure showing the water level as measured by the giant ruler fastened to one of the piers on the eastern side of the bridge. That was significant, for the hydrologist does not stop to take readings at secondary gauging stations such as Lawrence unless a flood is threatening.

In late June, the Kansas River rose almost to unprecedented heights.

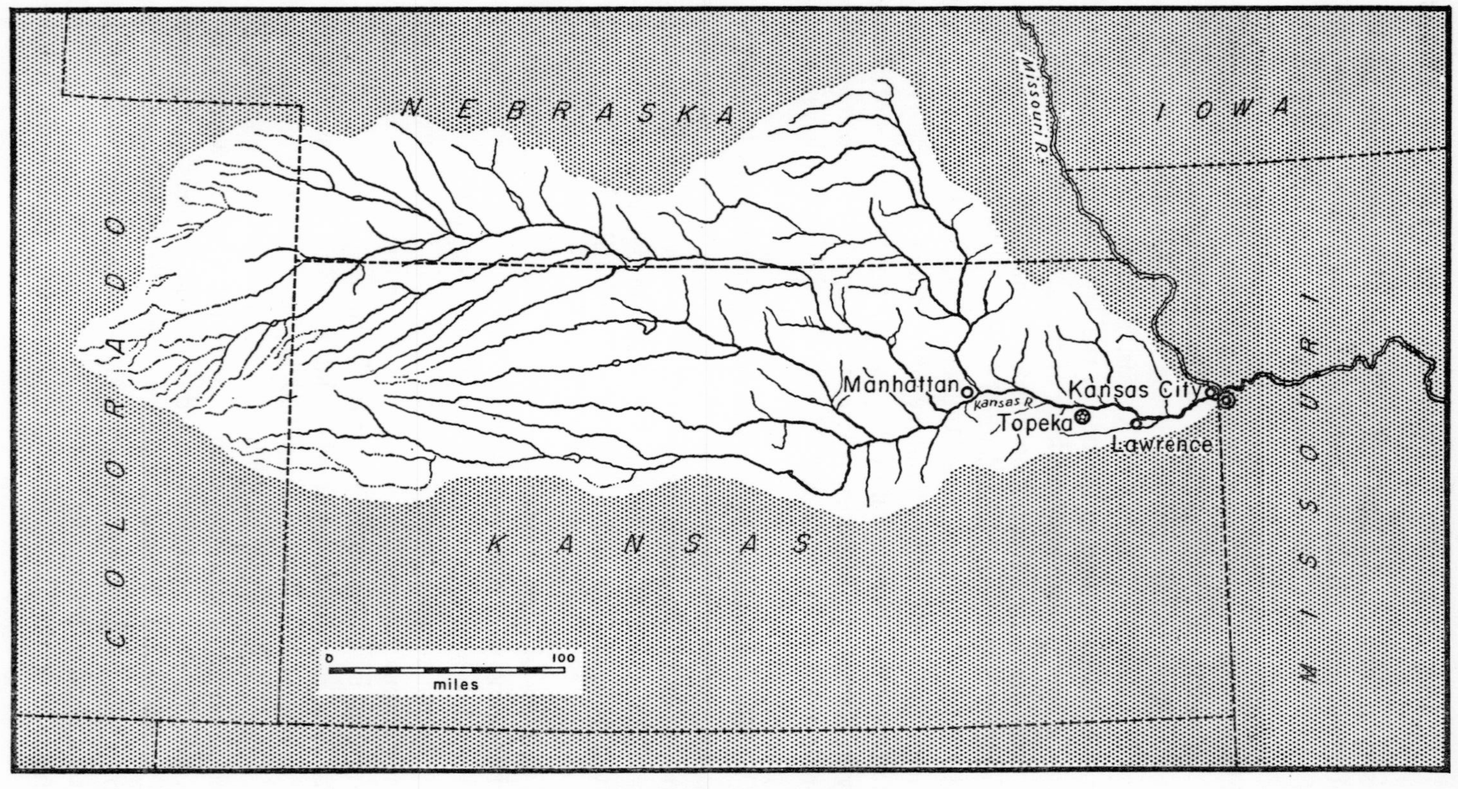

THE KANSAS RIVER BASIN

Workmen were called in to check and to bolster the levees that protected the low-lying industrial and residential areas in a half-dozen towns along the river. Nonetheless, at Lawrence, the water sluiced away part of the levee on the west bank and covered several square blocks of the low industrial area. Yet the floods were relatively minor.

When the river started slowly to fall during the first few days of July, fewer and fewer people stopped each day upon the bridges at Lawrence, Topeka, and Kansas City to stare at the swirling waters. By Sunday, July 8, despite occasional light rains throughout the previous week, the situation was markedly improved. Though the water of the river still stood at a height that was far above average, there seemed to be no need to worry about a major flood. The professional flood forecasters reasoned that rains of unprecedented intensity would be required to cause a flood; that the chances of such rains were no more than one in a hundred.

The average July precipitation in northeastern Kansas is 2½–3½ inches. The average precipitation for the entire summer is 10–12 inches. During the storm of July 9–13, 1951, the rainfall exceeded seventeen inches at one locality. Over extensive areas the total exceeded ten inches. One has to go back to 1844 to find storm rainfall amounts of similar magnitude for this area. The rains started on the afternoon of Monday, July 9, and continued without interruption until Thursday afternoon or Friday morning. During most of this period the rainfall intensities were not great; but on Monday, Tuesday, and Wednesday nights there were violent rainfall spasms, each of which laid down water to a depth of two to five inches.

Usually a storm that yields such great rainfall totals will be on the move and so will distribute its water burden across a path many hundreds of miles long. The storm of July 9–13 took place along a front that lay east-west, separating cool polar air to northward from moist tropical air to the south. Although this front wavered before the inward surges of moist air that beat against the cool polar air, for four days it remained almost stationary across the states of Kansas and Missouri. Disaster was the sure result.

The flood delivered its first major blow on Wednesday. At Lawrence and Manhattan, national guardsmen commandeered small boats of all descriptions to evacuate marooned refugees. A helicopter from Alton, Illinois, landed on housetops to remove the stranded inhabitants. The de luxe train, El Capitan, slid to a halt on top of a hill that the flood had converted into an island. In dozens of communities, thousands of people dragged their furniture upstairs in the hope that the flood would rise no higher than the first floor; then fled for higher ground, wading through water that was often hip deep.

It was 2 A.M. on Thursday when the river topped the levees at Topeka and the waters began their swift advance to batter and surround 5,000 homes in the northern part of that city. Many houses were demolished, and with each new demolition the rapidly flowing water acquired new battering rams with which to smash the foundations of other buildings. At Forbes Air Base, Massachusetts, amphibious planes of the Air-Sea Rescue Service took off for the flood scene. Kansas State College of Agriculture and Applied Science at Manhattan was converted into a hospital and a depot for refugees. Bill Brandt, of Burns, Kansas, landed his light plane on a relatively dry strip of highway near the stranded El Capitan. Three times on that Thursday he made round trips to the train, carrying fresh milk for the children aboard and airlifting the ill to safety.

The major flood crest passed Manhattan early Friday morning, Topeka on Friday afternoon, and Lawrence late Friday night. Meanwhile the river was rising rapidly at Kansas City. By Friday noon, three major levees had been topped and the water soon covered wide sections of the industrial district. The flood swept away bridges, put a pumping station out of commission, washed out roads and railroad tracks, drove thousands from their homes, and destroyed the Last Chance Tavern, which straddled the Missouri-Kansas line and which fifty years ago was a favorite hangout for gamblers, who could escape from the police of either state merely by pushing the gaming tables across the white line on the floor that marked the location of the state line.

Saturday noon the crest of the flood moved past Kansas City and into the Missouri River. One day later it would reach Lexington, and in three more days Jefferson City. Then would come St. Charles, and after that the Mississippi River itself, which would carry the flood on down to afflict the river shores at St. Louis and beyond. Everywhere the same kinds of things would happen, in different ways, perhaps, and certainly to different people, but the major theme would be the same, one of suffering and devastation.

Such a major flood completely disrupts a community; it drastically alters the lives of thousands of persons whose homes have been destroyed, whose businesses have been injured, or who have suffered the loss of a family member. Deprivations like these cannot be measured and totaled. The Kansas-Missouri flood damage totaled one billion dollars.

When a flood hits a modern city, the effects are much the same as if the city had been bombed. Communications are disrupted. Suddenly the city dweller is deprived of all the various services that in the past he has come unthinkingly to expect. Water mains burst, and pumping stations are put out of commission. Though the streets and yardways are filled with water, the faucets in the houses run dry, and there are serious shortages of drinking water. To boil the water in the cellars and so make it safe for drinking is impossible because gas and electric service has also been disrupted. Since kerosene lamps and candles are being used to provide illumination in areas where the power lines are down, the hazard of fire is particularly great; and if a fire breaks out, it is apt to spread quickly, for it may be impossible for fire engines to reach the scene.

If the flood lasts several days, food shortages develop. Even though some grocery stores may have escaped damage, there still remains the difficult problem of food distribution. Disease may also be an acute problem, both because of the unsanitary conditions and because it may be impossible for a doctor to reach a stricken household. Even after the flood waters have receded, many weeks are required to restore all major services. Months may be required in some instances before buildings are repaired, flood debris is cleared away, and the city has returned to a fully normal condition.

Recovery from the Kansas-Missouri floods was not complete until November. Indeed, their impact is still felt indirectly today, because many small commercial and industrial enterprises in Kansas City, Topeka, and elsewhere were put out of business by the floods and many people whose homes had been destroyed or severely damaged moved away to other areas. Industrially and economically, the cities hit hardest by the flood were set back many years in their development.

In all parts of the inhabited world, occasional flood catastrophes are inevitable. It is impossible to predict more than a few hours in advance that a fifty- or hundred-year flood will occur, and it is impracticable to erect impenetrable defenses against such floods. An experienced flood forecaster working in an area that is well equipped with rain gauges and with gauging stations on the major streams can do a highly creditable job nine times out of ten in predicting a flood of moderate intensity. But so far as major floods are concerned, this same forecaster cannot do more than indicate that a serious threat exists. The difficulty is that when conditions are ripe for a major flood, the difference between nine and ten inches of precipitation may be the difference between a large flood that causes relatively little damage and a much larger one that is devastating.

A good weather forecaster can predict that rainfall will be heavy; but even the best forecaster, using the most modern forecasting techniques, may easily be 20–30 per cent off in predicting the precise amount of rainfall. No one could possibly have predicted on July 9, 1951, that there would be ten to seventeen inches of precipitation over the Kansas-Missouri watershed during the next three days. No one could have predicted that there would be seven to ten inches in twenty-four hours at Chicago on October 10, 1954. In both instances, throughout the storm period such a precarious balance of the forces that produced the abnormal rains and that caused them to be concentrated in one particular area was maintained that the merest variation in any one of a dozen meteorological factors would have reduced the rainfall total by 20 per cent or more, thus averting a disastrous flood.

The same holds true for the prediction of flash floods in arid regions. A competent weather forecaster can predict correctly that there will be scattered thunderstorms in an area such as Arizona or western Texas. He cannot know that a relatively small current of ultramoist air will curl upslope in one particular drainage basin in exactly such a way as to cause the storm to score a bull's-eye on the basin in an area where slopes are steep and natural vegetation is sparse. Yet when such a hit is scored, the runoff must converge rapidly along the valleyways and rush violently downslope as a wall of water.

It is not practicable to erect absolute defenses against the fifty- or hundred-year flood. Theoretically, such floods could be eliminated even on such a large river as the Mississippi through construction of a whole series of dams and reservoirs throughout the drainage basin. But if this was done, at a cost of billions of dollars, and if the flow of water was then regulated for the sole purpose of preventing floods, there might be times when the river would be so low it would be impossible to meet the water needs for navigation, for domestic use, for industry, and for many other purposes.

Theoretically, also, it would be possible to move the population concentrated along the Mississippi sufficiently far upslope from the river so as to place it well beyond the reach of even the hundred-year flood. But this concentration of population is no accident. Cities and towns are located on rivers because the advantages of such locations far outweigh the disadvantage posed by flood hazard; and this holds true not only on the Mississippi, but on the other rivers of the world.

Extreme floods cannot be completely repressed, but their effects can be diminished through control measures that at the same time will eliminate somewhat lesser floods that would otherwise create great damage. It is both possible and practicable to build more levees to protect densely populated areas in the lowlands along large rivers; to construct additional dams and reservoirs not only for flood control but also to provide hydroelectric power and to provide water for industrial, domestic, and agricultural uses; and to place reasonable restraints upon the practices of lumbering companies so that hill and mountain slopes are not completely stripped of trees. These and other control measures have already proved effective.

In lesser ways, flood damage can be diminished through individual originality and initiative. The scheme worked out by the Catholic fathers to protect their mission house from the annual floods of the Nelson River is representative of what even a few individuals can accomplish.

The Nelson River flows northeastward into Hudson Bay, so that, in the spring, melting of the river ice takes place first in the southerly, headwater region of the river rather than near the mouth where the mission house is located. Invariably, in the spring the melt water floods downstream on top of the ice, with considerable overflow of the river banks. For many decades it was the habit of the fathers to move out of their mission house just before flood time, to wait patiently at a safe distance while the flood waters lifted the wooden structure from its stone foundation and carried it downstream; and finally, after the flood had subsided and the ice in the lower river had melted, to float the house back upstream and with much labor return it to its foundation.

Then one of the fathers, thinking deeply on this problem, hit upon a far more practical approach. He cut several large holes in the first floor of the building, in such a way that they could be plugged like manholes when the first floor was in use. Today when flood time is near, the fathers move their belongings to the second floor, remove the plugs, and await the rising waters. Now, instead of lifting the building from its foundation, the water merely moves up through the holes to a depth of a few feet above the first floor. After the flood has subsided, the fathers come downstairs, clean out the debris, and repossess the first floor for another year.

Not all flood problems are as easily and neatly solved as was this one, but there is still ample opportunity for discovering new ways to minimize flood damage. Though floods can never be wholly eliminated, much can still be done, even by the individual, to ameliorate their effects.

Irrigation

Irrigation was the first major triumph of man over his hydrologic environment. Possibly the first irrigationist lived in the Nile Valley, 4,500 years before the time of Christ. Probably irrigation was invented independently in several different early agricultural societies in places far removed from one another. In any event, at the dawn of history in Egypt, Babylonia, India, China, Mexico, and many other regions, irrigation was being practiced. Man's conquest of the arid and semiarid lands was already well begun.

The first irrigation techniques were relatively crude. One of the earliest, pictured on tablets in ancient Egyptian tombs, was simply to carry water from the stream to the field in pots swung by a yoke from the shoulders of a man. Early also there came into use the sideswipe, a device still employed in parts of the Near East. It consisted of a lever with a water basket on one end and a counterweight on the other. The basket and its counterweight were so closely balanced that even a child could push up the counterweight to lower the basket into the river and then pull the weight down to raise the water. Since the wooden lever could be rotated freely about the post top on which it rested, the water basket was readily swung round and emptied into a cistern at the head of an irrigation ditch.

Far more efficient and sophisticated than these simple contrivances were the water wheels and canals that by the time of Hammurabi, *ca.* 2000 B.C., had reached a high stage of development in Babylonia. The water wheel was typically driven by oxen. Earthen pots attached to the perimeter of the wheel scooped the water from the river on the uptake and dumped it into an irrigation trough as the pots became inverted upon passing over the top of the wheel. Though highly useful on streams and rivers, the wheel and other irrigation machines were unnecessary on the canals, which were constructed at an elevation slightly above the surrounding fields. It was only necessary to open the sluice gates along the sides of a canal to send the water coursing into the irrigation ditches.

Dozens of canals, many twenty miles or more in length, were in existence in Babylonia during the time of Hammurabi. In those days the fields of springtime were green with barley and spelt. Date palms and fig trees flourished. Today in this same region most of the land is barren desert. Only traces remain of the canals of 4,000 years ago.

Unlike a river, a canal cannot purge itself of its accumulated sediments. As it is tapped at successive points for irrigation, the carrying power of its waters decreases. Sediments are deposited. Unless the canal is dredged almost constantly, it chokes itself to death. Such in time was the fate of the canals of Babylonia.

The rulers of Babylonia and Egypt were ever vigilant in maintaining irrigation works to the fullest possible extent and in augmenting the water supplies whenever possible. No ruler ever forgot that water was the very substance on which, above all others, the existence of his kingdom depended. Therefore even the digging of a solitary well, an event that today would hardly warrant comment in western Europe or the eastern United States, was an accomplishment that required commemoration in the written records of the time. One such account, from the thirteenth century B.C., reads in part as follows: "His Majesty said to the master of the royal writings: 'Cause a well to be excavated at once halfway along the road towards the valley of AKITA. Cause in a day a month's work to be done.' " And, when the work had been completed, "There is abundance of water in immense quantities . . . the fishes rejoice; they make signs to one another. . . . Let us call this well, the well of Ramses-Meiamun the valiant."

Not only in Egypt and Babylonia but also in other parts of the world, the practice of irrigation is almost as old as the practice of agriculture itself. Living as they did in a land where only the summer rains are sure, the early cultivators of China drew water from rivers, lakes, and ponds to nourish their rice crops. In this way they realized two harvests every year: one based on natural rainfall, the other on irrigation. When the Spaniards first arrived in the New World, they were astonished to discover advanced and complex agricultural systems among the Incas of Peru and the Aztecs of Mexico. Both maintained elaborate irrigation works.

The Pueblo Indians of the southwestern United States also were practicing irrigation upon the coming of the Spaniards. They, like the prehistoric Egyptians, were able to support a high population density, the highest among the Indians north of the Rio Grande, through intensive agriculture in a riverine location in the middle of a dry land; and their culture, though different from that of the prehistoric Egyptians, was equally complex and barely below the threshold of true civilization.

Despite its great antiquity in the New World, irrigation was of minor importance in the early development of the United States. As late as July, 1847, it was being practiced only in the rice regions of the Mississippi Delta area and on a few small cultivated plots upon the widely scattered estates and mission lands of California, Texas, and the Southwest. Nor was there in the public press or in the modes of thinking of that time the slightest indication that the United States stood at the threshold of an irrigation era that would alter the national economy and change forever the character of the arid West. In July of 1847, the regions between the Rocky Mountains and the Sierra Nevadas-Cascades were virtually uninhabited by Americans or Europeans. The Pacific coast was only sparsely settled. To the man in the street in New York, Atlanta, or even St. Louis, little was known of faraway California. Nothing was known of that region of the Utes that was soon to be called Utah.

Within six months, in two widely distant places, there came about two unrelated events which in their consequences were to result in the irrigation revolution. On July 24, 1847, a band of Latter-day Saints, led by Brigham Young, arrived upon the desert at the foot of the Wasatch Range, just southeast of Great Salt Lake. Soon they had dammed a mountain stream, and fresh, cool water was flowing through man-made trenches, carrying life to the parched desert floor. Exactly six months later, on January 24, 1848, 700 miles away in the Republic of California, James W. Marshall reached into the waters of the South Fork of the American River and picked up a pebble of gold. In four months the Gold Rush was on.

Step by step, the Mormons built and enlarged their desert domain, their "home in the valleys among the mountains." They improved their irrigation works, augmented their agricultural lands, laid out towns, and formed teams of colonists. The colonists went forth in all directions across the desert, upon trails blazed by Mormon scouts, to found, strengthen, and enlarge dozens of irrigation communities extending from Ogden all the way to southern California. By 1856, these communities held 22,000 Mormons.

The Gold Rush pulled people westward by the hundreds of thousands. Many came by the Overland Trail, through Ogden and Salt Lake City. They saw the neat green fields of the Mormon farmers and made the acquaintance of Mormon merchants who were happy to buy eastern manufactured goods from the overloaded tenderfoot at prices far below their New York cost or to sell him a mule for $200. To the Mormon irrigationists the Gold Rush was a boon, an unexpected benediction that gave them the means to conquer the desert at an even swifter pace.

As for the gold seekers, in the years to come they would recall the watered fields upon the desert and some would put to use their scanty, half-remembered knowledge. At the time, eager and unthinking, they pressed on westward to California. Sooner or later all but a handful would be down from the hills, empty-handed, disillusioned, their meager grubstakes gone. Many would return to their homes in the East. Tens of thousands would remain in the West to provide the population basis for the coming irrigation boom.

It happens often in history that great events are imminent, that their coming is manifestly certain, and that nonetheless they continue on and on to hover just offstage, like an actor waiting in the wings until he hears his cue. So it was with the irrigation boom. Mormon enterprise and the Gold Rush had set the stage, but there were other events to be acted out before the boom could begin. In the fifties, the East was concerned with growing tensions between the North and South; the West, outside the Mormon realm, was gold-crazy. Almost to the end of the sixties, the East was involved in war and Reconstruction; the West had its lesser mining strikes, its Indian wars, its expansion of cattle kingdoms. Then in 1869 the transcontinental railroad was completed. Suddenly, in the minds of the people, East and West were one. By the early seventies the western surge was on. With it came the irrigation boom.

As farmers flocked in from the East, a private California company built a forty-mile irrigation canal in the San Joaquin Valley. Other companies followed suit. Soon vineyards, orchards, and dairy farms were invading the cattle and wheat lands. At Phoenix, Arizona, the construction of the Maricopa Canal enlarged by thousands of acres the tiny area previously irrigated by the "Swilling Ditch." At Greeley, Colorado, settlers from the East established an irrigation colony. Similar ventures were started in Nebraska, Wyoming, and other states and territories.

Congress passed the Desert Land Act in 1877, permitting anyone to purchase 640 acres of dry public lands for $160 provided he irrigated some portion of them within three years. Though the act was used fraudulently by cattlemen to enlarge their holdings, it nonetheless further quickened the tempo of dry-land settlement. The move to the arid West was hastened also by the government's publication in 1879 of the *Report on the Lands of the Arid Region,* in which J. W. Powell and his associates assessed the irrigation potential of the West. So great was the demand for this report that a second edition had to be issued within a few months after initial publication.

By 1889, there were extensive areas under the ditch in every state and territory west of the Mississippi except North Dakota. Irrigated land had come to total four million acres, an area larger than the state of Connecticut. Within two decades, with government financing through the recently established Federal Reclamation Service, this acreage had been doubled. With so much bustle and haste, it was inevitable that there would be irrigation failures. Where there were marginal irrigation lands or marginal farmers, projects had to be refinanced time and time again. Repayment contracts held by the federal government were extended from ten years to twenty, from twenty to forty, and sometimes even to eighty years.

It was discovered that even with water available not all dry lands are irrigable; that in places sodium salts deep in the desert ground are brought to the surface through irrigation, and thereafter no amount of downward drainage will loosen the hold of these plant-killing salts. It was learned that on irrigation projects professional land speculation is difficult to thwart, and that such economic factors as distance from market can be decisive in determining the success or failure of a project.

Today, in the area between the Pacific coast and the tier of states extending from the Dakotas through Texas, there are 26 million acres of irrigated land, nine-tenths of the national total and one-eighth the world total. These western acres produce crops valued annually at close to $3 billion, almost one-fourth the national total. Fruits, nuts, vegetables, cotton, and sugar are the principal products. Yields are prodigious. On the irrigated tracts in California a single acre produces on the average as much cotton as do three acres of unirrigated land in the southeastern United States, or as many cantaloupes as four acres in Illinois or North Carolina. With these yields, land values and water duties can be maintained at a sufficiently high level to finance and maintain elaborate and costly irrigation works.

Irrigation is not confined to regions of scanty rainfall. In the humid eastern United States, where the annual precipitation averages forty inches and more, and there is no dry season, supplemental irrigation is commonly practiced in intensive truck-farming operations. If a drought threatens or temperatures are in the nineties, causing the plants to transpire rapidly and to pull moisture from the soil at an excessive rate, the farmer turns on the sprinkling system and makes up the water deficit.

The rate of growth of crops can even be controlled by lessening or increasing the supplemental irrigation. Different fields in the same crop can be brought to maturity at intervals of two or three days, and a relatively small crew moving from field to field can harvest the entire crop without its overripening. If he does not pace the growth of his crops in this way, the farmer with several hundred acres in beans or peas or melons must suddenly hire a large crew of pickers for a short period and must all at once transport great quantities of products to market, at far greater expense than if his was a planned operation.

In humid lands as in arid ones, economic factors ultimately determine the extent of irrigation. And there are decisive differences between the economics of supplemental irrigation in humid areas and full-scale irrigation in dry lands. The situation in the United States is typical. The eastern farmer rarely owns more than a few hundred acres. His unit installation costs for sprinklers and tile drains are therefore very high. He can afford to practice supplemental irrigation only if he raises high-priced fruit or vegetable crops on an intensive scale and is within quick trucking distance of market or of a frozen-food concern that will contract to buy his produce.

In the arid West, a single irrigation project provides water to hundreds of thousands of acres of farmland. Unit costs are relatively low. Federal and state governments often help to finance initial construction and installation. On the larger projects, the sale of hydroelectric power and water for industrial and domestic users lessens the charges to be borne by the farmer. Arid-land irrigation is big business. Humid-land irrigation remains small business that can be practiced only by a few.

Nonetheless, with world population increasing at an alarming rate, it is encouraging to know that through irrigation, even in the humid regions, the bounty of the land can be increased. There are problems of water supply, of poor soils, of maintenance of irrigation works; but in most parts of the world, in humid and arid regions alike, the limits of irrigation have not even been approached. More and more the civilizations yet to come may have to depend on it.

The Complexities of Water Management and Supply

There are few problems more complex than those of water management. And the complexities are especially great in the industrial society of the western world, in a situation where there are competing demands upon the limited water resources of a single major river. The case of the Delaware River is an excellent example.

"A river is more than an amenity; it is a treasure. It offers a necessity of life that must be rationed among those who have power over it." These words, written in 1931 by the late Justice Oliver Wendell Holmes, define what has become the accepted American philosophy that governs the use of fresh-water resources. The words were contained in the majority decision of the Supreme Court of the United States in the case of *Commonwealths of New Jersey and Pennsylvania* v. *Commonwealth of New York*. Beneath the doctrine established by the decision lay the reality that in all parts of the country, the humid East as well as the arid West, there is not sufficient fresh water to meet all requirements. In the case in question, it was the Delaware River whose water resources were under dispute.

The Delaware River rises in the State of New York, where its two main branches, one from the east and one from the west, join to form the main stream that first flows southeast along the boundary between Pennsylvania and New York, then follows a zigzag course southward along the boundary between Pennsylvania and New Jersey until the river reaches its estuary at the northern end of Delaware Bay, just below Trenton, New Jersey. Below the juncture of its east and west branches in the north, the river is 280 miles long. Together with its tributaries, it drains an area of almost 7,000 square miles. At the falls at Trenton, where the river enters tidewater, the average discharge is about 8,000 million gallons of water a day. If this average could be maintained without fluctuation season in and season out, day after day, the problem of allocating the water of the Delaware would be relatively simple. Actually, the stream volume fluctuates so much that the flow has risen to 150,000 million gallons per day, almost twenty times the average, and has fallen to 800 million gallons, only one-tenth the average.

Sixteen million people depend wholly or in part upon water from the Delaware for domestic and industrial purposes. New York City draws up to 800 million gallons of water daily from two tributaries of the Delaware, the Neversink and the East Branch. Philadelphia, Wilmington, Trenton, Camden, and many other cities and towns also depend upon the Delaware for their water supplies. Among them they require an additional 800 million gallons daily, bringing the total to 1,600 million. Were it not that domestic and industrial water users return water to the stream and that the reservoirs that supply New York City can discharge impounded water downstream during times of drought, the Delaware could not possibly support such a heavy water draft. Even so, some cities, like Chester, Pennsylvania, have been forced to abandon the Delaware as a source of water because supplies were inadequate; and in the future, many communities and industrial plants in New Jersey, Pennsylvania, and Delaware will have to look elsewhere for new sources of water to meet increased needs.

As a natural resource, the Delaware River is more than a supplier of water. It is a sewage disposal system, a source of food, a recreation ground, a line of transport, and a real-estate asset. These aspects of resource use frequently conflict with one another and with use of the water for domestic, industrial, and irrigation purposes. Conflicts are not merely local; what happens at one place on the river or its tributaries has repercussions at many points throughout the valley. Build a dam on the East Branch and the flow of water changes at Trenton, 300 miles downstream. Dump 100,000 tons of sewage at Phillipsburg and eliminate fishing for twenty miles downstream. Log

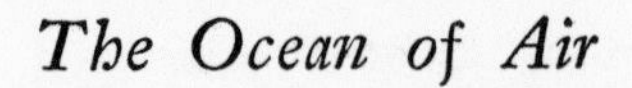

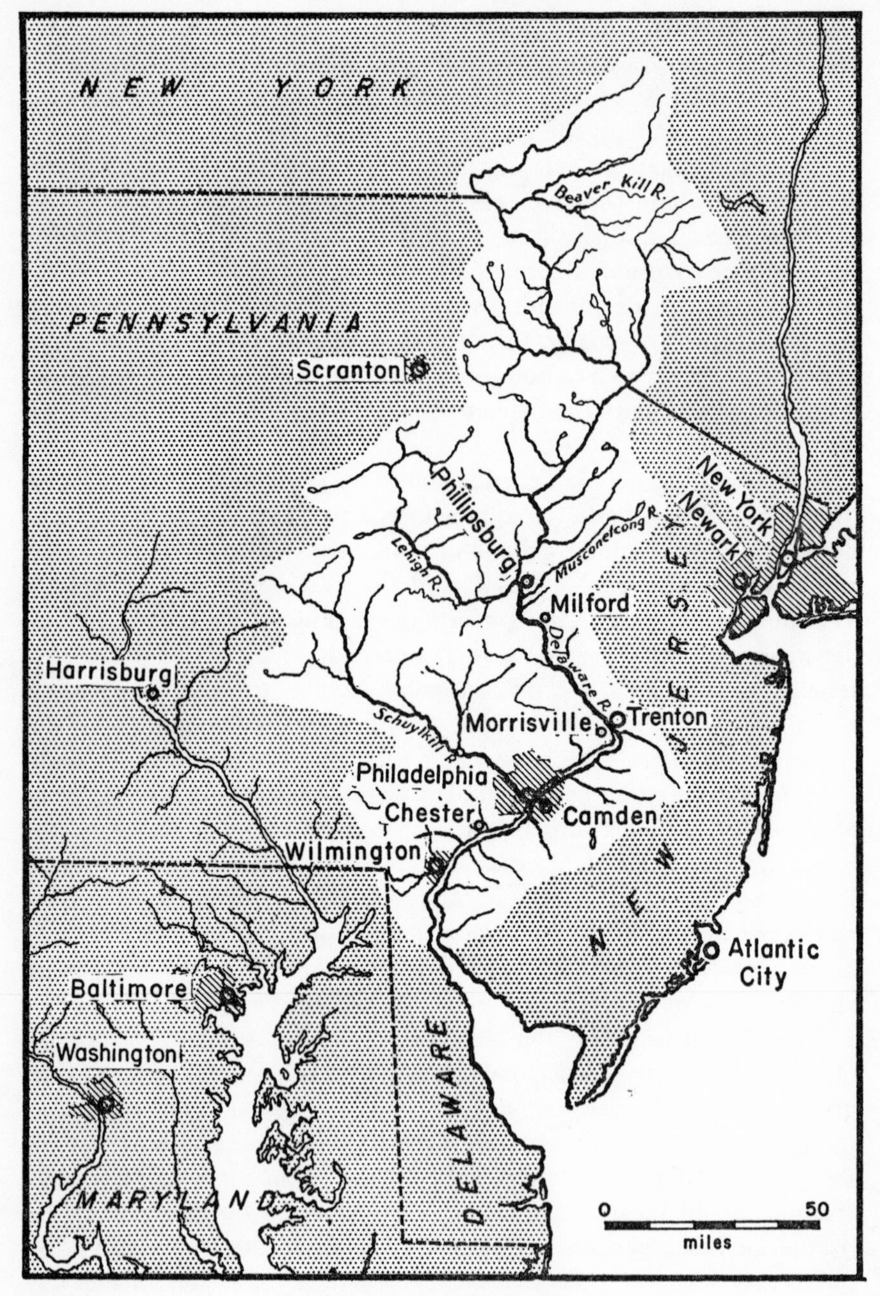

THE DELAWARE RIVER BASIN

off some forested slopes in the Musconetcong Valley and the next big springtime flood at Milford on the Delaware is larger than ever. Increase the soil erosion in Mercer County and silting increases in the estuary. From the viewpoint of water economics, the entire valley with all its tributary valleys and inward-facing slopes is an organic unit. Any action anywhere in the watershed that strongly influences the water economy has broad economic and social repercussions, good or bad.

Not even a Solomon endowed with all the knowledge of the many relevant sciences could answer to everyone's satisfaction the questions that have arisen concerning the use of the water resources of the Delaware. Should a channel be dredged to a forty-foot depth from Camden thirty miles upstream to Trenton and Morrisville? Yes, because it will permit ships from Venezuela to deliver iron ore directly to the Fairless Steel Works at Morrisville. No, because with dredging, sediments may well be swept far out into the estuary and upset the natural balance in the oyster beds that are a major fishery resource. Should Philadelphia, Camden, and other large cities be permitted to continue to dump raw sewage into the river? Yes, because the cost of installation of a sewage treatment plant is prohibitively high. No, because with treatment of sewage, the shad industry, which fifty years ago provided 16 million pounds of fish annually, can be restored. Should the Beaver Kill and Willowemoc Rivers be used as sources of water? Yes, because additional supplies are required. No, because these famous trout streams are among the most important recreational resources of the Catskill Mountains. In planning the use of the water resources of the Delaware or of any other river, there are scores of questions of these kinds that must be resolved. Whatever their resolution, it is inevitable that some interests will be disappointed.

Each drainage basin has its own peculiar problems of water supply and competing demands. Yet there are certain general principles involved in planning the use of all fresh-water resources wherever found. Planning must be carried out on a long-range basis with a view to the situation that will exist a hundred years in the future. Such plans must allow for increased population and for increased water use per capita. The first waterworks company in the United States was constructed in Boston in 1652. At that time the per capita water consumption in Boston was less than twenty-five gallons per day. Today the Boston consumption is over 150 gallons. By the year 2500, consumption may easily reach 300 gallons, a figure that has already been approached in some large industrial cities.

Planning must provide for water use for multiple purposes. With modern methods of sewage treatment, fresh water need no longer be contaminated to the point where the fish resource is destroyed. With modern methods of water purification, there is no reason why reservoirs should not be sites for recreational fishing, boating, and even swimming. Philadelphians have without ill effect long drunk their own sewage water, since the water intake pipes for that city lie downstream from the sewage discharge pipes. Finally, plans for the use of fresh-water resources must envisage the development of all such resources, not merely of those that are most readily accessible. With reference to the Delaware River watershed, this means making the utmost use of the water that lies underground in southern New Jersey, such as the water in the Cohansey sands, which can easily provide 1,500 million gallons of water daily.

Underground water resources are more than merely supplementary to surface resources. The majority of farmsteads in the United States depend exclusively upon wells for water. So also do half of the towns and cities; and although most of these are small, three—Houston, Memphis, and San Antonio—each have a population of over a quarter-million. Ground-water supplies are particularly important in arid and subhumid regions, where the occasional lakes are apt to be saline and streams with a permanent flow of water are a rarity. Palisade, Nevada, is on the Humboldt River, which has an average flow of 100 million gallons daily and a maximum flow equivalent to 4,000 million. Yet, like virtually all towns in Nevada, Palisade uses well water since in the autumn it is impossible in a twenty-four-hour period to collect from the stream so much as a single glass of water.

The art of digging wells is ancient. At Chanpudaro in the Indus Valley is a well that dates from the third millennium before Christ. The Babylonians and Egyptians dug many wells, some of which reached to depths of over 200 feet. The Romans, too, were skillful well diggers. The well at Pompeii attests their skill in this art, for it pierces two tough beds of lava, one thirty feet thick and the other sixteen feet, and the well itself extends to a depth of 116 feet and is five feet in diameter. The digging of these ancient wells must have been difficult even as recently as Roman times; for at best the chief tools that were used were the pickax and the sledgehammer, and they were made of relatively soft iron rather than steel.

The modern well digger drives his truck up to the appropriate spot, rigs a drill, turns on the motor, and then stands by only to regulate the rate of spin or to change bits or add extension rods as required. Occasionally a modern well is dug by hand, but only if it is shallow and does not involve piercing a rock formation. Deep wells and hard-rock ones are drilled.

With well digging such a difficult and often vital task in early times, it was inevitable that techniques would be developed for locating underground water supplies. Pliny, the Roman naturalist and writer of the first century, recommended that to locate underground water one should go out just before sunrise and lie face downward on the ground with chin resting on the earth. "If vapor is seen to rise, dig; for that will not happen in places without water."

Much earlier than Pliny's time, the divining rod had come into use. Evidently it was first used in China, some four thousand years ago. Ever since, it has been widely used to locate subsurface water, and there have always been and are today many people who believe in its effectiveness. With only slight variations, the method used has remained unchanged. The waterfinder picks a small branch or switch of some suitable wood, such as willow, and walks slowly across the ground, holding the switch in front of himself with the point drooping earthward. What happens when a favorable spot for digging is reached is described in a book on the subject written by Tompkins, a Wiltshire diviner, in 1893:

> After walking a distance of 80 yards or so, I suddenly felt a running or creeping sensation come into my feet, up my legs and back and down my arms, which caused me to look to see what had happened. I noticed the rod began to rise in my hands. I gripped it still tighter to prevent it and kept walking; still I found the sensation got stronger and stronger, and that I was being led in a zig-zag course, the twig at the same time exercising a greater determination to turn up. So strong had this influence become that I was powerless to keep it down and eventually after proceeding some distance farther, it attained a vertical position and revolved over and over. So great was this sudden and unexpected pressure or influence on me that I fainted and became very ill and I at once threw the rod away thinking Old Harry was not far off.

Except for the fainting and illness, this description applies generally to the experience of diviners. As for the effectiveness of their method, most scientists ridicule it. It is simply a matter of whether one believes, as the physicist Sir Oliver Lodge did, in the verity of psychic phenomena.

In less dispute than the technique of the divining rod are various scientific methods for determining where ground water will be found. In arid regions the sediments beneath a dry stream bed will usually yield water at quite shallow depths. Away from a stream bed the presence of water near the surface is sometimes indicated by the relative profusion of vegetation. The presence of good water supplies at greater depths is related chiefly to the structure of the underlying layers of rocks and sediments and to whether or not these layers are porous and so capable of containing good quantities of water. Sands are more apt to contain large quantities of water than are finer silts or clays. Sandstone, which not infrequently has a porosity of 20–30 per cent, is apt to be a far better aquifer than shale, limestone, or other less porous rocks. There must also be a source of water to supply the aquifer, but the initial supply is not necessarily related to present climatic conditions.

Water often moves only slowly underground. Movement as slow as ten feet a year in a gently sloping bed of sandstone is not unusual. The water now drawn from wells that tap the Dakota sandstone in the region of eastern Wyoming, eastern Montana, and the Dakotas may well have been derived in large part from the melting of ice during the last glaciation, 12,000 years or more ago.

When a well is sunk to tap an aquifer of sediments or solid rock, the water may have to be pumped upward or it may rise of its own accord. In the Artois region of France, the wells flow freely, making pumping unnecessary. From the name of this district has come the adjective *artesian*, which is applied to a well that yields such free-flowing water. The conditions necessary for artesian wells seem to have been understood by Leonardo da Vinci 500 years ago. What is required is that there be water in an aquifer that slopes downward and is overlain by an impervious stratum. The aquifer is analogous to a hose that draws its water from a water tower high aloft. The impervious layer is the cover for the hose. When the hose is pierced, the water spurts upward and emerges in the well without pumping or otherwise being lifted.

Among the famous artesian water basins of the world are those in Australia, in northern Illinois, and in the Santa Clara Valley of California. Unfortunately, every time a well is sunk to tap an artesian aquifer, the pressure that forces the water upward is lessened. And with thousands of wells being sunk in some locations, as in the Santa Clara Valley, the pressure may finally diminish to the point where none of the wells flow freely any more. Even where there is no artesian situation, where the wells have been pumped from the very first, there is the same kind of fundamental problem. Ground-water resources are not unlimited; where too many wells have been sunk to tap the same aquifer, there may be such a diminution in ground water that the supplies are threatened over wide areas, thousands of square miles in extent. Here again, as in the problem of allocation of the waters of the Delaware River, the only practicable solution appears to be to regulate the demands that are placed upon the water resource.

In coastal locations and along rivers that are swept by ocean tides, there is an additional problem of conservation of underground water resources. Saline water from the ocean and from tidal rivers tends to underride the land. Generally, since this salt water is denser than fresh water, it does not immediately contaminate wells that are sunk to moderate depths. But in time, if enough water is drawn from fresh-water aquifers in coastal locations, the well will bring up salt in such quantities that the water is no longer potable. Sea water has about 35,000 parts of salt per million parts of water. In drinking water, if the salt content exceeds 400 parts of salt per million, the water tastes slightly brackish. If it exceeds 5,000 parts, it is undrinkable, even if taste is not considered. If it exceeds 15,000 parts, neither horses nor cattle can live on it; and if it exceeds 16,000 parts, even sheep cannot live on it.

Atlantic City, New Jersey, has long depended on wells for its water supplies. At first the wells were dug to 100 feet, where there is an unconsolidated aquifer that yields a good amount of water. Then aquifers were tapped at 200 and 800 feet. Today the 100- and 200-foot supplies are useless because of salt-water intrusion. In time, if the draft upon the supplies is too great, even the 800-foot aquifer will cease to supply potable water because of the invasion of salt water into the wells.

There is a real chance that soon the whole complex of the water-supply problem will be altered radically. All that is required is that someone devise an economical method for converting sea water to fresh water. Physically, there is no problem. One can distill salt water and obtain fresh water through condensation, as was done during World War II, using solar stills. The problem is purely economic. A method of distillation that can yield fresh water at an economic rate will certainly be developed in the years to come.

Unfortunately, not all places in the world lie on the coasts. Even when a cheap distillation method is found, there will still be, for most of the parts of the world, severe problems of water allocation. Fresh water will always remain "more than an amenity." It will always be a treasure.

10 The Upper Regions

To leave the regions along the floor of the ocean of air and to ascend many miles, into the stratosphere and beyond, is to enter an unfamiliar realm. Heat waves and cold waves as known upon the earth are left behind within the lower troposphere. No longer are there trade winds or monsoons or breezes of the land and sea. Nor is there any water. The highest cirrus clouds and even the mother-of-pearl clouds of the lower stratosphere lie far beneath. Though there is physical continuity between the lower and upper air, and though the physical events in one are often related to events in the other, the upper air is in many ways a unique realm.

Only relatively recently within the span of scientific history has man begun to comprehend how complex the upper regions of the air really are. In 1714, Edmund Halley of England, the foremost astronomer of his time, confidently observed: "The theory of the air seems now to be perfectly well understood, and its different densities at all altitudes, both by reason and experiment, are sufficiently defined." Halley's conception was simple. He calculated that the earth's atmosphere was forty-five miles high and that the air became steadily thinner and colder toward the top until it merged into outer space.

For almost two centuries Halley's views remained in general agreement with all observations. In the last half-century, however, scientific advances have radically altered man's concept of the nature of the upper regions of the atmosphere. First came the studies of Arthur Edwin Kennelly of Harvard and Oliver Heaviside of England, who demonstrated, independently of one another, that there are charged air particles at heights well above forty-five miles. Then came studies of meteors, of the auroral lights, of sound waves that are reflected downward from the high upper atmosphere, and of the faint light that is radiated from air high aloft. Much more recently, these indirect studies have found their culmination in direct observations from rockets and satellites, so that now it is possible to describe the upper regions of the ocean of air from both indirect and direct evidence.

As more evidence accumulates in the future, man's concept of these upper regions will certainly change further. There will be radical findings that will necessitate major revisions of the physical theories now called upon to explain what little is known of these vast upper regions. Nonetheless, the general descriptive outline is already beginning to be well known, and there will not again have to be such a revolutionary revision of man's concept of the ocean of air as that which accompanied the refutation of Halley's views.

The General Nature of the Ocean of Air

There are four great regions of the ocean of air, each one enveloping the solid-liquid earth, so that among them they comprise concentric, spherical shells in a layered arrangement, one on top of another. The lowest shell is the familiar troposphere, which reaches from the surface of the solid earth to heights of about five miles above the poles and about ten miles above the equator. Next comes the stratosphere, already penetrated by man. The top of the stratosphere lies at a height of around fifty miles, after which the ionosphere begins. The ionosphere, in turn, continues upward to around 400 or 500 miles, where it merges with the exosphere, which extends to the very edges of the atmosphere, some 18,000 miles up. The exosphere is over one hundred times the size of the solid earth and accounts for more than 99 per cent of the volume of the entire atmosphere, yet it contains less than one-billionth of the total amount of the gases of the atmosphere.

The composition and structure of the troposphere are well known. By volume, 99.99 per cent of dry tropospheric air is composed of just four gases. Nitrogen constitutes about 78 per cent, oxygen about

21 per cent, argon not quite 1 per cent, and carbon dioxide .03 per cent. Dry tropospheric air also contains very small amounts of neon, helium, krypton, hydrogen, zenon, radon, and ozone. Because of the vigorous mixing of the air, the proportions of these various gases are remarkably uniform in samples taken at thousands of different points within the troposphere.

There are, however, wide and important variations in other components of the tropospheric air. Water vapor varies from 5 per cent in the air overlying the tropical oceans to .05 per cent or less at the top of the troposphere. The atmosphere also has variable amounts of dust, bacteria, carbon particles, and other solid material, nearly all of which has been blown up from the earth's surface, though an appreciable amount has been derived from meteors and from the dust of outer space.

As for its structure, in the troposphere, as throughout the atmosphere, both air density and air pressure decrease with increasing height. In middle latitudes, at the top of the troposphere, seven miles up, the air is only three-tenths as dense as at sea level and the air pressure is only one-fifth the sea-level pressure. Temperatures also decrease upward through the troposphere, at an average rate of about 3.3° for every rise of 1,000 feet. At the top of the troposphere the average temperature is 55° below zero in middle latitudes and 100° below at the equator, where the troposphere reaches to a height of about ten miles.

In the stratosphere the temperature begins to increase chiefly because of the concentration of ozone, which powerfully absorbs much of the ultraviolet light from the sun and so is warmed itself and helps to warm the other surrounding gases. This ozone is, however, chiefly concentrated in the lower stratosphere, at heights of ten to twenty miles, so that the temperature curve, after reaching a maximum of around 180° in the middle stratosphere, begins to decrease once again and has fallen to around 20° below zero by the time the top of the stratosphere is reached. At that point the density of the air has become less than one ten-thousandth of that at sea level and the air pressure has become so slight as to be almost too small for measurement.

The most fascinating of all the regions in the upper atmosphere is the turbulent, highly charged ionosphere. Upon the buffer region of the ionosphere there falls an immense electromagnetic cannonade:

light rays, ultraviolet and infrared radiations, radio waves and corpuscular streams from the sun, similar radiations from other stars, cosmic rays from interstellar space beyond the solar system. All these impacts produce a great variety of effects on the molecules and atoms of the upper air. The ultraviolet radiations, for example, knock electrons from the air particles, split molecules into atoms, and leave ionized molecules and atoms. Cosmic rays, shooting into the nuclei of air atoms at huge energies, produce a vast, energetic debris which cascades down through the atmosphere, creating powerful secondary showers.

It is in the ionosphere that there is a radical change in the composition of the atmosphere. Nitrogen and oxygen appear as individual atoms, instead of in pairs to form the usual nitrogen and oxygen molecules of the lower atmosphere. Free electrons are produced; these, together with electrically charged atoms, form great layers that are themselves electrically charged. These strata are the scene from time to time of the electromagnetic storms that disrupt radio communication, and they are associated with eruptions of auroral lights. The charged or ionized layers are not constant in thickness, but swell in size beneath the bombardment of the sunlight of daytime and shrink at night. Because they are least developed at night, radio reception is better then than it is by day.

In the extremely rare atmosphere of the ionosphere, the scattered atoms and other particles are energized by the scorching rays of the sun. Temperatures soar from a few hundred degrees in the lower regions of the ionosphere to 2,000° and more in the uppermost regions. Yet at these heights an individual would freeze to death during the night, since there would be no sunlight to keep him warm and the air particles would be too few to warm him by striking him and so conveying their heat. At the top of the ionosphere, about 50,000 billion air particles would strike each square inch of a person's body each second; but this would convey nothing like the heat conveyed by the atmosphere at sea level, where a square inch is struck by 10,000,000,000,000,000 billion air particles each second.

In the ionosphere, as in most of the stratosphere and all of the exosphere, heat can be effectively transferred only by radiation. A rocket at such altitudes is strongly heated during the day; but as soon as the sun disappears, the rocket begins to lose heat effectively through its own radiation, since there is no atmospheric blanket of any consequence to check its radiation losses. The rarity of the ionospheric air is demonstrated by the fact that Sputnik II is calculated to have encountered only a total of one-third of an ounce of air in one complete revolution. This is equivalent to one-third of an ounce in twenty-seven cubic miles, as contrasted with about 800,000 tons of air in one cubic mile at sea level. This figure applies to the mean height of Sputnik II, which was 330 miles.

Somewhere between the 350- and 500-mile height, the stratosphere merges with the exosphere. The distinction between the two is that in the exosphere the atmosphere has become so fantastically rare that the charged particles formed by action of the sunlight are too widely scattered to produce detectable charged layers of the kind that are found in the ionosphere. Instead, at much higher levels, the exosphere includes two enormously thick charged belts of a different kind. One is centered at a height of about 2,500 miles; the other, at about 10,000. The lower belt is hundreds of miles thick; the upper, thousands. Seemingly the belts consist of swarms of electrons and protons (hydrogen nuclei) that have arrived from the sun and have become trapped in the earth's magnetic field. The belts appear to thin out above the magnetic poles and to be thickest above the geomagnetic equator, the line on the earth's surface that is equidistant from the magnetic poles. Judging from the first analyses of observations made from the U.S. Pioneer vehicles launched in late 1958, radiation intensities within these two belts are extraordinarily high, so high that in less than two minutes a person exposed to this radiation would receive more than the total dosage that the United States Atomic Energy Commission considers safe for anyone to receive in an entire week. Because of their direct lethal effect, these intense radiation belts may make it extremely difficult for man to reach the surface of the ocean of air; and the difficulty may be compounded because the fast-moving particles that make up the radiation belts may, upon striking the hull of a space ship, create intense secondary showers of radioactive particles in the interior of the ship.

The exosphere is composed of more than radiation belts. These belts are immersed in an unimaginably rare atmosphere that is almost wholly composed of charged particles of atomic oxygen and nitrogen. Probably throughout the exosphere the particles are at temperatures well in excess of 3,000°. And they extend upward to a height of something like 18,000 miles.

This is the surface of the air ocean. Here stray particles from outer space fall into the ocean of air; and here also particles of air escape from the atmosphere and dart off into space at speeds of 25,000 m.p.h., leaving the earth behind to continue on its way around the sun, carrying with it an ocean of air so little diminished by the loss of a few million billion particles that the difference is negligible.

These, then, are the upper regions of the ocean of air. By their natures as well as by their special weathers, which include the welling up and dying out of vast air currents and swift changes in the bombardments from the sun and outer space, they are regions that are the scene of physical phenomena quite different from those of the troposphere. What is the character of the meteors that sweep these regions and how frequent are they? What of magnetic storms, auroral lights, and other electromagnetic phenomena? How dense and energetic are the primary cosmic rays of the upper air and how do they yield secondary showers? And what is the nature of the outermost limits at the surface of the air ocean?

The answers to these questions are not only of intrinsic scientific interest; they are also of the greatest importance in the design of manned rocket ships and satellites. Certainly today's answers to them are not identical with the answers that can be given tomorrow. But each question can be answered in some measure even now, and in each instance the answer is derived from a body of scientific knowledge that is surprisingly great considering that direct exploration of the high upper atmosphere did not begin until 1957.

Meteors and Meteorites

Over four billion million meteors enter the atmosphere every twenty-four hours. These are tiny particles, most of which are no bigger than a speck of dust and the largest of which is about the size of a pinhead. They are not, therefore, to be confused with meteorites, whose dimensions may be measured in feet or even hundreds of feet. A meteorite that struck a satellite or rocket ship would vaporize it in an instant. But meteorites are so rare that even if a rocket ship cruised in the upper atmosphere for several centuries, it would have at least a fifty-fifty chance of not being hit.

Most meteors burn themselves out through friction with the atmosphere before penetrating to great depths in the atmospheric ocean.

The minuscule meteor itself is invisible. Whizzing through the atmosphere at tremendous speeds, up to sixty miles a second, it leaves a cone-shaped train of incandescent vapor which may remain luminous for many minutes. Ordinary air could not retain an incandescent temperature for any such length of time. It is likely that the meteor ionizes and dissociates the air molecules, creating energized particles that continue to radiate long after the meteor itself has disintegrated.

Meteors first become luminous in the lower ionosphere, fifty to eighty miles above the earth. They nearly always disappear within the stratosphere, at heights of ten to fifty miles. Where do they come from? Why are they visible only in this specific portion of the atmosphere? How can they travel thousands of miles downward through the exosphere and upper ionosphere before beginning to vaporize?

Meteors shoot into the atmosphere from interplanetary space at such enormous speeds that the relatively few air particles they strike in the thin outer atmosphere radiate their tremendous energy almost instantaneously, and so do not have time to pass on that energy to other air particles to form a luminous trail. Under one theory, originated many years ago by F. A. Lindemann and G. M. B. Dobson of Oxford University, as the meteor descends into denser air, more and more air particles pile up in front of it and form a cap of compressed air ahead of it. Not until this cap is heated to a high temperature and passes its heat to the meteor itself does the meteor begin to vaporize. This is the stage at which the meteor makes its appearance. What the observer on the ground sees is the incandescent air cap and the trail of hot, luminescent vapor.

Because nearly all meteors burn themselves out so quickly, the chances are almost negligible that a rocket ship would be hit by a meteor at heights of less than sixty miles. However, at heights above 100 or 200 miles, there is a real hazard. A partial remedy is to navigate so as to avoid meteor streams, which are especially dense in that portion of the earth's atmosphere which lies in the path of the trailing tail of a passing comet. A further and necessary precaution is to design the rocket ship or satellite so that it has a thin outer jacket of aluminum or aluminum alloy to absorb the shock of a meteor encounter.

Even the largest meteor would probably not penetrate an aluminum jacket to a depth of more than two and a half inches, though in so doing it would form a craterlike depression rather than punch clear through. More dangerously, it would in effect create an explosion which would hurl debris from the outer bumper shell inward against the interior hull. Thus the hull itself might be punctured, with resulting rapid loss of air and sudden decompression. Various devices and mechanisms have been suggested for the rapid, automatic sealing of holes formed in this way; but the problem is by no means solved, nor will it be until still more is learned about meteor sizes, frequencies, and speeds, and until there is considerable direct information on the actual effects of meteor hits on satellites or rockets.

Electromagnetic Phenomena

In the upper atmosphere, as everywhere in the universe, electrical and magnetic phenomena are inseparably linked. Two of the primary principles underlying this linkage can be demonstrated through laboratory experiments that are relatively simple.

If a direct electric current, flowing continuously in a single direction, is passed through a wire, and if magnets in the form of miniature compasses are placed about the wire, the compass needles will swing around, parallel to one another and at right angles to the wire. Furthermore, the north ends of the needles will point in such a way as to show that the lines of magnetic force go round and round the wire in the same direction as would the encircling fingers of a person who grasped the wire with his right hand and with his thumb pointing toward the direction in which the current was flowing. (Actually to grasp a wire in this way is, of course, dangerous.)

The fact that an electric current creates a magnetic field is utilized in the electromagnet, which is essentially a soft iron core surrounded by a coil of wire through which a current is passed. When the current is flowing, the iron becomes a magnet that can be used to pull the clapper of a bell, bend the sensitive diaphragm of a telephone receiver, or lift an iron box weighing several tons.

Just as an electric current creates a magnetic field, so also, in the reverse sense, a magnetic field can be used to create electricity. If a permanent magnet, such as a common horseshoe magnet, is suspended in the air and a wire is moved in such a way as to cut across the lines of magnetic force, an electric current is induced in the wire. The stronger the magnet or the faster the movement of the wire, the greater is the resulting current. This principle is applied in the dynamo, which converts water power or steam power to electric power by using the water power or steam to provide the necessary relative motion of the permanent magnet and wire. The motion is relative because often it is the magnet that is moved rather than the wire, with the same result.

Electric currents are created in the ionosphere just as they are in a wire. The necessary magnet is the earth itself. The wires are the layers of free electrons and charged ions. The necessary motion is seemingly provided chiefly by the tidal movements of the atmosphere. How this complex system works is best seen after first considering its necessary elements: the earth magnet, the ionized layers, and the atmospheric tides.

The earth is a giant magnet surrounded by a magnetic field that permeates not only the surface rocks and oceans but also the atmosphere. Over 90 per cent of this magnetic field is created within the solid earth itself. A small part, however, of the order of 3 per cent, is created in the atmosphere; and another residual amount, approximately between 1 and 3 per cent, originates in ways that are still unknown.

The North Magnetic Pole is located near Bathurst Island, far to the north of central Canada. The South Magnetic Pole is in Antarctica. Neither pole coincides with the geographic pole, nor are they exactly opposite each other, as are the geographic poles. Furthermore, both the North and South Magnetic Poles keep wandering. The north one, for example, moved slowly northward over a distance of several hundred miles during the first half of the present century.

The wandering of the poles has never been satisfactorily explained, nor is there any well-accepted hypothesis as to why the solid earth should be a magnet in the first place. One is that the magnetic field is created by currents that are induced within the solid earth by its rotation. Though this is the most nearly acceptable theory at present, a suitable mechanism for creating and maintaining currents of the required magnitude has never been deduced and the hypothesis remains highly speculative.

Much more is known about the charged layers of the ionosphere, 40 to 300 miles above the earth's surface. They are layers only in the sense that they are broad zones within which the density of electrons and ions is higher than in the surrounding zones. Further, it is possible to distinguish among several sublayers within both the E region and the F region. Also there are other lesser layers outside the E and F: a D layer at lower heights, near the top of the stratosphere, and, perhaps, a G layer at around the 350-mile height, in the very high ionosphere.

The charged particles of the ionized layers of the upper air are in constant motion. On the smallest scale, the motions of the particles are of a molecular nature in that each particle darts back and forth and up and down at tremendous speed, changing direction only when it collides with another particle. Superimposed on this helter-skelter pattern of trillions of darting particles is a more orderly average large-scale motion that is produced by the atmospheric tides. Thus the differential pull of the moon upon the air and solid earth yields two bulging waves, one in the air on that side of the earth nearest the moon and the other on the opposite side, where the earth is pulled more strongly pound for pound than is the more distant air, so that a bulge is left behind. As the earth rotates, these bulging waves move round the earth as tidal surges that are analogous to the tides of the oceans. In this general manner, though with many complications in detail, the air is set in motion.

The motions of the charged air particles constitute electric currents on a grand scale. The currents in turn generate their own magnetic fields which reinforce and modify the much stronger magnetic field of the solid earth itself. In addition, because the moving particles are cutting across the magnetic field produced by the earth, there is a further generation of electric currents in the charged layers. These and other factors result in an electromagnetic environment of great complexity.

Two effects of the electromagnetic conditions of the ionosphere are readily discernible to man upon the earth beneath: one is the effect on radio waves; the other, the production of the auroral lights.

At long wave lengths, which are those used by ordinary radio broadcasting stations, radio waves cannot pass through the E and F layers but are, instead, reflected from them. The reflection is not direct, as is the reflection of light from a mirror, but involves the refraction of the wave, so that it enters the ionized layers, begins to bend around, continues to bend still further, and emerges again on a downward path headed for the earth. The radio wave is reflected by the solid earth or ocean surface, turns upward once more toward the charged ionosphere, is once again bent back toward the earth, and so in this manner travels back and forth between the ground and the ionosphere. In this way, long-wave-length radio waves remain within the lower air and they can, accordingly, be received at great distances, even at a point on the earth that is directly opposite the place where the broadcasting antenna is located.

As radio wave lengths decrease and as frequencies increase correspondingly, the waves are refracted less and less by the E and F layers. Commercial television stations broadcast at moderately short wave lengths that overlap the high frequency and very high frequency range. At these frequencies, the transmitted waves nearly always penetrate the ionosphere, with considerable refraction but without enough to turn the waves back to earth. Occasionally, however, where the broadcast is only in the high frequency range, as on channels below Channel 10 in the United States, the wave is refracted in an unusual manner and turns up thousands of miles away at the surface of the earth. In one instance, for example, the program from an Australian TV station was received in Canada.

At ultrahigh frequencies, and especially at superhigh frequencies, radio waves punch through the ionosphere with only slight refraction. At superhigh frequencies the wave lengths are very short, from about one to four inches long. This is the radar band, and it is this band that is used in bouncing radio signals off the moon and picking them up on their return to the earth's surface. In contrast, most of the satellites that have been placed in orbit round the earth broadcast only at very high frequencies.

Whatever the frequency of a radio wave and regardless of whether it is emitted from the earth's surface or from a satellite or rocket, the wave is distorted and sometimes virtually wiped out when there are ionospheric disturbances such as magnetic storms. Pronounced magnetic storms also affect wire communication and may even induce such an overload of current in a power line as to trip master fuses and so black out whole sections of a city. Magnetic storms also produce unusually pronounced auroral lights.

According to the most generally accepted theory, magnetic storms and accompanying auroras occur when the earth is engulfed in a vast cloud of greatly rarefied gas ejected from the sun. The gas is comprised of electrons and protons so widely spaced that even though one is negatively charged and the other positively charged, they do not combine to form hydrogen atoms. As this wind of gas comes streaming past the earth, bound for the outermost reaches of the solar system and beyond, the particles approaching the earth bend inward under the influence of its magnetic field. They pour into the great radiation belts of the high exosphere, causing the belts to swell in size. Almost simultaneously, perhaps because the overloading of the radiation belts causes leakage both downward and poleward, the charged ionospheric layers also grow larger and rise to greater heights. Greatly augmented electric currents speed through the ionosphere. A weak current is induced within the solid earth. Auroral lights flare up, not only near the magnetic poles, but even downward into middle latitudes.

The auroras are among the most spectacular sights of nature. On some nights they flame up with such intensity that it is possible to read by their light even though there is no moon. With their changing patterns, which include sheets of light, streaks, and rays seemingly emanating from a single point, they yield an endless variety of vividly luminous forms. Though they commonly occur in the lower and middle ionosphere, at heights of 60 to 150 miles, they have been known to extend to its top, 500 miles up. Auroras are most pronounced and most frequent in polar regions. They are caused by the excitation of the air by the charged particles from the sun.

Major magnetic storms and auroral displays occur several times each year, and minor occurrences a few times each month. Whether the storm is major or minor, it may last from a few hours to a few days, and during this time there is at least some disruption of communications.

Magnetic storms are not the only events in the high upper air that are related to activity in the sun. Solar flares, which consist of the sudden energetic flaring up of small regions within the disk of the sun, produce an instantaneous burst of extremely intense ultraviolet light that excites the particles of the ionosphere. The sun also emits radio waves that sweep through the atmosphere, sometimes with rapid fluctuations in intensity. Like magnetic storms, these and other solar phenomena produce radio interference and fade-outs. More fundamentally, however, they are to be viewed as physical events that are strong determinants of the environment of the upper air. It is even likely that, in ways that are still not understood, these physical events within the sun may, through the medium of the upper air, help determine the broad-scale features of the weather in the lowest atmosphere of the planet earth.

Cosmic Rays

All of space throughout the universe is constantly traversed by tremendously energetic particles that consist of the charged nuclei of many different kinds of atoms. These particles are cosmic rays. They apparently originate in stars, including our sun. They are densest within the galaxies, as within our own Milky Way. Nowhere, however, are they really dense; for, despite the fantastic energy of a single particle, all the cosmic rays that plunge into the earth's atmosphere account for a total energy intake no greater than that from starlight.

Cosmic rays enter the atmosphere from every direction. About 83 per cent of them are charged hydrogen nuclei, or protons. About 16 per cent are charged helium nuclei, or alpha particles. The remaining 1 per cent are the charged nuclei of heavier atoms, such as lithium or iron. Because they are charged, as they enter the outermost atmosphere they tend to move toward the magnetic poles. However, because they are vastly energetic, cosmic rays speed downward through the atmosphere with only a minor swerving toward the poles, so that even at the equator there are constant showers of cosmic-ray debris.

There is a wide range in the energy of cosmic rays. The most energetic rays are more than a billion times more powerful than the least energetic. Yet even the weakest cosmic ray is extremely vigorous. If an average-sized man had as much energy, weight for weight, as the weakest cosmic ray, he could lift 5,000 billion tons to a height of one mile. If he had the energy of the strongest ray, and if he had a solid platform to stand upon, he could lift the entire earth the same distance.

At these great energies, the incoming primary cosmic rays rip through the outer electron barrier of ordinary air molecules and split the nuclei, thus producing showers of secondary rays that cascade downward. In terms of number of collisions, virtually all of this splitting of nuclei takes place in the middle and lower ionosphere, so that only the secondary showers reach the stratosphere and troposphere. The secondary showers include electrons, alpha particles, newly created protons, and mesons, which are spinning particles of subatomic size. Some of the mesons smash into new air particles and so yield more disintegration products, including more mesons. Other mesons decay and change in such a way that they are not easily captured by air molecules. Because they can penetrate matter, these mesons comprise most of the cosmic radiation at sea level and underground.

One of the products of secondary cosmic-ray showers is gamma rays. Gamma rays are like X rays, but of a shorter wave length and higher energy. Like X rays, they have the property of penetrating the tissues of plants and animals. When they enter the sperm or egg cells of the reproductive organs, they may disrupt the cell structures to produce changes that are reflected genetically in the offspring of the plant or animal. Such occurrences are unusual, but nonetheless they probably account for a high percentage of the natural mutations that occasionally take place. Through such mutations, "sports" come into being, as when some new and completely erratic trait suddenly appears in a strain of sweet peas or in human beings. Usually these new traits are not spectacular, but in rare instances they are as extreme as is the appearance of six fingers on the hands of a newborn baby.

The presence of primary cosmic rays in the ionosphere and beyond may pose severe problems for space travel. As in the case of the particles that comprise the radiation belts, cosmic rays striking the hull of a ship may produce secondary showers that will be hurled inward toward the occupants of the ship. The fact that the dog of Sputnik II lived for at least several days would seem to indicate that these effects will not be lethal; but it is, however, no proof that they may not be deleterious. Here again, as in the case of meteors, more knowledge is required. Doubtless, as further information is gleaned from rocket and satellite observations, the problem will become better defined and so, at last, will be solved in a practical manner. At the same time, more will be learned of the nature of cosmic rays and of the multitudinous effects they yield within the atmosphere.

The Outermost Regions of the Air Ocean

Far beyond the ionosphere lie the edges of the ocean of air, where the rare gases of the exosphere mingle with the equally rare gases of outer space. No clean-cut spherical surface marks the outermost boundary of the true terrestrial air. Rather there is an ill-defined zone, hundreds of miles deep, with gases beneath and downward which, however rare, still for the most part follow the earth about the sun; and with gases above and outward that for the most part, when the earth travels onward, are left behind. Even if the occasional darting particles of gas were visible, this would appear not as an ocean stretching away toward the horizon, but more as a chaotic realm with particles swarming in all directions.

So far as any definite knowledge is concerned, the nature of the outermost regions of the air ocean remains a matter of conjecture. This conjecture is, however, far from haphazard. It rests upon physical theories whose central features have been derived both from laboratory experiments and from observations, and it incorporates many new ideas that have been advanced only in the last few years. These views require that the earth's outer atmosphere be envisaged in two different, yet complementary, ways: as a boundary region with reference to the earth itself, and as a mere and almost insignificantly small inclusion within the outer atmosphere of the sun.

As a boundary region, the zone at the top of the ocean of air is a realm in which the gases are so rare that a charged particle may race hundreds of miles through empty space before encountering another particle and so being bounced one way or another. Often a particle races outward into true outer space and so is lost to the earth. Often some other particle comes racing in and so is gained. At the same time, cosmic rays stream inward from all directions at an almost constant rate, night and day.

Over the months, there are frequent inward bursts of protons and electrons from the sun. Over the years, there are sudden inroads of whole swarms of meteors, but mostly there is only a fluctuating influx with occasional minor swarms. Over the millennia, there are episodes when hydrogen and other light elements from the interstellar dust fall into the air ocean at an unusually high rate. These episodes occur when the sun and its earth and other satellites pass through a dust-cloud region as they speed around the enormous rim of the Milky Way galaxy.

The earth in relation to the sun, 93 million miles away, is a minor object in the outer solar atmosphere. It exists as a speck in a field of intensive solar radiation. Clouds of solar gas burst outward and stream past it. Solar radio waves are barely interrupted by it as they travel onward toward Mars, Neptune, Pluto, and the edges of the universe. The outer reaches of the atmosphere of this planet owe their primary character to the fact that the earth is embedded in the solar atmosphere. Heat and cold, wind and storm, rain and drought—in the last analysis all these happen because the earth is a satellite of the sun and from it draws the energy that is the driving force of weather.

Part Two

The Ocean of Air: Observation, Prediction, Control

Arts of publique use . . . are Power: And though the true Mother of them, be Science . . . yet, because they are brought into the Light, by the hand of the Artificer, they be esteemed (the Midwife passing with the vulgar for the Mother,) as his issue.

—Thomas Hobbes

11

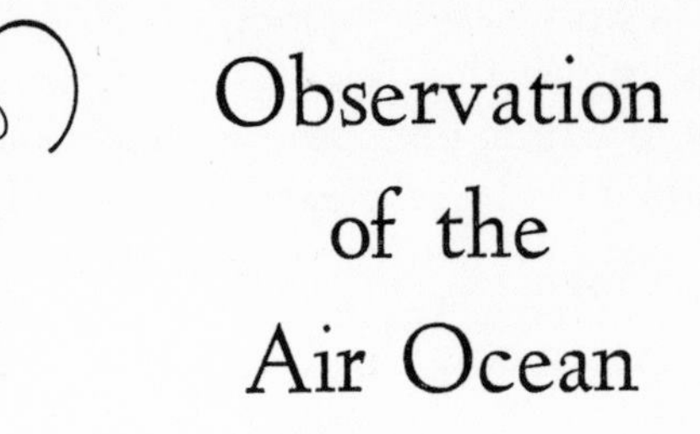

Observation of the Air Ocean

There is no better illustration of the difference between science and technology than in the history of man's observations and studies of the behavior of the ocean of air.

The scientist observes and studies nature that he may better understand it. His curiosity is general. His hope is that some day he may be able to make general statements that will without exception describe the relations among all observed facts. The technologist observes and studies nature that he may solve some specific, practical problem. His attention is focused on items that will help him in his task. His hope is that he will find a perfect, practical solution to his problem.

In terms of quantity, 99 per cent of the observations of the ocean of air have been made for technologic reasons. They have been made to help man predict atmospheric phenomena, to forecast what the weather will be. This technologic emphasis will always exist because the weather will always be of immediate, practical concern to man. However, there have been many observations of a purely scientific nature. Furthermore, as scientific comprehension of the behavior of the air ocean increases, the benefits to the weather technologist also increase. Technology rests on science. It also helps science, because the observation of natural phenomena, even within a limited range and for limited purposes, provides added knowledge that helps the scientist to formulate, to test, and to modify his views.

Within this framework of science and technology, the observation of the air ocean came about and thrived and grew. At first almost the sole object was technologic: to read the sky and so foretell what the weather might bring. This was the first of the four great periods in the history of observation of the air ocean. One of its chief characteristics was that observations were nonquantitative; they did not rest on physical, quantitative measurements. The second period came into being during the early stages of modern science, in the seventeenth century. During this time also, the primary emphasis was upon the use of observations to forecast weather, but now quantitative measurements were developed and became commonplace. The third period overlapped the second. It had as its hallmark the investigation of the upper air, away from the surface of the solid earth.

The fourth period is just emerging at the present time. Only in the past several years has the range of observations been extended to much greater heights, all the way to the top of the air ocean. So new is this period, and the information garnered from it is still so relatively slight, that not enough has been learned to apply the new findings effectively to weather forecasting. Yet the general principle still holds: where science leads, technology will follow, and the latest era in the exploration of the ocean of air will in time yield benefits of great practical consequence.

Early Weather Observations

By necessity men of all races and cultures, all places and eras, have observed the weather. Perhaps the men who 25,000 years ago roamed the forested hills of Europe felt at times strange wonderment upon gazing at some patterned sky. But it was not for aesthetic reasons that they watched the skies and weathers. The game they hunted must be stalked downwind. The berries they gathered must not lie in marshes made treacherous by heavy rains. Shelters must stand against the wind and lie above the swollen river's reach. The signs of the changing year must be read correctly so that man, like the other animals, might migrate with the seasons.

Not only man the savage but also civilized man has always been a weather observer. Twenty-five hundred years ago, the citizen of Athens walking through the market place stopped before a column to peer at the almanac posted there giving the latest information about the weather. Then, being of a questioning mind and perhaps suspicious of official weather reports, he looked to a nearby tree top to note the wind direction and scanned the sky to see and judge its aspect. So, too, in this present time, with an almost constant barrage of weather forecasts and reports, even the most urbanized city dweller checks the appearance of the sky in the hope of learning which way the weather will turn.

Regardless of their calling, watching the unfolding weather has always been almost instinctive for all people, but the really avid watchers and those of greatest skill have been the sailor and the farmer. It was they chiefly who formulated and passed along the early weather proverbs which served as rules of thumb for weather forecasting; and when these proverbs finally were given written form, it was often with reference to navigation or farming. Typical are two sayings from Hesiod, who, writing in the eighth century B.C., was the earliest classical recorder of weather lore:

> For fifty days after the turning of the sun, when harvest hath come to an end, the weary season, sailing is seasonable for men. . . . Then are the breezes easy to judge and the sea is harmless. Then trust thou in the winds, and with soul untroubled launch the swift ship in the sea, and well bestow therein all thy cargo.

And, with reference to farming:

> Take heed what time thou hearest the voice of the crane from the high clouds uttering her yearly cry, which bringeth the sign for plowing and showeth forth the season of rainy weather, and biteth the heart of him that hath no oxen.

With the coming of the era of exploration, it was the sailor and farmer whose weather observations did most to extend knowledge of the weathers of the world. In the logs of old sailing ships are records of the winds and weathers of far-off regions of the seas: of hurricanes off the Bahamas, of ripping winds that funnel through the Straits of Magellan, and of arctic cold that freezes the salt spray in the scuppers. In the diaries of early farmer-settlers are records of cruelly harsh winters in the northern English colonies, of hot, rainy summers along the Gulf Coast, and of the sharp turn of the seasons in lands whose climates have a vigor of seasonal extremes that contrast strongly with the mild-tempered climates of western Europe.

Despite the fact that most of these accounts—and all of the earliest—were lacking quantitatively, they contain excellent observations and descriptions. These people watched the weather for a purpose and with a skill that is rare today. Consider, for instance, a passage by Dampier, the famous English sea captain, buccaneer, and natural philosopher, whose skill as a weather observer has not been exceeded. It was July 4, 1687, when his ship encountered a typhoon off the China coast:

> It was now the time of the year for the S.W. Monsoon, but the Wind had been whiffling about from one part of the Compass to another for two or three Days, and sometimes it would be quite calm. This caused us to put to sea, that we might have Sea-room at least; for such flattering weather is commonly the fore-runner of a Tempest.
>
> Accordingly, we weighed and set out; yet we had very little Wind all the next night. But the Day ensuing, which was the 4th day of July, about 4 a clock in the afternoon, the Wind came to the N.E. and freshened upon us, and the Sky look'd very black in that quarter, and the black Clouds began to rise apace and mov'd towards us; having hung all the morning in the Horizon. . . . At 11 a clock . . . it began to rain, and by 12 a clock at night it blew exceeding hard, and the Rain poured down as through a Sieve. It thundered and lightned prodigiously, and the Sea seemed all of a Fire about us; for every Sea that broke sparkled like Lightning. The violent Wind raised the Sea presently to a great heighth, and it ran very short and began to break in on our Deck. One Sea struck away the Rails of our Head, and our Sheet-Anchor, which was stowed with one Flook or bending of the Iron, over the Ship's Gunal, and lasht very well down to the side, was violently washt off, and had like to have struck a hole in our Bow, as it lay beating against it. Then we were forced to put right before the Wind to stow our Anchor again; which we did with much ado: but afterwards we durst not adventure to bring our Ship to the Wind again, for fear of foundring, for the turning the Ship either to or fro from the Wind is dangerous in such violent Storms. The fierceness of the Weather continued till 4 a clock that morning . . .

Because they provide a total picture such as can never be provided by instruments alone, visual weather observations will always be important. They indicate in broad outline the general plot of the story that is the changing weather. But to follow that story in detail, to read the paragraphs and sentences and words, one must look to the information provided by weather instruments.

Visual and instrumental observations go hand in hand. One sees that there is a light rain falling in the form of drizzle, that the overcast fills the sky to the horizon, that the clouds from which the rain falls are strato-cumulus, that the visibility is half a mile to a mile, and that there is a light breeze blowing. One reads from instruments that there has been .15 inch of rain in the last hour, that the temperature is 58°, that the wind is blowing at 5 m.p.h. from the southeast, that the ceiling height is 1,800 feet, that the relative humidity is 98 per cent, and–from balloon observations–what the temperature, wind, and humidity are along on ascending line up to a height of 100,000 feet.

When man began to measure the physical nature of the ocean of air, a new era was ushered in. These observations provided the quantitative information that would later be used both in the development of weather forecasting and in describing and coming to understand the physical nature of the lower atmosphere. These first quantitative measurements stemmed from the invention of instruments that are for the most part still in use today.

Weather Instruments

One of the oldest of all weather instruments is the rain gauge. Its date and place of origin are both unknown, but it must have existed in simple form in earliest historical times. Fundamentally a rain gauge is merely a receptacle for catching rainfall, the catch being measured to determine the amount of the fall.

The land itself provides a number of natural rain gauges. Hollows and closed depressions catch and hold the rain, and the depth to which they are filled is a rough measure of the rainfall. Streams and rivers gather in the rain from over widespread areas, and the amount to which the stream or river rises indicates roughly the amount of rain. But such natural rain gauges provide crude measurements at best. For accurate measurement of rain it is far better to have a closed container, such as a jar or can.

It is likely that the early peoples of Southeast Asia, who practiced irrigation many millennia before the time of Christ, may have set out containers to measure the rainfall as an aid to deciding whether it was necessary to use precious irrigation water after a light rain.

The simplest modern rain gauge consists essentially of a funnel into which rain falls and down which it flows, to be concentrated in a cylindrical tube beneath. Usually the funnel at its topmost, broadest end is ten times as large in cross-section area as the cylinder. Then if there is one-tenth of an inch of rain, it fills the cylinder to a depth of one inch. Multiplying the rain depth ten times in this fashion makes it easier to measure accurately the depth of fall by simply thrusting a ruler into the cylindrical tube and measuring the depth of the water collected there.

Rain gauges are used to measure snowfall as well as rainfall. The snow collected in the gauge is melted and the melt is then weighed to determine the water-depth equivalent. Snow may be light and fluffy, in which case it may require as much as fifteen inches to equal one inch of melt; or it may be dense and well packed, and only six inches may equal an inch of melt. Measuring the snow melt equates these differences and provides a standard measure that gives a true picture of the amount of water added to the ground.

The only weather instrument other than the rain gauge which probably existed in simple form in early times is the wind vane. Once again, definite proof is lacking, but one may surmise that the people of earliest history may well have devised a simple wind vane of one or another kind. After all, even a reed attached at the top of a pole in such a manner as to pivot freely serves as a sensitive indicator of wind direction.

The rain gauge and the wind vane are essentially instruments quite easily conceived. No great knowledge of the nature of the atmosphere was required for their conception, nor was a knowledge of physical principles needed for their construction.

In marked contrast, the weather instruments that followed required for their conception a high order of scientific sophistication. Earliest and foremost among these instruments were the thermometer and the barometer, which were invented in the first part of the seventeenth century. The time of their invention was no accident. This was the beginning of the period of the great philosophers, the founders of modern science. It was a time when a few great thinkers were beginning seriously to challenge methods, concepts, and whole modes of thought that so far as the western mind was concerned had not been markedly revised for almost 2,000 years. It was a period of new ideas, experimentations, and inventions.

In this climate of vigorous inquiry, the thermometer and barometer originated. Their inventors were among the most distinguished natural philosophers of the time. Galileo Galilei not only devised the thermometer and conducted experiments with falling bodies; he also developed the telescope, discovered the moons of Jupiter, did much to establish the Copernican system, and formulated the basic laws governing the behavior of pendulums. Evangelista Torricelli made major contributions in the fields of mechanics and mathematics, besides discovering the principle of the barometer.

Galileo's thermometer was of the gas type. It was essentially a U-shaped tube sealed at one end, the sealed arm containing air at the top and water below, the water extending around the U and part way up the open arm. With an increase in temperature, the air expanded and forced downward the water below; with a decrease in temperature, the air contracted and the water rose beneath the air. The position of the surface, where water and air met, was a measure of the volume occupied by the air and hence of the temperature of that air.

The expansion-contraction principle underlying the working of Galileo's gas thermometer was soon applied to the development of both liquid and solid thermometers. Today the most common thermometers involve contraction and expansion of liquids, such as mercury or alcohol. Expansion and contraction of solids is also commonly used, as in recording thermometers that employ bimetallic strips. Such strips are useful for other purposes also. Highly accurate watches and other precision instruments employ bimetallic elements designed to compensate for the expansion or contraction resulting from temperature changes.

The notion of the barometer was far more complicated. Galileo knew that air had weight. He knew also that a pump could pull water upward only to a height of about thirty-two feet. Yet he failed to relate these two—failed to see that it was the pressure of the air that forced the water upward to thirty-two feet but no higher.

Both Galileo and, at first, Torricelli believed that "Nature abhors a vacuum." At first, when Torricelli constructed his mercury barometer and saw that the column remained supported only to a height of some twenty-nine inches, he ascribed this behavior to nature's horror of a vacuum. But then he noted that the height of the mercury varied from day to day. This caused him to conclude that the variation must be owing to changes in air pressure. Because, as he said, "Nature would not, as a flirtatious girl, have a different *horror vacui* on different days."

A barometer simply weighs a column of the atmosphere. The mercury barometer is like a two-pan balance. A mercury column within an inverted tube sealed at the top and devoid of air acts as the weight on one pan of the balance. If the tube containing the mercury curves round in the form of a U, then the air pressing downward upon the mercury in the open arm of the U represents the substance that is being weighed. The greater the weight of the overlying air, the greater the pressure on the mercury in the open arm and the greater the height to which the mercury in the closed arm is forced upward. The early mercury barometers were actually U-shaped. Today, in the common mercury barometer, the mercury column within the tube rests in a well of mercury, and the pressure of air on the mercury surface in this well forces the mercury upward within the tube in the same manner as in the U-shaped barometer.

The general association of high air pressure with fair weather and of low air pressure with storminess was noted within a few years after the discovery of the barometer. Soon in common parlance the barometer became known as a "weather glass." About 1670, Hooke invented the wheel barometer, which consisted of a U-tube mercury barometer to which was attached a dial face with a pointer that moved as the pressure rose or fell. Then the term "weather glass" assumed even more explicit meaning, for the dials of wheel barometers were inscribed with words such as "Very Dry," "Fair," "Rain," and "Stormy." For the first time an instrument directly related to weather forecasting had come into use.

The relation between weather and barometric pressure is not nearly so strict as the first users of the weather glass believed. Only at the extremes do pressures indicate impending weather with a good degree of reliability. In low latitudes a falling glass, with the pressure descending below 28 inches, nearly always means that a hurricane is approaching. At all latitudes a rising glass, with the pressure ascending above 30.5 inches, nearly always means dry weather. But between these two extremes there is considerable variability.

By 1650, the weather observer had available to him four major instruments: the rain gauge, wind vane, thermometer, and barometer. In 1667, Hooke added another: the anemometer, for determining wind speed. Hooke's anemometer consisted of a plate attached to an arm that was free to pivot upward against a spring. When the plate was held into the wind, the force of the moving air pushed the plate upward. The amount of the upward swing was a measure of the wind speed.

Anemometers of this kind have generally been replaced by the cup anemometer or the pressure-tube anemometer. In the former, cups are fastened to crossarms as to the ends of spokes of a rimless wheel, the "wheel" being free to rotate in the horizontal so that as the cups catch the wind they spin the wheel around at a rate proportional to the wind speed. In the latter, an open-ended tube is mounted on a wind vane so that the tube will pivot to face constantly into the wind. A pressure gauge within the tube measures the force of the oncoming wind and so provides a measure of wind speed.

The anemometer did not take to the seas as did the thermometer and weather glass. For one thing, wind-speed measurement is tricky business even on land. Moving air is skittish. It is thrown off and its flow is interrupted by any obstruction, even an obstruction as slight as an anemometer pole. Eddies are created, so that the anemometer does not measure the true wind but only an approximation of it. So far as use at sea is concerned, an even more important consideration is the fact that when a ship is in motion a relative wind is created. Even if this is allowed for and discounted, the moving ship itself sets up all manner of eddies and currents as it plows through the surrounding air.

The force of the wind at sea is determined by observing its effects upon the ship and particularly upon the water surface itself. This method of determining wind force is ancient. Among navigators everywhere, in as many languages as there were peoples who sailed open waters, there grew up a terminology for describing wind force in terms of its effects on ships and on the state of the sea. Terms such as "calm," "smooth," or "windless" were used to denote an utter lack of wind, when the sea lay still and flawless. "All-powerful wind" denoted the ripping winds that bite deep into the surface of the sea, creating a jumble of towering, fast-riding waves. There were also terms for winds of lesser force, such as "light wind," "full wind," "heavy wind," "storm wind," and scores of others.

By the sixteenth century a scale of descriptive terms to identify winds of different force had come into common use among the sailors of western Europe. This scale became formalized when, in 1806, Admiral Sir Francis Beaufort of the British Royal Navy related the descriptive terms to the effects of the corresponding wind forces on a typical British man-of-war. He noted, for instance, that when the wind was of such force as to be called a "light breeze," a "well-conditioned man-of-war, under all sail and clean full, would go in smooth water from 1 to 2 knots." Beaufort assigned numbers to the wind-force terms, the result being a scale that ran from 0, which corresponded to calm, up to 12 for a hurricane, representing a wind to which the British man-of-war "could show no canvas."

The Beaufort scale was officially adopted by the Royal Navy in 1838. From the Navy it spread to the British merchant marine, and then to the merchantmen of other countries. Only a few years ago the scale was still used on the weather maps of the United States, the countries of western Europe, and many other countries, even though wind of a certain Beaufort force actually covers a range of wind speeds.

Determining wind speed and direction from a ship is difficult enough—from an airplane it is even harder. A plane drifts with the moving air on which it rides. The navigator of the plane plays a constant game with the wind. If he can see the stars or sun, if he can see a recognizable landmark, or if his radioman can pick up signals from a beacon, then by charting his successive positions he can figure backward and see what the wind must have been to account for the drift of the plane. Average wind values must then be used, together with the forecast weather map, to estimate what the wind drift will be over the next flight leg.

Suppose the plane is three hours out of Gander, eastward bound for Ireland, flying at 19,000 feet beneath a night sky filled with guidepost stars. It is 0300 and the navigator has obtained a three-point fix, one based on observation of three stars, and has entered it on the flight chart. The plane is at 52° N., 50° W. The pilot has been holding a heading that would correct for a northwest wind of 40 knots—the wind given by the weather forecast. But the plane is farther along than expected and is much farther north than it ought to be. Figuring backward, the navigator calculates that the average wind since the last fix an hour ago has been 45 knots from due west. Consulting his weather map, he sees that as the plane moves eastward the winds should strengthen and should turn clockwise—from west to northwest to north. So once more he tries to outguess the wind. He passes the word to the pilot to correct for a northwest wind at 50 knots. An hour later, when he takes his next fix, he will find out how well he guessed.

Despite the special problems of estimating wind speeds aboard ship or from an airplane, the anemometer remains the fundamental instrument for measuring the winds of the lowest atmosphere. After the anemometer was invented, only one other major weather instrument remained to be devised. This was the wet-bulb thermometer, which was probably invented by Hutton and which made it possible to measure humidity in a relatively simple manner.

Though still widely used today, the wet-bulb thermometer has one disadvantage: it does not lend itself readily to continuous recording of humidity data. For this special purpose, a hair hygrometer is used. A hair has the property of lengthening when the humidity increases and shortening when it decreases. Human hair responds better to humidity changes than does the hair of any other animal, and blond hair behaves best of all. Yet even blond hair has its disadvantages: it responds too slowly to changes in humidity; it behaves erratically at very high or very low humidities; it is difficult to keep free of oil and grease, which upset its sensitivity as a humidity-measuring element. Hair hygrometers are therefore used only in recording instruments. The hair is attached by a series of levers to a recording arm that moves up and down across a rotating drum as the hair lengthens and shortens. At the end of the arm is a pen point that traces a line on paper wound around the drum to give a record of humidity.

The invention of the wet-bulb thermometer completed what was to be the standard surface weather observatory for almost one hundred years, until the 1940's. Within that hundred years other instruments were to be devised: for measuring the duration and intensity of sunlight, for estimating the speed and direction of movement of clouds, for determining the intensity of the electrical field of the atmosphere, and for measuring many other properties of the lower regions of the ocean of air. Nonetheless, the rain gauge, the thermometer, the barometer, the wind vane and anemometer, and the wet-bulb thermometer remained the primary, standard instruments so far as surface weather observations were concerned. Then came the Second World War, which brought with it two major innovations, one involving a new observational technique and the other an entirely new kind of weather observation. These innovations were the automatic weather station and radar storm detection.

None of the thousands of weather observers and forecasters who in 1943–45 were charged with watching the weather in the Southwest Pacific will fail to remember a solitary station that appeared to be misplaced on the weather map. It stood as a circle in the center of the Coral Sea, seemingly in the midst of open water. Actually the station was mounted on a barely emergent coral reef, which on stormy days was sure to be awash. Clearly no ordinary weather station could be maintained there. Yet it was essential to have weather observations from the Coral Sea, known to be the birthplace of hurricanes that might swing westward to hit Australia or curve off to the east across the New Hebrides, New Caledonia, or others of the hundreds of South Pacific islands.

To solve the problem an automatic weather station was developed. The New Zealanders flew it in, landing just beyond the reef in their Catalina flying boat, and bringing the heavy equipment ashore in a small raft. They filled the station's reservoir tank with gasoline; tested the recording barometer, thermometer, anemometer, and radio transmitter; then took off, leaving behind the first automatic weather station to be put into use. Every three months a flying boat returned to refuel the station, retest the equipment, and make adjustments if required.

The observations from the Coral Sea were welcome indeed to forecasters trying to outguess the tricky weather of the Southwest Pacific. On days when, because of radio interference, the signals failed to come through, they were sorely missed, even though the station was by no means perfect. For one thing, the aneroid barometer never behaved quite properly. But the forecasters soon caught on and made allowance for the fact that the pressure gave a reading that was progressively more and more below the actual pressure until the three-month inspection rolled around. Then the barometer readings would jump up to their proper height before slipping downward again.

The automatic weather station was deliberately planned and developed to meet a special, urgent need. Another modern weather instrument, even more important, was developed as a by-product of radar research. In the late 1930's, when the British were conducting their early studies of radar, they found that strange, unexplained images showed up on the radar screen when there was no plane in the sky or any other obvious target to account for the echoes.

Careful study showed that in many of these instances the echoes were produced by raindrops or large flakes of snow. This atmospheric effect was a nuisance that had to be at least partially eliminated if radar was to serve its purpose as a wartime instrument for detecting aircraft and ships. So the British and, later on, the Americans at the Massachusetts Institute of Technology Radiation Laboratory made special studies of the effects of the atmosphere on radar beams. They found that the beams were reflected by raindrops and snow, and that they were bent by the atmosphere, especially when the lower atmosphere contained contrasting layers of air at markedly different temperatures or with sharply contrasting moisture contents.

Except for trying to predict and minimize the effects of the atmosphere on radar performance, nothing much was done about the findings until several years later, in 1944, when Colonel J. T. Wilson of Canada decided to apply these results by using radar as a weather instrument. The radar scope picked up rain. Why not use it as a rain-detection instrument?

The results of Colonel Wilson's tests, using radar in this fashion, were phenomenally successful. On the circular, maplike face of the radar scope one could actually "see" a cold front moving in from the northwest. A whole mass of raindrop targets would first appear at the edge of the scope—the edge that revealed what was happening in the extreme northwest, 160 miles away. Over the succeeding hours the line moved inward toward the center of the scope, which marked the location of the observing station. Almost to the minute, when the line touched the scope center, the patter of rain could be heard on the roof of the radar shack overhead. Here was a weather instrument uncanny in its accuracy and unique in performance. It viewed the rainfall over a wide area simultaneously, and although it might miss the areas of very light rainfall—since small droplets are not good reflectors of radar beams—it made it possible to track large storms with heretofore unthought-of precision.

Radar storm detection has already come into use at a few major weather stations in the United States. The Army Signal Corps radar at Orlando, Florida, is used to detect hurricanes still far out at sea. Shortly after the war, the Air Force made a motion picture of this radar scope, showing the approach of a major hurricane. In the actual picture the views are speeded up, so that in the space of twenty minutes one can see what actually covered a time interval of forty hours.

Seeing the picture, one has something of the feeling he might have were he suspended in mid-air, 100 miles up, looking obliquely downward on the storm through a telescope. First, scattered rain areas appear at the edge of the scope face. Then the jagged, ill-formed edges of an outer ring of churning cloud and rain are seen, the whole ring rotating counterclockwise. Hard on the first, a second, more even ring appears. It, too, is churning and rotating. Then come three more rings packed closely together, and finally the clear center area that is the rain-free heart of the storm. Now the outer ring reaches the center of the radar screen, and the film begins to jump. The photographer is having a hard time keeping his camera steady as seventy-mile winds pound the heavily constructed radar building. The jumpiness gets worse as the hurricane moves overhead, subsides when the clear "eye" touches on the center of the screen, then starts with added fury as the storm moves away. The picture continues to follow the hurricane as it swirls northeastward, back out to sea.

Wartime experiments in radar and communications led to still another weather application of electronics. Electric discharges in the atmosphere, especially strong discharges accompanied by lightning, produce static in radio receivers. By using special radio direction-finding instruments, it is possible to locate the source of such atmospheric disturbances. As part of the wartime craze for abbreviations, the word "atmospherics" became shortened to "spherics." Then, to obtain a unique, designating word, the "spherics" was changed to "sferics," the present name for this type of detection system.

Sferics networks were set up in the Caribbean and the Southwest Pacific late in 1945 for operational trial, after preliminary tests at the University of New Mexico had shown the feasibility of locating electrical disturbances in the atmosphere by this method. The trial networks proved useful in locating storm areas hundreds of miles away; but unfortunately they had to be abandoned with the end of the war, and to date little further work has been done with this new weather-locating instrument.

As of today, the progress being made in the improvement of surface weather observations is chiefly in the direction of designing more accurate instruments and devising new methods, often electronic, for automatic recording and transmitting of observational measurements.

So far as entirely new techniques and instruments are concerned, the emphasis has shifted from observations at the earth's surface to those aloft from rockets and earth satellites.

The advances in this new field have been so spectacular during the past several years that the impression is often given that little or no knowledge of the upper air had been acquired prior to the first rocket soundings. Actually, a surprising amount was learned long before modern rockets were developed. How this information came to be obtained and how it made possible the design of successful rockets shows that even the most remarkable scientific advances do not arise spontaneously out of nothingness but instead evolve from the scientific achievements of the past.

The Upper Air

About the middle of July in the year 1749, on a morning unusually bright and clear for that place and season, there appeared in an open field in the Camlachie district of Glasgow, Scotland, two scholarly-looking gentlemen, burdened down with kites, strings, thermometers, notebooks, and other paraphernalia. The rumor of their undertaking had preceded them, so that already the field was surrounded by a crowd of townsfolk eager to witness the experiment that was to take place.

Professor Alexander Wilson of the University of Glasgow and his helper, Thomas Melvill, unfurled a chain of six paper kites that varied in length from four to seven feet, the smallest kite being uppermost. To the tails of the smaller kites thermometers were attached, to each of which was appended a paper tassel. The thermometers were hung beneath the kites by strings. Joining each of these strings was a waxy match line that was ignited before the kites were launched, so that, shortly after the kite chain reached its maximum anchored height, the gradual singeing of the match line disengaged the thermometers, which fell to the ground unbroken, being protected in landing by the paper tassels. Melvill held the kite rope, while Professor Wilson raced across the field to pick up the thermometers so as to note their readings before a change in the readings occurred.

Professor Wilson continued his kite experiments throughout the summer. Although at best, in this manner, he sounded the atmosphere only to a height of a few hundred feet, still his studies were of great interest. One hundred years previously, Pascal had ascended the old tower of Saint-Jacques de-la-Boucherie in Paris, carrying with him the newly invented barometer, to determine how air pressure varied with height. And in the intervening century, many scientists had climbed the slopes of mountains to obtain both pressure and temperature readings. But Wilson was the first investigator to obtain observations from the free upper air, from air unaffected by close contact with the ground. A whole new line of study was opened up by his work.

Wilson's experiments established the use of the kite as a meteorological equipment. Three years later Benjamin Franklin conducted his famous kite experiment to learn the nature of lightning. In a letter to Peter Collinson, a Fellow of the Royal Society of London, Franklin described his experiment and the results obtained therefrom:

> Make a small cross, of two light strips of cedar; the arms so long, as to reach to the 4 corners of a large thin silk handkerchief, when extended: tie the corners of the handkerchief to the extremities of the cross: so you have a body of a kite: which being properly accommodated with a tail, loop, and string, will rise in the air like those made of paper: but this, being of silk, is fitter to bear the wet and wind of a thunder gust without tearing. To the top of the upright stick of the cross is to be fixed a very sharp-pointed wire, rising a foot or more above the wood. To the end of the twine, next the hand, is to be tied a silk ribband; and where the twine and silk join, a key may be fastened.
>
> The kite is to be raised, when a thunder gust appears to be coming on, and the person who holds the string must stand within a door, or window, or under some cover, so that the silk ribband may not be wet. . . . As soon as any of the thunder clouds come over the kite, the pointed wire will draw the electric fire from them. . . .
>
> From electric fire thus obtained spirits may be kindled, and all the other electrical experiments be performed . . . and thus the sameness of the electric matter with that of lightning is completely demonstrated.

Franklin carried out many experiments on the nature of lightning, not only with kites but also with his newly invented lightning rod. He tested the effect of the "electric fire" on various kinds of animals and, having himself been knocked unconscious by an electric current, cautioned other scientists against repeating his various experiments without taking all manner of precautions. Despite Franklin's warnings, Professor Richman of the St. Petersburg Academy of Sciences, one of several scientists who followed Franklin in the study of lightning, was electrocuted when he stood too near the ball-shaped terminal of a lightning rod constructed for scientific purposes.

For over thirty years the kite remained the only equipment for sounding the free atmosphere. Then, on October 15, 1783, Jean François Pilâtre de Rozier of Metz made the first balloon ascent. His was a fire balloon, fed by hot air rising from a brazier. A few months later J. A. C. Charles in England ascended in a hydrogen-filled balloon. With this improvement, heights of several thousand feet were reached.

At first the greatest difficulty was in landing; for although the balloon could be slightly deflated so that it drifted earthward, there was no one to grab and hold fast the two lines. Nearby folk, seeing the strange round thing descending, would run and hide so that in many instances the balloonist had to jump for it, abandoning his balloon and taking his chances of being injured. This situation did not prevail long; soon balloons were common sights in the skies surrounding London, Paris, St. Petersburg, and many other cities.

Scientists were quick to see the advantages of the balloon over the kite for making observations in the upper atmosphere. The year after Charles' ascent from London, Dr. John Jeffries and the aeronaut, Blanchard, made balloon observations of pressure and temperature and brought down with them samples of air for chemical analysis. Two decades later began what amounted to an international contest to see who could collect the most observations from the greatest heights. In 1804, Sacharof of St. Petersburg and E. G. Robinson ascended to 8,000 feet. In the same year, Gay-Lussac and Biot of France rose to 13,000 feet, and then to 23,000 feet, where the temperature was found to be 14.9°. For the next several decades many other ascents followed.

Specially notable were those of Welsh and Green, who reached heights above 19,000 feet on several occasions, and of Glaisher, who in 1862 claimed to have reached 37,000 feet. The enthusiasm of the scientist-balloonists was suddenly checked when, on a spring day in 1875, only Gaston Trisandier among a crew of three survived an ascent to 27,950 feet. His companions died for lack of oxygen.

Shortly thereafter, Hermite and Besançon started work on designing an unmanned balloon to be used for meteorological soundings. In November of 1892 they successfully tested the first "balloon sonde," which rose several hundred feet in the air and then, as the hydrogen inside it expanded, burst and floated down by parachute to deposit its weather instruments undamaged on the ground.

The sounding balloon quickly became a standard weather equipment and remains so to this day. Balloons were improved so that they rose to thousands of feet, and now heights of 100,000 feet or more are probed in this manner. Meanwhile improvements were made in methods of balloon tracking and in the instruments carried. If the purpose of the balloon ascent is to measure the winds aloft, then all that is required is to track the balloon as it rises and so to compute the movement of the air on which it drifts. Tracking is accomplished visually, using theodolites, or by radar, in which case the balloon appears as a target on the radar screen. Radar tracking has one enormous advantage over visual tracking: the balloon can be followed even though it rises out of sight above the clouds.

If the purpose of the ascent was to measure temperature and humidity, the initial practice was to chase the balloon so as to be on hand when the instruments descended or to hope that someone would find the instruments and turn them in. Now a radiosonde is used—an airborne instrument which contains a radio transmitter that sends out signals giving the temperature, humidity, and pressure values at periodic intervals. The balloon can be tracked visually, by radar, or by radio direction finders that can be kept trained on the balloon's transmitter. The instruments themselves are tiny elements of ingenious design, consisting of a bimetallic strip for measuring temperature, a metal aneroid barometer, and a coated metal measuring device whose electrical resistance varies with the humidity.

Even before the radiosonde was developed, information was being obtained from different sources about the nature of the upper atmosphere, to heights that were not to be reached until modern rockets and satellites came into being. This information was obtained indirectly, in remarkably ingenious ways. It led to knowledge that was at least sufficiently accurate to permit the successful design of rockets and satellites many years later. It profoundly altered the scientific concept of the nature of the stratosphere and of the ionosphere beyond.

In 1918, at the end of World War I, it was supposed that the stratosphere and ionosphere were very cold and that the atmosphere as a whole was not more than fifty to a hundred miles deep. There were a few disquieting bits of knowledge that did not fit this concept, such as the known existence of at least one charged layer in the ionosphere and the observations of auroral lights at great heights; but not enough was known about these phenomena to refute the concept of a shallow atmosphere of quite simple structure, a concept that was supported by balloon observations to heights of 30,000 feet and more.

The first break-through occurred as a direct result of World War I. During the war it had been noted that the sound from a violent explosion behaved in a peculiar way. A large explosion was audible to everyone nearby in every direction; was inaudible to everyone at middle distances, within the circular zone from about thirty to fifty miles away; and then was audible, again, to those in a more distant zone, beyond fifty miles.

The only explanation was that the sound waves from the explosion must have traveled outward and upward through the first zone of audibility and overhead above the inaudible zone, and that the waves must have been bent downward upon reaching the stratosphere and so returned to earth within the outer zone of audibility. Yet if such downward bending occurred, the stratospheric air must be at a high rather than a low temperature to produce the necessary refraction.

Acoustical studies conducted after the war confirmed this view. At the same time, Lindemann and Dobson were studying the behavior of meteors, and their results also favored a high temperature zone in the stratosphere. After these earliest indirect studies, the new findings were further supported and elaborated upon by indirect observations of several different kinds.

Great advances were made in the spectroscopic analysis of the light of the aurora and of the light emitted during the nighttime by air particles at great heights. New methods were developed for bouncing radio waves off the charged layers of the ionosphere and so learning more about air density, temperature, and composition at heights of fifty miles and more. Observations of cosmic rays and of geomagnetism contributed still more indirect information.

Thus by World War II, during which the first very high altitude rockets were designed, at least some information was available about the general structure of the atmosphere to heights of 100 miles. It was known that the middle stratosphere was, like the lower ionosphere, at very high temperatures, and that the atmospheric density was much greater at these heights than had ever before been supposed. This knowledge was accordingly "written in" in the design of the first modern rockets.

The rockets and satellites that today probe the atmosphere are providing many kinds of new information. So recent is this observational program that it is still in an experimental stage and will remain so for many years to come since both the vehicles themselves and the instruments and communications devices they carry are undergoing constant improvement. Yet, as in the recent discovery of the radiation belts, important observational data have already been obtained and highly ingenious instruments and communications systems have been successfully employed. Some of the accomplishments thus far make it clear that a new era of atmospheric exploration has begun and that in the coming decades the entire ocean of air will begin really to be known for the first time, in all its physical complexity.

Observations from Rockets and Satellites

The rocket was invented more than 2,000 years ago. It has been used as an instrument of war for over 500 years. Yet it was not until the present century that the rocket came to be viewed in a serious scientific sense as the one vehicle that could probe the atmosphere to tremendous heights, far above the heights that might be reached either by balloons or by such missiles as artillery shells. This realization resulted largely from the work of Robert H. Goddard, the American physicist, whose research studies and rocket experiments over a period of more than twenty-five years laid the foundation for modern rocketry. Many of Goddard's ideas and techniques were employed in the development of such rockets as the German V-2, during World War II. And it was these wartime rockets that were first used for atmospheric exploration immediately after the war.

The first rocket observation techniques were relatively simple. They involved flights to modest heights only—less than 100 miles. They involved such observations as obtaining photographs of cloud systems and the earth beneath, taking of air samples, and measurement of cosmic-ray intensities, using devices such as the Geiger counter. In the beginning, just as with the sounding balloon fifty years before, the observations were parachuted to earth. Afterward, radio communication systems were installed that permitted the monitoring of observations while the rocket was in flight.

By the time of the International Geophysical Year such great advances had been made that it was possible to plan a comprehensive observational program. The IGY extended from July, 1957, through December, 1958. It was a period when countries all over the world joined in making hundreds of different kinds of observations of the nature and behavior of the solid earth, the oceans, and the atmosphere, following an elaborate observational schedule that had been worked out in advance and that covered wide regions of the earth, from pole to pole. So far as the rocket portion of the program was concerned, seven countries participated. These were Australia, Canada, France, Japan, the U.S.S.R., the United Kingdom, and the United States. The program envisaged the launching of rocket satellites, and this phase began on October 4, 1957, with the launching of Sputnik I. This satellite and the others that followed had a great advantage over rockets that were used just as probes, along a single-line track reaching upward; for satellites remain in orbit for weeks, months, or even years, and so permit continuous observations along paths that traverse the atmosphere through many different regions the world around.

During the IGY and in the time since, rocket probes and rocket satellites have obtained and relayed to earth observations of air temperature; cosmic rays; meteor sizes and frequencies; the intensity of the magnetic field; the concentration of charged particles; spectrographs of the sun, the aurora, and the glow of the night sky; and many other physical properties of the regions of the very high atmosphere. Grenades have been exploded from rockets, and the transmission of sound waves downward from these small explosions have been analyzed to provide information on air density and temperature. Metal confetti has been released and tracked by radar during its descent to learn more about the winds at great heights. Nuclear bombs have been exploded and the spread of electrons around the earth has been observed and interpreted to give a better understanding of the electromagnetic environment of the ocean of air.

The very movements of rockets and satellites provide information on such items as air density, because vehicles are slowed down either more or less by the thickness of the air. The satellite radio signals also provide direct information quite aside from the data they transmit, because in traveling from the satellite to the surface of the earth the radio waves are bent more or less, depending on the depth and nature of the intervening charged layers of the ionosphere.

The observational data obtained during the IGY and afterward are still being analyzed. They are so voluminous and their interpretation is so much slower than the data-taking that there is and always will be a lag in comprehension. There is, however, also the excellent possibility of obtaining and using a few simple kinds of observational information on a current basis. This possibility is well represented by the information from what has been called the "weather rocket."

The first weather rocket was launched on December 5, 1958. It was designed specifically to photograph cloud systems over a wide area. The rocket carried a gun-sight camera and used sensitive film with a red filter. Taking continuous pictures for not quite four minutes, the camera turned slowly over and over during descent and so alternately recorded views of the clouds across a vast area beneath and of the sun above. It obtained excellent cloud shots from heights between about sixty and ninety miles.

The advantage of the weather rocket is that it can detect the cloud systems associated with major storms that lie across regions where there are few weather observations, such as uninhabited polar lands and the oceans. Even more valuable will be weather satellites, which can be programed to patrol the skies on a regular basis and to send their photographic findings back to earth as radio signals. This will eliminate the expense of recovering camera capsules, although the photographic information received will not be as precise as if the photographs were actually recovered and viewed directly. Indeed, when a weather satellite is developed it will not produce a photographic film at all, but will scan the clouds and earth beneath with a television camera which will then directly transmit the required visual information.

The significance of cloud observations and of all the other kinds of observations from rockets and satellites is still not certain. But it *is* certain that among them they will permit a further extension, on a major scale, of the knowledge of the nature of the ocean of air. And it is equally certain that in time this new knowledge will lead to improved weather forecasts at the surface of the earth, where the majority of mankind will continue to live for untold centuries, as well as to the development of a closely related technology: the forecasting of "weather" for all parts of the air ocean, even upward to its very surface, some 18,000 miles away.

12 Weather Forecasting

Few technologic achievements would be a greater boon to mankind than development of a method for making perfect weather forecasts. If there was such a method, the farmer could prepare for droughts, ships at sea could avoid hurricanes, reservoirs could be emptied well in advance to prepare to receive and hold the waters from excessive floods, and the sportsman could plan with confidence for a week end of perfect skiing weather in the mountains. Unfortunately, perfect weather forecasting is impossible and always will be impossible.

To many people it is puzzling why this should be so. After all, the astronomer can forecast an eclipse centuries in advance. Why, therefore, cannot a meteorologist make perfect forecasts a week, or at least a day, in advance? He cannot do so simply because weather is determined by scores of different kinds of physical events that take place at different rates in different parts of an atmosphere that is by no means uniform, but differs from place to place in water-vapor content, density, transparency, and many other ways. In contrast, eclipses are determined solely by the motions of three astronomical bodies: the earth, the moon, and the sun. Weather forecasting is at least as difficult as forecasting the behavior of the stock market; and, just as in forecasting the behavior of stocks, it is far more difficult to make predictions one week in advance than to make them a day in advance, and virtually impossible to do more than make an intelligent guess as to what the conditions will be a year hence.

For technologic reasons, it is usual to distinguish among several kinds of weather forecasts, each of which poses somewhat different prediction problems. There are short-range forecasts, which are generally for periods not more than forty-eight hours in advance. Extended forecasts, on the other hand, cover longer prediction periods. There are general weather forecasts, such as those printed in newspapers and broadcast by radio, and these require the prediction of rain or snow, high winds, storms, and other weather elements that are important in planning activities of many different kinds. There are many different special forecasts, such as those for agriculture or for floods, and these require only that certain specific conditions be forecast. One special forecast, useful to aviation and to civil-defense officials concerned with what the fallout pattern will be should a nuclear bomb hit their area tomorrow, requires only the prediction of wind conditions aloft, at levels well above the earth's surface. This type of forecast is of particular interest because it is the only one that has proved sufficiently simple to be solved by machine computer methods. Other forecasts, especially general ones, still require the talents of an experienced weather forecaster.

The Weather Map

The weather map is the one absolute link between weather observations and weather forecasting. It shows the geographic relations that are the essence of the shifting, changing weather. It gives the shapes of weather systems upon an earth comprised of oceans, continents, mountains, hills, and plains. Even when it is not actually drawn upon an actual base map, but instead is visualized within the brain of a map-minded forecaster, the weather map is by far the single most important tool in weather forecasting.

There are several kinds of weather maps. They vary chiefly as to the height levels they represent. There is the surface map, upon which is plotted the observations at the level of the sea or solid ground. There are also maps that show conditions at various pressure heights. It is common, for example, to use a map that shows the conditions at heights where the air pressure is 700 millibars, about seven-tenths that at sea level. The 700-millibar map closely represents the conditions at an actual height of 10,000 feet above sea level. Similarly,

500-millibar and 300-millibar maps are commonly drawn; these correspond to heights of about 18,000 and 30,000 feet.

Among these maps, by far the most important in everyday weather forecasting is the surface map. The character of this map and the ways in which it comes into being illustrate the nature of all kinds of weather maps and show how they are formulated. They also illustrate the paramount role of the observer, who fundamentally makes the forecast possible, and show some of the ways in which he goes about his tasks.

At first glance a full-fledged weather map is a confusion of symbols and figures. Here are long sweeping lines in red, blue, and purple; there is one of alternating red and blue dashes. Here are areas of shaded green and a few green triangles and commas. There are black, curving lines, some of which turn back upon themselves to form closed ovals, others of which run off the edges of the map. In the background, forming an uneven polka-dot pattern, are hundreds of tightly packed groups of numbers and symbols, each group clustered around a tiny circle. Viewed at a distance or through squinting eyes, the surface weather map looks not unlike a painting by a symbolist.

Look again at the map, but this time through the eyes of a weatherman. The blue lines become the leading edges of cold air butting into warm. The red lines show where warm air slides upward over cold. The purple line is a fragment of a shattered, twisted front squeezed upward into the middle air. The red-blue line is cold air, standing next to warm, neither moving. Green shading: steady rain. Green triangles: heavy showers, splashing water downward by the ton. Green commas: drizzle. As for the black lines, they show air pressure. Here is a group of concentric ovals surrounding a HIGH pressure area. There is a LOW. Toward the bottom of the map there are no closed pressure areas at all, just a general region of LOW pressure, the pressure decreasing southward.

What of the figures and symbols grouped around this or that small circle within an area no larger than a dime? Each group tells a story of weather at a particular station—a story that is amazingly complete. *Temperature 68°. Dew point 56°. Sky half-covered with clouds. Ceiling unlimited. Visibility 7–10 miles. Puffball cumulus clouds at 800–1,000 feet, moving from the northeast. Middle layered stratus*

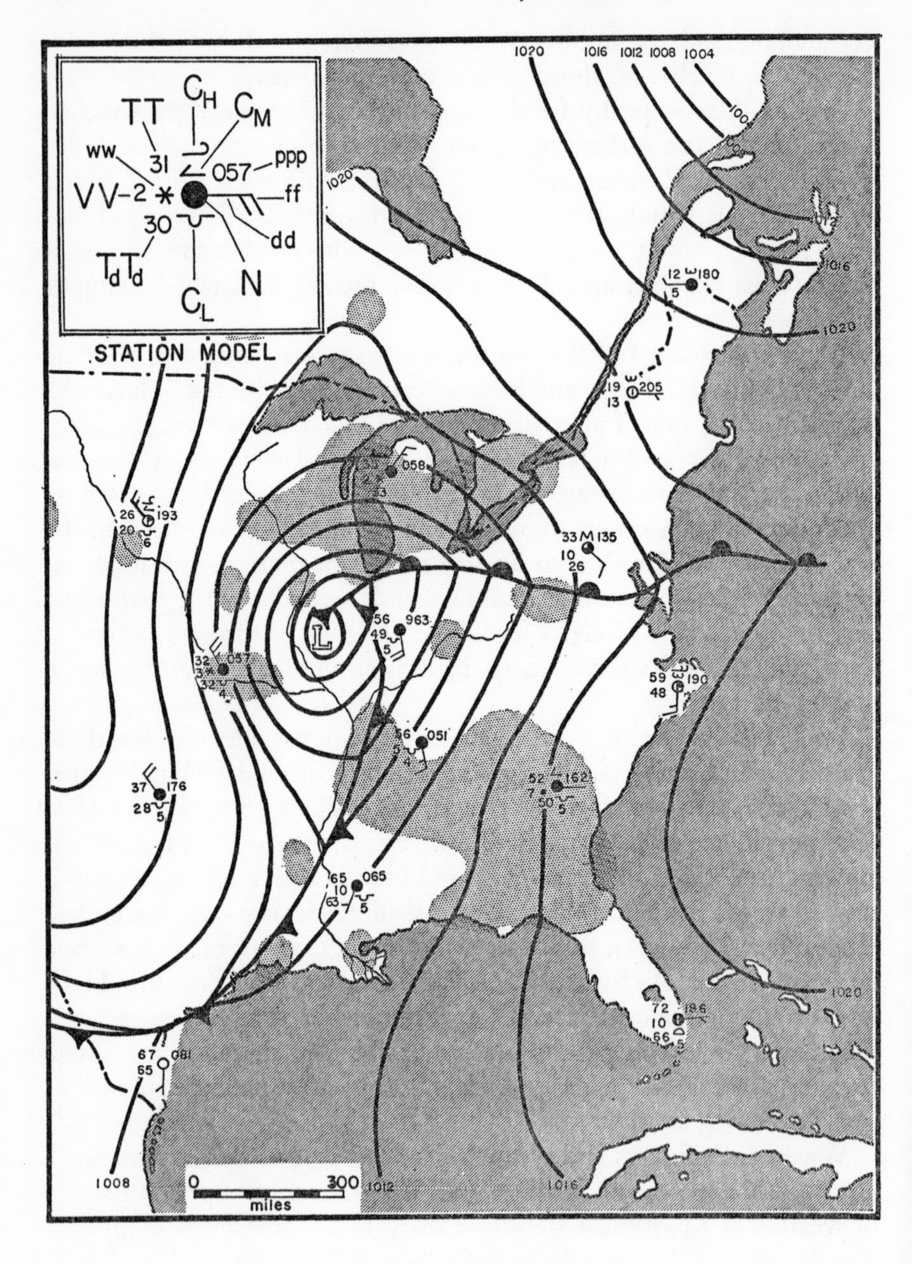
STATION MODEL
TT
C_H
C_M
ww
31
057
ppp
VV-2
ff
30
dd
T_dT_d
N
C_L
1020
1016
1012
1008
1004
L
miles
0
300
1008
1012
1016

SECTION OF A WEATHER MAP

Weather Map of Eastern United States, 6 A.M. Greenwich Time, March 15, 1959. This simplified map shows a storm system (LOW) that is yielding considerable rain and snow. It is based on an actual U.S. Weather Bureau map, which, being more detailed, showed about twice as much weather information for each station and included about five times the number of stations shown here. Shaded areas indicate where precipitation was occurring at map time. Lines without triangles or semicircles connect points of equal sea-level air pressure, and the values at the ends of these lines are in millibars (average yearly value at sea level for the United States: 1013 millibars). The line with semicircles is a warm front; that with triangles, a cold front. The abbreviations in the Station Model are as follows: *ppp,* sea-level pressure in tens and tenths of millibars (thus 057 equals 1005.7 millibars); *ff,* wind speed in knots, with each full barb representing 10 knots and each half barb 5; *dd,* direction from which wind is blowing, as shown by orientation of arrow (from east in the model); *N,* tenths of total sky covered by cloud; T_dT_d, dewpoint temperature; *VV,* visibility in sixteenths of a mile up to 10 miles, after which values are omitted; *ww,* present weather, for which there are 100 symbols, of which two generalized ones are shown here: a dot for rain and a star for snow; *TT,* temperature; C_H, C_M, and C_L are high, middle, and low cloud forms, with the partly curved symbols representing different kinds of cumulus-type clouds and the flat-based symbols different kinds of stratus-type clouds.

clouds moving from the east. No upper clouds. Surface wind 8–12 knots from the north-northeast. Air pressure 1,012.4 millibars. Air pressure has risen steadily .9 millibar in the last three hours. Trace of rain in last six hours. No rain at present time but lightning sighted in distance. All this information is in an area no larger than a dime. And there is equally detailed information for three or four hundred other stations, not to mention special data from some forty stations on conditions in the upper atmosphere.

No wonder a weatherman, looking at such maps, at hundreds of them, month after month and year after year, gets so that he can "see" the weather on the move. He sees the surging masses of warm and cold air, of moist and dry air, overrunning mountains, flowing down river valleys, draining off the land and onto the sea. He sees them collide and climb one atop the other, stacking up two and three deep. He sees thunderstorms well up, tornadoes whirl across the land, hurricanes build and move, clouds bank up across the sky, and winds come whipping in. He visualizes all this in three dimensions on an earth that curves away to east and west and north and south with air piled up across it. In three dimensions he sees the winds and weathers not only as they vary across the land and water from Peoria, Illinois, to New York to Kidderminster, England, but also as they vary from 1,000 to 5,000 to 30,000 feet at height within the atmosphere.

The earth rotates on its axis once every twenty-four hours. As it does, the sun, which is the timepiece of the world, in effect moves round the earth from east to west so that time everywhere is never the same. When it is midnight in London it is 5 A.M. in Calcutta, noon at Suva in the Fijis, and 9 P.M. in New York. Regardless of what time it may be in this place or that, the weather observations that appear on the surface weather map must all be taken at the same time to give a true synoptic picture. So by international agreement all standard weather maps carry observations taken at 0000, 0600, 1200, and 1800 Greenwich time. When the master clock at the Greenwich Observatory, just outside London, reads one of these times, it is as though a world-wide signal had been sounded. Then weather observers everywhere—in the gray of early morning, in the glare of high noon, in the blackness of late nighttime—start reading the weather.

Uneventful and dull, or eventful and even dangerous, either way the story of the weather observer is there for the reading in the symbols and figures on the weather map. At several hundred land stations, at a dozen weather ships, on a score of merchantmen, out along the half-dozen weather-plane routes, on the commercial airlines where navigators act as weather observers—at all these places, in storm, calm, heat, cold, and every other imaginable weather, observers carry out their duties to provide the information that results in the weather map. They start at the click of a clock in Greenwich, England. They record and tabulate their findings. Then communications men take over. By radio, telephone, teletype, and telegraph the weather messages funnel in to weather collecting centers.

These centers collate the reports they have gathered. Out the reports go in the form of "weather collectives": lists of reports covering the weather of a general region. Ottawa sends out the Northeast Canada Collective. Chicago handles the Midwest. London handles all of Great Britain. From Berlin, Paris, Rome, Los Angeles, Cairo, Buenos Aires, Sydney, and twoscore other major cities, four times a day, come lists of weather reports. Onto the weather teletype circuits they come and into the offices of the weather forecasters—from the part-time forecaster at Paducah Airfield, whose chief responsibility is to pass on to pilots the official Weather Bureau forecast, to the forecaster in Chicago, who must issue several dozen kinds of forecasts covering all or part of the Middle West.

Weather maps are drawn at all major weather forecast offices. A specially trained clerk plots the map from the collective lists fed in by teletype. He works with amazing rapidity. In forty to fifty minutes he must plot the reports from over 200 stations—a task requiring the writing of over 3,000 symbols read at a glance from the code reports and written in a small, neat hand. By his labors he is summing up on one piece of paper the work of some 2,000 weather observers and communications men. All of their work was directed toward this end so that a view of the weather would be available to the forecaster.

The weather forecaster will analyze the plotted map. He will prepare additional charts and aids, such as upper-air weather maps and diagrams showing the vertical structure of the air at selected places. He will consult the supplemental hourly weather reports arriving from certain key weather stations. Finally, he will make his prediction. If he makes it well, it is to his credit as well as to the credit of the thousands of men who helped to "draw" the weather map and subsidiary charts. If he makes it poorly, only he is to blame.

The Human Factor

Jones was an outstanding forecaster, surely among the twenty best in the world. His scientific background was first-rate, but there are hundreds of practicing forecasters with better. His intuitive judgment was uncanny, but so is the judgment of several dozen other forecasters. His temperament was unexcelled.

There is something impressive about the temperament required of a really superior forecaster. He must look at the last several weather maps. He must draw on his knowledge and intuition to analyze properly the weather map at hand: to draw in the fronts, the pressure lines, the whole synoptic view of the weather. Then, without hesitating or hedging or thinking of consequences, he must draw on a map or in his mind a picture of the weather to come and must make an irrevocable forecast. He must ignore the fact that if he is wrong, some ship may go down at sea or a friend may crash while trying to get into San Francisco Airport. He must detach himself completely from any thought of consequences. If he cannot do this, he will never be a really good forecaster.

Jones was really good, but even the best forecaster is wrong occasionally. In weather forecasting there is no such thing as perfection. Jones was one of two AAF forecasters solely responsible for calling the turn of the weather for bomber raids in a major wartime theater. Every other day when his turn came up he would make his forecast, then brief the top brass on the weather situation. Forecasting in an area entirely new to him, he displayed surprising skill for two solid months. Where Smith, the forecaster with whom he alternated, would worry and hedge, Major Jones would call them as he saw them. Time and again Smith would play it safe, and so a primary target would be ignored in favor of some secondary target; yet it would turn out that the primary target might have been hit. Jones called them close to the line and with great accuracy. But there is no such a thing as perfect forecasting—and that is where temperament comes in.

"Bombing conditions will be visual at Target A. Cloud tops en route and return will extend to 17,000 feet. Route conditions wholly operational, but aircraft will have to fly close to their ceilings to maintain formation." That was the forecast issued by Major Jones; and in issuing it, he assigned to the forecast a high confidence rating.

Target A was a juicy melon that weather-wise had luckily avoided being hit for a long time. With the weather outlook still favorable, the generals decided to lay on the heavy attack.

In the predawn darkness of the next day the planes took off. Two hundred miles en route, the cloud tops started rising. The planes climbed to 18,000 feet, and then to 20,000. Still the clouds ahead towered even higher. The planes struggled upward to 22,000. Then they were surrounded by clouds. The neat formations split up. Six or eight planes collided. Of the 500 ships that started out, only 300 reached the target; the rest turned back or got hopelessly lost, so that crews decided to bail out rather than crash-land.

Major Jones could read the score: "30 planes, 240 men, missing because of weather." The report might just as well have said, "Because of Major Jones."

A serious forecast error cannot be forgotten. Ten years after, in the midst of other things, at a place 5,000 miles away, some combination of random thoughts will awaken Jones's memory. He will find himself thinking, sweating out a forecast ten years dead, seeing suddenly with superclarity the look on the face of the general who sat in the first row when he next appeared to brief the brass after that forecast bust.

Mistakes will happen, and the good forecaster comes to realize that they are unavoidable. If he has the right temperament, he will be able to go on turning out top-notch forecasts in spite of occasional blunders.

Waiting out difficult forecasts is bad enough for an old hand at the business, but it is particularly hard on new forecasters. Many of them give up then and there or take to hedging their forecasts so badly that they cannot hold down their jobs. Many forecasters who are excellent in practice forecasting are not worth much in actual operations, especially when the forecast obviously involves human lives, as in military forecasting, airline work, and hurricane forecasting.

Proper supervision is all-important in breaking in a novice forecaster. The senior forecaster must train his new men technically. He must build their self-confidence. He must know them so well that he can tell precisely when to put them on their own. If he is wrong in his timing, the senior forecaster will have on his hands a man who fails because he either is not ready to accept responsibility or has lost confidence through relying on the senior forecaster for too long.

No one is better at breaking in new forecasters than Charlie Stiefelmeyer, Senior Forecaster for Pan American Airways' Pacific Division. No one is better at nursing along a neophyte who lacks skill or confidence. No one is better at brusquely dumping that neophyte on his own when he is ready to perform.

In 1944 Pan American was flying the Pacific under contract to the Navy and handling the forecasting not only for its own planes but for the Naval Air Transport Service also. In June of that year they acquired a new man whose theoretical background was adequate and who seemed to be all right temperamentally, but who never had done any forecasting, practice or otherwise. So they put him through three months of intensive practice forecasting and then flew him out to Charlie, who was holding down the job of Chief Forecaster for the South Pacific, south of the line.

For six weeks Charlie worked with the new man, checking his forecasts, giving him hints, explaining the peculiarities of weather behavior in the crazy equatorial regions where the trade winds of the hemispheres converge to form the intertropical front. Then at lunch one day Charlie said, "Beginning tonight, Jim, you'll take the mid-watch. Thereafter you'll be on regular watch in the usual rotation from mid, to daytime, to swing—seven days on and one off." That was in the New Hebrides at Espiritu Santo.

From Espiritu the transport-plane routes led south and west and east: south to New Zealand, west to Brisbane, Australia, east to Funafuti and Canton Island before turning north to Hawaii. The weather was relatively easy to forecast for the run south to New Zealand and west to Australia, but east to Funafuti-Canton was apt to become nasty. The explosively moist, unstable air just south of the line could kick up stormy weather and seas in no time at all. The mid-watch handled the eastbound run that left at dawn.

Funafuti is a coral atoll eight degrees south of the line in mid-Pacific. The main island itself is a strip of land of ridiculously small dimensions, considering that in 1942 it had been a basing point of major importance. But it was not the mile-long strip of land that was so important; it was the twelve-mile-wide lagoon protected by circular coral reefs on all sides but the northwest, where a broad channel led to open sea. In terms of what the mid-Pacific had to offer, the lagoon was an excellent harbor for ships and seaplanes. By late 1944, Funafuti had become an island by-passed by the war. It remained important chiefly as a stopping-off and refueling point for aircraft. There was no better landing place in the South Pacific for the seaplanes of the Naval Air Transport Service and Pan American than the broad waters of Funafuti lagoon.

The en route forecast seemed simple: moderate easterly winds at flight level, shifting to northeasterly as Funafuti was approached, with a couple of patches of not-too-stormy weather. But what about the winds at Funafuti itself? A six-hour-old report from Kwajalein, far to the north, seemed to indicate that the wind at Funafuti might shift to the northwest before the plane arrived. If that happened, the long-sweeping wind would pound the waves inward through the entrance of Funafuti lagoon and make for a seaplane landing that would be dangerously rough at the very least.

Jim argued with himself for five minutes, then decided definitely that the winds would go into the northwest. But when? Before or after arrival? Mentally he gauged the pace of the shifting weather, scribbling faint pencil lines on the map to help him visualize the progressive changes. Then he made some quick calculations. With his forecast winds the plane should reach Funafuti in five and a half hours. The wind should not shift to northwest until three hours after the plane reached Funafuti. That was figuring things unpleasantly close, particularly considering that much of the analysis hung on a lone weather report from Kwajalein.

He cursed the fact that Tarawa and Jaluit had not reported in. After all, between Kwajalein and Funafuti lay over a thousand miles of water without a single reporting station. He went through his reasoning again. Again came the answer: the plane would have about three hours to spare. That was too close for comfort. It was much too close for an inexperienced forecaster like himself. He decided to wake Charlie and have him take a look at the map.

The Chief Forecaster's reaction when he awoke was explosive: "Listen, you! When I put anyone on watch it's because he can, should, and will handle the watch. Get out of here."

The plane went out on Jim's forecast. Jim fretted by the teletype to get any stray weather reports that might be of help. Three hours out, the plane would reach the point of no return. Three and a half hours out, it would pass the point where it could still divert to Wallis Island, 150 miles off track, the only alternate for a seaplane headed for Funafuti. If within three to three and a half hours it became clear that Funafuti would close to seaplanes before estimated arrival time, it might still be possible to radio the plane to return or divert. No helpful weather reports arrived.

Finally came the report that the plane had landed safely. Then, a scant hour later, another report came through: FUNAFUTI CLOSED TO SEAPLANES. WINDS NORTHWEST. STATE OF SEA FIVE. WILL ADVISE WHEN AGAIN OPERATIONAL.

Charlie never referred to the incident of the night before. He never had to. Jim's temperament as a forecaster had been proved.

The Funafuti wind forecast illustrates two general principles. Even though weather behaves in more regular fashion over the smooth oceans than over the wrinkled continents, weather forecasting over the oceans is fully as difficult as over the lands because of the scarcity of weather reports. Where the continental forecaster has several hundred reports, the ocean forecaster has but a few score from scattered islands, merchantmen, weather ships, and planes.

The forecast illustrates, too, the importance of judging the rate of change of the shifting weather. Ninety-five times out of a hundred, the weather forecaster can give the correct answer on *what* will happen. The real question is *when* it will happen. When will it rain? When will the winds shift? When will the hurricane reach the Florida coast? When will the cold front come through, dropping the temperature from a mild 40° down to 22°?

To answer the question "when," and the co-ordinate questions "what" and "where," the forecaster needs not only the proper temperament but also scientific knowledge and intuition. Without the temperament he will not be a good forecaster. Without the knowledge he will not be a forecaster at all.

Knowledge and Intuition

Knowledge is acquired in three principal ways: through formal training, through informal study, and through actual experience. The knowledge required for weather forecasting is no exception. Most forecasters have had formal training in meteorology and forecasting at universities, colleges, or trade schools. Many, including several of the best, have learned through individual study and by trial and error through actual experience.

Whatever his source of knowledge, a forecaster learns many things. He learns that if the polar winds behind a cold front are driving straight outward, the front will move with the speed of the cold wind; whereas if the polar winds are edging outward, the front will move at only a fraction of the wind speed. He learns that at the western edge of oceanic HIGHS in the Northern Hemisphere, the winds veer aloft so that if winds at the ground are southerly they become southwesterly and then westerly with increasing height. He learns how to calculate when fog will form on clear, cold nights; how to recognize a hurricane in the making; how to plot a simple diagram that shows whether moist, warm air will breed a thunderstorm; how to estimate the rate of movement of a cyclone; and how to outguess the weather in a hundred other ways. A few of the rules he learns are invariably true. Many of them are true most of the time. Some of them are seldom true at all because there is still a wide gap between the weather as it should behave according to theory and as it actually behaves.

A competent forecaster uses the tools and knowledge provided by the science of meteorology; but he uses them with caution. The rules, charts, formulas, and other paraphernalia of formal science are excellent in theory. In practice they often break down. The forecaster therefore applies his scientific knowledge and rules unless or until he senses that they are leading him astray. Then, seemingly without reason, he may arrive at an answer that scientifically is not indicated at all. Such answers rest wholly on intuition.

Every successful weather forecaster relies to a large degree on intuition. Every once in a while he *knows* that the weather is going to develop in a certain way, and yet he cannot explain how he arrives at this knowledge. Nothing is learned by trying to pry an explanation from a forecaster who has made an intuitive decision.

At a gathering of meteorologists at the Massachusetts Institute of Technology a number of years ago, there was considerable discussion concerning the daily weather forecast. It was midwinter, and the forecast for the New England area hinged on the behavior of a cold front that was moving in from the west. The front had been sweeping along at a steady 30 m.p.h. pace. If it continued its steady advance, it would move across New England the next morning, there would be a brief snow flurry, the temperature would drop, and then the weather would "clean out," becoming clear and cold. Nothing on the weather map clearly indicated that the front would not continue to roll along. Therefore the forecaster from the Institute, who was in charge of the forecast discussion, made some straightforward calculations as to rate of frontal movement and predicted cold, clear weather for the following afternoon. A visiting forecaster took sharp exception. He predicted that warm air driving against the cold would produce a wave along the cold front, causing it to stall over New England. According to him, New England was in for a three-day blizzard.

"Where do you get that from?"

"Well, I don't like the look of these pressure tendencies down here."

"What about them? The pressure's falling sharply, isn't it?"

"Yes. But taken in conjunction with the winds here at Scranton . . ."

And so the two argued back and forth. At no time was it possible to get a definite answer from the forecaster who was calling for a blizzard. He didn't like the look of this; or something looked strange; anyhow, the thing just didn't look right.

The next day New England got its blizzard, which lasted just three days.

Many forecasters believe that intuitive judgments are derived from unconscious memory of previous weather situations. They believe that, without being wholly conscious of the fact, the forecaster who makes a supposedly unreasoning judgment is really remembering some similar weather situation that confronted him months or years before. Quite likely this is often true. Certainly the mind retains many more impressions and much more information than is contained in the realm of conscious awareness. And certainly such "near-conscious" thoughts can be drawn upon without well-defined conscious knowledge of what the underlying thoughts are.

But there may be some other factor at work also, something in the nature of a hunch. If intuition in forecasting was solely a matter of unconscious memory, it would be difficult to explain how a novice forecaster with but a few weeks' experience could suddenly "know" that the weather was going to violate all usual rules, even though he had never before seen anything like the weather situation depicted on his map. Yet novice forecasters have had such hunches, and the weather itself has vindicated their judgments.

A man who never uses intuition is not a good forecaster. For this reason theoretical meteorologists are rarely good forecasters. They insist on complete and absolute logic. They hold that weather predictions can be worked out precisely on a mathematical basis. When they fail, which is quite often, they usually blame their failures on lack of sufficient time to make all required calculations or on lack of comprehensive or sufficiently accurate observations. Occasionally they see that the accepted theory is not wholly adequate, and then they revise that theory accordingly. In this manner, some progress has certainly been made in forecasting, but that progress has been dishearteningly slow.

The past three decades have witnessed impressive advances in theoretical meteorology, but little advance in the accuracy of weather forecasting. The weather is too complex and gigantic to fit closely any theories yet devised. A forecaster with minimum scientific knowledge but with keen intuition can still turn out far better weather predictions than can a highly logical scientist who has studied and fully understands all the latest meteorological theories but is completely lacking in intuitive judgment.

The ultimate in scientific forecasting is represented in the work of L. F. Richardson of England, who set out to make a weather forecast entirely on the basis of mathematical calculation. As an astronomer calculates the predicted position of a comet, using the equations of celestial mechanics, so Richardson calculated the predicted weather, using the numerous complex equations that described the behavior of the atmosphere. It took him several years to set up and solve all the various mathematical equations required for his forecast, but Richardson eventually completed his calculations and arrived at a forecast that was reasonably accurate.

Until something over a decade ago, Richardson's work remained merely a mathematical curiosity. Obviously, it was impractical to take several years making a forecast of tomorrow's weather. Then came the development of electronic calculators. These amazing machines, such as that developed by the Radio Corporation of America at Princeton, can handle as many as 2,000 calculations per second. They also have memory devices that permit them to retain the numerical answer to an equation and to re-enter that number into later calculations at any desired point and in any desired manner. With such machines it became possible for the first time to envisage making weather forecasts, at least of limited kinds, without a human forecaster.

Machine Forecasting

Richardson's work set the stage for machine weather forecasting; and after World War II, he and Jules Charney, at the Institute for Advanced Studies at Princeton, led the way in developing and refining new mathematical models of the atmosphere to make machine forecasting possible.

In a practical sense, what was needed was a battery of equations that could be "set up" in a machine so that when observational data were entered, the machine could solve the equations and produce a series of answers that would predict what the weather conditions would be at many different points in the atmosphere after a specified period of time. In theoretical terms, what was needed was a model of the atmosphere, expressed mathematically, that was sufficiently simple to be worked out, yet sufficiently sophisticated to result in predictions that would be at least as accurate as those of a human forecaster.

Virtually all of the postwar work on this problem, by Richardson, Charney, and many others, was devoted to formulating models that would permit the prediction of the density-pressure field and of the resulting winds. To do this it was necessary to make many simplifying assumptions. Whereas the atmosphere is really a compressible medium of great complexity and is not at all homogeneous as regards density, water-vapor content, and many other properties, it was necessary to assume that it was composed of just one, or one and one-half, or two, or three different layers, each of which was essentially uniform. Then, using the greatly simplified and idealized equations developed initially for the behavior of such simple fluids as water, and modifying these equations only slightly, it was necessary to work out relations between the state of the atmosphere at a given moment and its state at some later interval, such as twenty-four hours afterward.

Through proceeding in this way, the necessary equations were worked out. Now it is possible to forecast by machine what the wind and pressure-density conditions will be twenty-four hours hence at height within the troposphere, and to do so with a degree of accuracy that is greater than that achieved by most human forecasters.

There are those who believe that some day mathematical models will be improved to such an extent that it will be possible to make general weather forecasts by machine—forecasts of rain, snow, hail, droughts, heat waves, and other kinds of weather immediately important to people everywhere. They hope and believe the day will come when all incoming weather observations will be fed electronically into a computer that will automatically type out the weather forecast an hour or so later.

This vision is an attractive one, but it is contrary to all that is known about the enormous complexity of atmospheric behavior. Probably the human weather forecaster, despite his frailties, will always be depended upon for most kinds of weather predictions. He will surely continue to prepare and issue at least general forecasts for many years to come. And in doing so, he probably will follow procedures that will not differ greatly from those he follows at the present time.

Forecast Procedures

The routine of weather forecasting as it is actually practiced varies in detail from one forecast office to another and from forecaster to forecaster at the same office. Yet, in general, procedures and the kinds of thinking that go into a forecast are the same.

When he first comes on duty, the forecaster spends half an hour or so catching up on the latest weather developments. Together with the outgoing forecaster, he goes over the most recent weather maps and special charts. They discuss the general weather trend and such scientific questions as the character of a moist-air mass that has started to travel inland, the speed with which a front is moving, or the chances of having sufficient nighttime cooling to produce fog. If the two forecasters differ in their views, they try to reach agreement. If they are unable to agree, the incoming forecaster wins out automatically. While he is on duty, it is up to him to interpret the weather as he sees it.

If his is the daytime forecast duty and this is a major forecast center charged with making regional predictions, the forecaster will have to work fast. In two hours he must have the forecasts ready for the first editions of the evening newspapers, which will be on the street by mid-afternoon. Six hours after that, at 4 P.M., he must be ready with another forecast in time to catch the late evening editions of the morning papers. In between times he must "sit on the forecast" so that if it becomes clear that the weather will depart from its predicted course, the forecast can be immediately changed.

Already the morning weather map is being plotted. The signals have been rolling in on two teletype machines that stand against the wall, next to the large drafting table on which the weather map is spread. An assistant tears a sheet of reports from a teletype machine, returns to the table, and rapidly plots the latest weather observations. Decoding the reports as he goes along and working with a fine-pointed pen, the assistant plots the observations at an average rate of a station each fifteen seconds, a dozen items or more for each station.

There is no time to wait for all the reports to come in, or even for those already in to be completely plotted. So the forecaster and his assistant work on the map simultaneously, the one studying and analyzing the map in those regions for which observations have already been plotted, the other filling in the blank spaces with his fast-moving pen. By the time all reports are in and the map is completely plotted—a process that takes some ninety minutes—the forecaster has already roughed out in pencil the position of the principal fronts, the pressure lines showing the location of HIGHS and LOWS, and such other special lines as may be helpful in understanding the particular weather situation.

One hour remains until forecast time. Before finishing his analysis of the surface weather map, the forecaster goes to the latest upper-air maps, on which are plotted the wind and temperature observations at pressure heights of 700, 500, and 300 millibars. After sketching in the lines of equal pressure height and those of equal temperature, he studies the map for a few minutes to make certain that his analysis of the surface weather situation is borne out by conditions in the upper atmosphere. Then he returns to the surface map, makes an adjustment in the location of a front, and, working with an eraser in one hand and a pencil in the other, quickly completes his roughed-out map.

In thirty minutes the forecast is due. Now the forecaster focuses attention on the area for which he must predict the weather. This region occupies only a fraction of the area covered by the surface and upper-air maps. To clarify his thinking, he rapidly draws a predicted map, one showing what the weather in the region will look like six hours later. This front will move from here to here. That HIGH will weaken and be squeezed up into a ridgelike thing shaped like a rounded Greek letter *delta*. Pressure will fall here as the front approaches and warm air is pulled up ahead of it. This LOW will deepen. Because of all these factors, the weather map will look like this six hours hence.

Now for the forecast. Is this warm air sufficiently unstable to produce thunderstorms? The forecaster looks at the graph of a sounding that shows the temperature-moisture distribution from the ground up through the air in question. No. No thunderstorms here, just scattered cumulus. But over here there will be rain as the front comes through. And behind the front, in this area, the present cloudiness will clean out and the temperature will rise to a maximum of only 50° because the warmth from the afternoon sun will be almost balanced by the coolness of the polar air moving in from the northwest.

By such reasoning and cross-checking the forecaster pieces his prediction together:

> New Jersey, Delaware, and eastern New York: Increasing cloudiness late this afternoon, followed by moderate rains in the early evening. Clearing by midnight. Maximum temperature 60°–65°; nighttime minimum temperature 38°. Eastern Pennsylvania and central New York: Scattered showers in mid-afternoon, clearing by evening. Maximum temperature 50°–55°; minimum temperatures 28°–30° in valley locations, 30°–36° on uplands.

Before issuing his predictions, the forecaster checks the latest hourly weather reports to make certain that nothing unexpected is happening. Until it is time to start on the afternoon map analysis and forecast, he will continue to check the hourly reports, will supervise preparation of several special charts, and will make special forecasts as requested by telephone.

The business manager of the local college may wish a forecast for the following evening, when an outdoor musicale is planned. There will be several requests from amateur pilots for forecasts along a dozen different air routes. A construction company may phone to inquire whether tomorrow's weather will be suitable for laying cement. A local photographer wants to take some seascape pictures at dawn tomorrow. Will it be raining or cloudy and how will light conditions be? There will be fifty or more telephone inquiries of less importance that will usually be handled by one of the assistants. Questions such as these will all be answered as accurately as possible.

The most critical element in general weather prediction is analysis of the surface weather map. The surface map is the text from which is read the pace and character of the shifting weather. Upper-air maps and special charts provide important footnotes, but their chief function is to check the surface map. Any one map must show a reasonable picture. If the forecaster draws pressure lines that are packed closely together around a HIGH, showing that the pressure decreases rapidly from the center of the HIGH outward, the resulting pressure picture must be supported by observations of speedy winds, 40 m.p.h. or more. As a ball rolls faster down a steep incline than down a gentle one, so the winds move more speedily around a steep HIGH or LOW than around a gentle one.

In drawing a cold front on the map, the forecaster must place it properly with reference to wind speed, wind direction, cloudiness, pressure, precipitation, and temperature as shown by the plotted observations. Ahead of the front the pressure will be steady or falling; behind the front, steady or rising. If this is the Northern Hemisphere, ahead of the front the winds will be southerly to easterly; behind the front, westerly or northerly. In the area around the front there will often be cumulus or thunderstorm clouds. Showers may precede or accompany the front, but will not persist long once the front has passed. Factors such as these must quickly be inventoried and appraised in drawing the map.

One of the greatest difficulties in the preparation of general weather forecasts on an hour-to-hour, day-to-day basis is that the forecaster must work under considerable time pressure. When the forecast is a difficult one, he seldom has time to make all the analyses he would like to make.

In this respect his situation is different from that of the forecaster who makes extended predictions, for periods more than forty-eight hours in advance. When a forecast must be issued only once a week for the following week, or once a month for the following month, there is considerably more time in which to carry out many kinds of complex analyses. Because there is more time and because the extended-forecast problem is a special one, the techniques of extended forecasting differ greatly from those of short-range forecasting. These techniques, which are by no means standardized but differ from one school of practice to another, illustrate even better than does the short-range forecast the great complexity of weather prediction.

Extended Weather Forecasts

When the meteorologist uses the phrase "weather forecasting," he means a particular thing: the application of special techniques to make more accurate predictions than can be made through the use of climatological statistics alone. This distinction is highly important. It is, for example, possible to state with confidence that there will be no rain in San Francisco on July 15, 1990. In a general sense this is a weather forecast; but it is one that rests solely upon the analysis of the climatological record for San Francisco, which shows that the chances are more than twenty-five to one against having rain on July 15 in any particular year.

Climatological odds of this kind can be worked out for any location and for any aspect of the weather. Such statistics are useful for many practical purposes, as for designing water catchments in areas where rainfall must be relied upon to provide potable water, or designing storm drains in a modern city. The computation of climatological odds does not, however, constitute a weather forecast; to be successful, a true weather forecasting technique must give results that are distinctly better than those that would be obtained from climatic analysis alone.

As compared with climatological probabilities, extended-forecasting techniques have yielded significant positive results. In discussing this subject, Namias, who has long been the leader in the United States in the extended-forecast field, remarks that even though really reliable extended forecasts cannot be made, "medium-range forecasts covering periods from a few days to a week are already proving economically valuable in many countries," and "forecasts of general weather conditions for periods a month in advance have shown promise." There is, however, no proof that any forecasting technique can produce predictions of significant value for more than one month in advance.

The difference between the short-range and the extended-range forecast problems is best understood through an example. Suppose a major storm system is approaching the coast of British Columbia and Washington-Oregon from the west. The radius of the well-defined storm system is 350 miles and the center of the storm is 500 miles off the coast. It is early spring and the storm structure is complex, so that it carries with it not a well-defined surface front but a frontal discontinuity that has been squeezed high aloft and is riding slightly ahead of the storm center, while the following surface front is poorly marked and is more a zone of heavy rain than anything else. Farther to the west, between this storm and Hawaii, is a second storm system, smaller but more distinct. Still farther away, beyond Hawaii toward Japan, is a still smaller storm, which has just begun to form.

In this kind of situation the short-range forecaster who must predict conditions for the following day at Vancouver, Seattle, Portland, and other west-coast locations can concentrate almost exclusively on the major storm system immediately off the coast. In so doing, he can draw upon knowledge as to whether the storm movement has been accelerating or decelerating; whether or not the storm has begun to move northward, as it often does off the coast; whether or not the HIGH ridge of pressure just back of the coast is intensifying and so may tend to block out the storm; and upon many other important features whose trends have already been established. It is true that he must allow for sudden erratic behavior; but if he is an experienced forecaster, the chances are good that he will already have learned what the signs of such behavior usually are. Since such signs usually manifest themselves a day or so in advance, he is in an admirable position to make a forecast that will be correct at least as to general content.

Suppose, however, that the forecaster must predict what the weather will be a week hence. At once the difficulties are greatly compounded. If he attempts to apply the techniques of the short-range forecaster, he must decide what the course and development will be, not only of the major storm just off the coast and the HIGH over land that may block it out, but also of the second storm and the third one, far to westward. If he decides that the HIGH will develop and block out the first storm, he must decide further whether it will weaken and admit the second storm after the first one has sidled northward to the Gulf of Alaska. And maybe the slight HIGH ridge between the first and second storms will build up and cause the second storm to change course and move in over California rather than British Columbia and Washington-Oregon. All these and many other possibilities must be weighed. Even with considerable experience the forecaster might well find it difficult to predict what the weather would be two or three days hence, much less a week.

To develop extended-forecast techniques that did not involve becoming enmeshed in such sequences of detailed problems, it was necessary to take a much broader view of weather relations and their evolution. This was done on a modern basis for the first time in the nineteen-twenties and thirties, when Baur in Germany and Multanowski in the Soviet Union independently developed extended-forecasting systems that were similar in principle, though they differed considerably in detail.

Through the comparative study of thousands of daily weather maps, Baur and Multanowski concluded that the weather over large areas is often dominated continuously, for periods of five to seven days, by a few large pressure systems, such as the major LOW storm systems that frequently stagnate in the Iceland-Scandinavia area or the oceanic trade-wind HIGH that sometimes persists for many days as a pronounced ridge extending into the Mediterranean area. They realized that these systems often were strong determinants of the weather in areas hundreds of miles away, because the systems with their encircling wind flow helped set up and guide the major air currents on a grand scale. With a major LOW off Scandinavia, Atlantic air was shunted eastward across Germany and into Russia. With a LOW over the Arctic Sea, to the east northeast of Murmansk in summertime, cool air was shunted southward across Russia and the Baltic Sea.

Starting with such simple precepts as these, Baur and Multanowski formulated classifications of weather situations in terms of the location and orientation of major pressure systems. These classifications formed the basis for extended-forecast systems that were reasonably successful chiefly because they sharpened the wits of the forecaster and gave him a broad-scale perspective of the kind needed to make predictions several days to a week in advance.

The forecasts were by no means infallible, but they were at least slightly better than climatological probabilities; and it is significant than when World War II arrived, it was Baur and his colleagues who successfully forecast many days in advance the sunny, rainless weather that aided German tanks and planes in their invasion of Poland, while later still, when the Soviet Union was drawn into the war, Pagava and his Russian colleagues made excellent use of the techniques they had learned from Multanowski.

The Americans also had an extended-forecast system during the war. It also was based on a method of classifying weather maps, though not simply with reference to a few major pressure systems. Eaton, Holzman, Krick, and George—all officers in the Army Air Forces Weather Service—were chiefly responsible for developing the system. Eaton and Holzman inaugurated a program for analyzing all Northern Hemisphere weather maps for a forty-year period. The maps were then arranged by weather types, which were given code designations. In actual forecasting in the European Theater, the current daily weather map was identified as to type, and past maps of the same type and for the same season of the year were then pulled from the files and studied to learn how the weather had evolved. In this process particular attention was paid to past maps that were part of a day-to-day weather sequence that closely resembled the current sequence. Thus it was not sufficient to have the current map for March 21, 1943, correspond to that for April 15, 1925. More valuable was the map for March 10, 1931, because the two preceding daily maps for March 9 and 8 were closely similar to the two daily maps preceding the current map of March 21, 1943.

This method of consulting weather history was most helpful to the AAF forecasters in short-range forecasting, as well as in making "outlook" forecasts a few days in advance. This was pointed up during the heated discussions that took place among the three forecast teams that participated in making the D-day forecast for the invasion of Europe in June, 1944. Two of the teams were British, representing the British Admiralty and the Royal Air Force. One was American. The forecast situation was exceedingly difficult, as a complex storm was due to move through the invasion zone and there was considerable question whether it would clear out sufficiently to permit an amphibious assault.

Holzman and Krick, the principal AAF forecasters, had what one of the European forecasters thought was too optimistic a forecast, even though it was one that hardly called for ideal weather. "After all," said he, "you haven't the years of experience in European forecasting that I have." Krick was the one to reply. He patted the stack of Northern Hemisphere weather maps that were at his elbow and said, "Well, it *is* true, we have only forty years' experience, right here!" As things turned out, the resulting weather lay somewhat between the two differing forecasts; but, if anything, Holzman and Krick were more accurate than their colleague because of their weather typing system.

Somewhat different from the weather classification systems of Baur, Multanowski, and the AAF group is the system developed by Namais and his colleagues during the past twenty years. One of the key elements of their system was derived from the work of C. G. Rossby, who may well have been the most brilliant theoretical meteorologist of the twentieth century.

Rossby had observed, as others had done, that at times there are vast movements of air from north to south and from south to north. These are the situations in which polar air rides far equatorward in several different sectors of the Northern Hemisphere, while at the same time, in adjacent sectors, warm tropical air moves far northward. At other times there is relatively little interchange of air between polar and tropical regions. Instead, the air flow is dominantly from west to east in middle latitudes. Rossby developed an index number that was a general measure of whether the flow was chiefly between higher and lower latitudes or chiefly zonal, from west to east. This index and how it varied proved to be exceedingly important in extended forecasting.

Today, using Rossby's index and also analyzing the air-flow conditions of the Northern Hemisphere in several different ways, Namais and his coworkers in the United States Weather Bureau issue five-day forecasts that have proved to be distinctly more accurate than climatological probabilities, even though, as Namias himself points out, they leave much to be desired. The Namias group has also experimented with monthly forecasts, which only recently have begun to yield results of real significance.

There is still one other important school of extended-weather forecasting: the school that would relate weather changes from season to season and even year to year to variations in the energy output of the sun. This notion was first developed extensively by Clayton of the Smithsonian Institution in the United States. More recently, it has been given new meaning and has been elaborated upon by

Hurd C. Willett of the Massachusetts Institute of Technology and by the group headed by Roberts at the High Altitude Observatory at Climax, Colorado.

It has not yet been possible to demonstrate the nature of sun-and-atmosphere relations in sufficiently strict form to permit forecasting the weather conditions over broad regions many months or years in advance. Nonetheless, recent advances on a number of different fronts give hope that a major scientific break-through is imminent. Most of these advances have centered not about the problems of short-range or extended weather forecasting but about the far more fundamental problem of the nature and causes of climatic change. It is likely that within the next few years a solid physical link will be demonstrated to exist between solar output and climatic change. If this occurs, it will certainly be followed by a technologic revolution in the field of weather forecasting.

13 Climatic Change

The Ice Age, in which we now live—a time of critical climatic change—has been in progress for between 250,000 and 1,000,000 years. Four times during this period, massive glaciers have covered almost one-third of the land area of the world. Between these glaciations, the masses of ice have wasted away, and the water from the ice has been transferred from the lands to the seas, either by runoff through glacial rivers or else more directly by the breaking away of millions of icebergs along the edges of the glaciers wherever they bordered upon the sea and through subsequent melting of the icebergs as they drifted equatorward upon the water. In each instance, with the melting of the glaciers, the sea level was raised several hundred feet. So also, today, the seas stand about 300 feet higher than they did at the peak of the fourth, and latest, widespread glaciation.

The great glacial icecaps of Antarctica and Greenland still exist, along with thousands of much smaller glaciers in the Alps, Himalayas, Andes, Scandinavia, Alaska, Baffinland, the Rocky Mountains, and many other places. Were all these to be melted, the sea level would rise an additional 200 feet and for miles inland great areas of the coastal lands of all the continents would lie beneath the sea. This is what will happen if the fourth great glacial period is really on the wane.

In contrast, it is possible that we live at a time when the glaciers have retreated only temporarily, so that instead of further melting with a rise in sea level there will be renewed growth of the great ice sheets accompanied by a lowering of sea level. Then Stockholm, Paris, London, New York, Chicago, and thousands of other places will once again be covered with ice. It is this possibility that seems the more likely. It will not occur in this generation, or the next, or the one after next; but it may occur within 10,000 to 20,000 years and so, in time, may drastically influence the future of mankind. And long before the ice actually advances, there will be major, accompanying side effects, consisting in a progressive lowering of the sea level and significant changes in the climate.

Which way will the pendulum swing? How rapidly will it move? These related questions comprise one of the great scientific puzzles of our time. Their solution lies in learning more about the climates of the past and in then determining what the fundamental causes of those changes have been. Once the causes are known, it will be possible to extrapolate, to project these causal mechanisms into the future. Only then will it be possible to predict with any real certainty what the climates of the future will be and hence whether the present glaciers will melt or there will be a resurgence of full glacial times. When this knowledge is achieved, mankind will have, as a technologic by-product, not only a general view of things to come thousands of years hence but also a tool for forecasting the nature of the broad climatic conditions five, fifty, or even five hundred years in advance.

The fundamental causes of climatic change may soon be known. Recent applications of nuclear physics to the problem of the dating of past climatic events have provided new and far more certain knowledge of the pace of climatic changes. Recent advances in geochemistry have yielded data of a new order of accuracy concerning temperatures of the distant past. The astrophysics of solar phenomena are coming to be better and better understood and their relation to the behavior of the earth's atmosphere is just beginning to be comprehended. Rocket and satellite observations of the high atmosphere are starting to reveal new and critical information about the physical interaction between solar emanations and the middle and upper regions of the ocean of air. Advances on all these fronts and increasing skill in the use of electronic computers to analyze complex problems pertaining to the circulation of the atmosphere make it likely that the processes that underlie climatic change will soon be determined.

The Time Scale of Climatic Changes

The natural forces that produce major climatic changes operate so slowly that the results are hidden from the eyes of any one man; the span of his life is far too scant to permit him to perceive the long-term trends that are masked by the wide swings in the weather from one year to the next.

Major climatic changes have been occurring throughout the three billion years or more of earth history. It now seems likely that the Ice Age began about 290,000 years ago. On this basis, the chronology of major glacial and climatic events within it is approximately as follows:

Years Ago (in thousands)	*Glacial Event*	*Climate*
290–265	First glaciation	Cold
265–200	First interglacial	Warm, wet
200–175	Second glaciation	Cold
175–125	Second interglacial	Cool, dry
125–103	Third glaciation	Cold
103– 75	Third interglacial	Warm, wet
75– 11	Fourth glaciation	Cold
6		Warm, moist ("Climatic Optimum")
5 (to date)		Cooler, but still warm, with fluctuations in temperature and rainfall from century to century

To make this chronology more comprehensible, R. J. Russell has suggested an analogy. Suppose that the Ice Age occupied a single year, from January 1 through December 31. The proportional chronology, including a few historical events for comparison, would then be as follows:

January 1–February 1	First glaciation
February 1–April 24	First interglacial
April 24–May 25	Second glaciation
May 25–July 27	Second interglacial
July 27–August 25	Third glaciation
August 25–September 29	Third interglacial

September 29–December 18	Fourth glaciation
December 25, in the evening	Warm, moist Climatic Optimum
December 28, about noon	Birth of Buddha
December 29, late morning	Birth of Christ
December 30, about 7:30 P.M.	Battle of Hastings
December 31, 9:30 A.M.	Columbus discovers America
December 31, about 8:50 P.M.	Assassination of President Lincoln
December 31, 11:58 P.M.	Events of one year ago
December 31, midnight	Today

Many scientists who have studied glacial chronology would not agree in detail with Russell's chronology. Nearly all, however, would confirm its salient features, such as the great length of interglacial as contrasted with glacial times, the great variation in the length of glacial periods, and the extremely short time that has elapsed since the end of the last extensive glaciation. Its broad features provide the basic reference scheme for considering the climatic regimes of the past and those that seem most likely to follow in the future.

Climates of the Past

The geologic period that preceded the Ice Age is known as the Tertiary period. The Tertiary lasted for fifty to one hundred million years. Throughout this great span of time the climates of the world were far milder than they have been at any time since.

During the first ten or twenty million years of the Tertiary, tropical palms and fruits abounded in the area that is now London. In North America, magnolias and tropical ferns thrived in the region of the Yukon Basin. Anthropoid apes and monkeys lived in the tropical and semitropical forests of Europe, while crocodiles and alligators were found in the waters offshore even as far north as 50°.

Toward the end of the Tertiary, about ten million years ago, the climates began slowly to worsen. Palms and other tropical vegetation began to move toward the equator. The warmth-loving creatures disappeared from Europe. In both of the Americas, and in Asia and Africa as well, there were similar changes. Even in Antarctica these changes were marked. In the middle of the Tertiary, Antarctica was well vegetated, although with such trees as conifers rather than with tropical forms. Only at the very end of the Tertiary were the trees eliminated by the coming of the glacial cold.

With the gradual deterioration of the climate, the Tertiary came to an end and the Ice Age came into being. Within a few thousand years ice sheets formed and moved outward across the continents, especially in the Northern Hemisphere. In North America they spread outward from Greenland, Baffinland, Labrador, and the northern Rockies, and grew southward to overrun much of the northern United States. In Europe the principal center was Scandinavia; the secondary center was the Alps. In Asia there were lesser ice sheets extending outward from the Himalayas and from other mountains, in Siberia as well as central Asia. In the Southern Hemisphere there were relatively small mountain icecaps extending outward from the Andes of South America and the mountains of east central Africa, while in Antarctica the icecap reached gigantic proportions, far beyond those of the present day. Even in Australia and Hawaii there were glaciers, though these never were sufficiently overriding to be true ice sheets with thicknesses measurable in thousands of feet.

The first of the four great glaciations lasted for about 25,000 years. Then the ice sheets wasted away and the first interglacial period set in, with markedly increasing warmth and rainfall in middle and high middle latitudes. In about another 65,000 years the swing of broad climatic events was once again the other way, and again the ice sheets formed and thickened and spread across the lands. Then in continuing sequence, though not with anything approaching regular periodicity, there followed the third and the fourth glaciations, each in turn being separated from the preceding one by a long interglacial period of comparative warmth.

That all this happened is known from the geologic, botanic, and zoologic evidence collected from thousands of different field investigations in many different parts of the world. In each instance the glaciers left their signatures in the form of grooves chiseled in bedrock, where hard rock fragments carried in the basal ice of the moving glaciers scraped the rock beneath, in the form of deposits of foreign materials picked up by the glaciers at one locality and deposited in another hundreds of miles away, and in many other forms of unmistakable glacial origin. The fossil remains and imprints of plants and animals also provide highly important evidence, especially as to climatic change. For as the great continental glaciers spread equatorward, the plants and animals adapted to warmer habitats migrated equatorward ahead of them; and as the glaciers melted away, the plants and animals from warmer climes migrated poleward to take over regions from which they had been barred by the glacial cold. All this happened not in a simple, uniform way but with local variations and complexities, many of which have yet to be defined in detail. Yet this was the over-all effect, the broad sweep of the major events: the motion of glacial ice sheets to and fro and the migration of plants and animals retreating and advancing.

The relatively rapid climatic changes of the Ice Age continued after the last extensive glaciation. The nature of these later changes is especially well known for western Europe, where intensive analyses of pollen grains found in swamps and in lake sediments have been useful in reconstructing past climatic conditions. C. E. P. Brooks describes the general climatic succession up to 2500 B.C.:

> Generally speaking, the ground laid bare by the retreat of the ice was a maze of depressions and ridges. The hollows were occupied by lakes and ponds, and the ridges first by an arctic flora, which soon gave place to birch, followed by pine. By about 7000 B.C. the climate was dry and sufficiently warm in summer for the rapid spread of hazel. The rise of temperature continued, and with some increase of moisture . . . [by about 4500 B.C.] all the western half of Europe was occupied by a rich forest of oak, alder and elm, the alder being favoured by the increasing rainfall. This was the beginning of the "Climatic Optimum," with temperatures up to 5° F. higher than the present, permitting forests to grow much higher up the mountain sides than is possible now. The heavy rainfall, however, favoured the growth of peat, and . . . [within 1,000 to 1,500 years] large areas of forests were killed and buried by peat-bogs. This phase continued until about 2500 B.C., with gradually decreasing temperature. . . .

Between 2500 B.C. and the time of Christ there was an alternation of dry and wet periods in western Europe, with the dry periods occurring around 2200, 1200–1000, and 700–500 B.C. Thereafter there was an especially wet period from 800 to 1200 A.D., with dry and mild conditions dominating the remainder of the time. Similar, though not precisely synchronous, changes took place in other middle latitude regions of Europe and of North America as well.

Beginning as early as 1850 in some places, and by 1890 in virtually all localities of the Northern Hemisphere, the temperature began slowly to rise. This increase continued until the 1940's, when temperatures leveled off or, in places, started slowly to decline. These recent temperature changes were evidenced in many ways, as by changes in actual air temperatures; the retreat of glaciers in Scandinavia, Alaska, and elsewhere; the progressively longer and longer ice-free periods in inland lakes; and the migration of tree lines up mountain slopes. In middle latitudes, as in the central United States, the temperature rise from 1850 to 1940 averaged 2°. At higher latitudes, as in Scandinavia and Spitsbergen, the average was close to 10°. In lower latitudes, as in India, there appears to have been no significant change in temperature.

These sequences of climatic events—in recent times, in the 11,000 years since the last great glaciation, and in the 290,000 years or so since the beginning of the Ice Age—raise two questions. What will the changes in climate be in the near future, that is, over the next few centuries? And, on a longer time range, from 1,000 years on up, will the next great major change produce the melting of the present icecaps and a great rise in sea level or will it produce the return of the great ice sheets?

Future Indications from Present Evidence

Viewed in perspective, with reference to the climatic swings over the past fifty or one hundred million years, the temperature increase that began around 1850 and seemed to come to a halt around 1940 must be viewed as merely a minor fluctuation. The short-term prospect, over the next few centuries, is a fifty-fifty proposition. There is an even chance that the temperatures may shift slightly up or slightly down, and it is likely that there will be no pronounced changes in the immediate future.

For the longer future, three facts are of significance. First, there are still the great glacial sheets in Greenland and Antarctica, so that it is at least as reasonable to suppose that the glaciers have withdrawn only temporarily as that they are definitely, finally, receding. Second, today's climates are far colder in middle and high latitudes than they ever were during the tens of millions of years of the Tertiary. And third, temperatures are now lower than they were 6,000 years ago, at the time of the Climatic Optimum.

With icecaps already present, with cool conditions typical of an Ice Age, and with cooler conditions now than existed 6,000 years ago, it is somewhat more likely that the next great climatic episode will bring back the glaciers rather than progressive warmth and a return of Tertiary climates. Furthermore, it is quite possible, judging from the pace of past climatic changes, that the return of the glaciers will come about in the next ten to twenty thousand years.

This estimate of things to come is tentative, despite the greater weight of evidence that favors these conclusions. Far more positive answers will be forthcoming within the next several years from new knowledge, some of which is already at hand.

Radioactive Clocks, Chemical Thermometers, and Climatic Reconstruction

Until recently, only crude estimates could be made of the age of such climatic evidence as the fossil imprint of a palm tree, indicating a warm and moist climate, or the presence of pollen from a beech, indicating a cool climate. Among the cruder methods for determining age was to estimate the length of time required to deposit the sediments overlying the fossil imprint or pollen grains, or to cut a stream valley that had been formed since the time that the palm or beech was a living tree. One of the less crude methods for age determination involved counting the number of clay layers, or varves, laid down in glacial or postglacial lakes. Since these varves were laid down annually, in sets of two per year, with a fine clay layer alternating with a coarse one because of seasonal swings in the temperature of the lake water, this method sometimes gave good results. But even clay-varve techniques are not always reliable because the varve layers for several succeeding years may have been eroded away, or because in some years there may have been two or more double sets of varves.

Most geologic events and periods are still dated in such crude or semicrude ways as these. Thus highly reputable geologists cannot, for example, agree whether the Tertiary period began fifty or a hundred million years ago.

Hope that a reasonably accurate dating method might be available on a geologic time scale came in 1904, when Lord Rutherford first propounded the notion of the radioactive clock. In 1896, Antoine Henri Becquerel had discovered the radioactive properties of uranium, and soon thereafter Pierre and Marie Curie began their famous researches on radioactivity. In making his brilliant suggestion for a radioactive clock, Rutherford carried the hard-gained knowledge of Becquerel and the Curies one step farther, and in a direction that had not occurred to them.

Radioactive elements continually decay, atom by atom, through the emanation of different types of rays and particles. The decay products are chemical elements of kinds that are different from those of the original chemical element. Thus uranium, a naturally occurring element in the crust of the solid earth, decays to yield thorium, lead, and helium, among other products. The significant point that Rutherford made was that since the *rate* of decay was known, all that was needed to date the time of origin of the uranium was a measure of the mass of the decay products as compared with that of the remaining undecayed uranium.

Rutherford's idea was sound, but there were all kinds of complications. The helium decay product was a gas that rapidly diffused and was lost to the atmosphere, and it was difficult to measure accurately the mass of the lead and thorium. Yet, in the words of Kulp, "This pioneer work . . . established the fact that the earth was at least two billion years old and that an absolute geological time scale could be constructed."

The first really practical radioactive clocks were not developed until after World War II. Their development arose from the knowledge gained in nuclear physics and technology during the all-out drive to develop an atomic bomb. From this knowledge and from continuing studies that came afterward, there came into being several new radioactive clocks that were far more accurate than the uranium clock. Among these was the carbon-14 clock, the operation of which was probed and evaluated by Libby and his associates at the University of Chicago.

The earth's atmosphere is constantly bombarded by cosmic rays. This causes nitrogen atoms, with an atomic weight of 14 units, to change to radioactive carbon, also with a weight of 14. In contrast, ordinary carbon has an atomic weight of 12. Because of the thorough mixing of the atmospheric gases, carbon-14 is distributed quite uniformly throughout the atmosphere. It is therefore taken in by plants and incorporated in plant tissue along with ordinary carbon, carbon-12. Animals also acquire C-14 through feeding on plants.

Because of the uniformity of C-14 available to plants and animals, there is a certain, established ratio of C-14 to C-12 in the tissues of all living plants and animals, including man. Upon death of a plant or animal, however, there is no longer any further carbon uptake, either as C-14 or C-12. But whereas the C-12 diminishes in quantity after death only by such means as through physical erosion or chemical replacement, the C-14, being radioactive, diminishes not only in these ways but also through nuclear decay. Thus the ratio between C-14 and C-12 changes with the passage of time and so provides a kind of clock that can be read hundreds or thousands of years later, as in dating the wood from the carbon remains of a palm tree in Europe.

Carbon-14 decays at such a rate that it can be used only to date materials up to 45,000 years ago. Stated differently, if the plant or animal remains are more than 45,000 years old, there is too little C-14 now remaining to permit dating within known limits of accuracy. Even for events that occurred less than 45,000 years ago, the dating is not absolutely definite but is, rather, expressed in terms of the most likely date, plus or minus so many years. The resulting dates are like the following, which are actual examples determined in the laboratory at the University of Groningen in the Netherlands:

Description	*Age in Years Before 1958*
Peat with muck, oak and pine dominant, from a former lake in Spain	4270 ±120
Charcoal from a cave in Austria	34,000 ±3000

The C-14 radioactive clock is so much more accurate than other dating techniques that it has already revolutionized the chronology of the later Ice Age. It was formerly supposed that the fourth great glaciation essentially ended with the disappearance of the ice sheet from the remoter outlying areas, between 18,000 and 65,000 years ago. Yet C-14 dating shows that there was still an ice sheet in the state of Wisconsin 11,000 years ago, and this is now generally taken as the time of ending of near-maximum glaciation. Similarly, the warm, moist period of the Climatic Optimum was formerly thought to have occurred around 8,000 years ago, but the C-14 clock gives a reading of about 6,000 years. These revised dates lead to an important conclusion: even major climatic changes, of such a magnitude as to bring on widespread glaciation or to dissipate glacial ice sheets millions of square miles in extent, can occur in far briefer time than was ever before supposed, within a time span of a few thousand years.

If uranium and C-14 were the only radioactive clocks, great progress would still remain to be made in reconstructing and dating the climates of the past, for much has yet to be accomplished in improving these techniques and in applying them to date the thousands of significant climatic indicators whose ages are still imperfectly known. But actually, even greater progress is in view because there exist many other radioactive elements that are certain to prove more and more useful in helping to reconstruct past climates. Among these are ionium, which can be used to date deep-sea sediments up to 400,000 years old, and rubidium, for dating several kinds of igneous rock that are older than 100 million years.

The new understanding of nuclear physics has also provided a second kind of tool of great promise. This is the chemical thermometer. Until recently, estimates of past temperature conditions have rested almost exclusively upon the nature and distribution of plants and animals of the past, remains or traces of which have been found in rocks or sediments. In 1951, Urey and his associates showed that it should be possible to determine the temperatures under which organic sediments were deposited in the sea through measuring the proportion of different kinds of oxygen present in the molecules within the sediments. This finding stemmed from still earlier work by Urey, who had shown that oxygen atoms of slightly different weights than the standard 16 units were incorporated in new-formed molecules in different proportions, depending upon the temperature at the time of incorporation.

Using the findings of Urey and working with sediments whose age had been determined by C-14 and ionium methods, Emiliani was able in 1955 to reconstruct ocean-water temperature curves for the last 400,000 years. They show a marked lowering of temperature about 290,000 years ago, and this leads to the conclusion that the Ice Age started at about that time. The curves also show that the warm period of the Climatic Optimum occurred about 6,000 years ago, and that there has not been as warm a period since that time.

Urey's chemical thermometer is at present chiefly applicable only in measuring the temperatures under which organic sediments were deposited upon the floors of the deep oceans. Similar techniques will no doubt be devised to permit the reconstruction of temperature curves in lake sediments and, perhaps, even in sediments laid down upon the land, such as sand dunes. It is even possible that chemical techniques will in time provide analogous information about moisture conditions, for the moisture environment is often highly important in determining the precise chemical changes that occur in any situation.

The Causes of Climatic Change

Theories of the causes of climatic change are legion. It has been said that major climatic changes of the kinds experienced during the Ice Age are brought about by changes in the amount of carbon dioxide in the atmosphere, by the drifting of continents, by volcanic eruptions that pour dust into the atmosphere which cuts down the incoming sunlight, by the wandering of the north and south poles, by mountain-building that changes the patterns of temperature and snowfall, by the precession of the equinoxes that progressively changes the date at which the earth is closest to the sun, by changes in the energy output of the sun, and by the alternate melting and thawing of sea ice in the Arctic. This last theory, recently advanced by Ewing and Donn, has enjoyed a certain vogue and thus warrants mention.

The keystone of the Ewing-Donn theory is that warming produces the melting of sea ice in the Arctic and that this in turn brings about the flow of cool water into more southerly latitudes to produce a general lowering of temperatures throughout middle and low latitudes. Simultaneously, according to their views, the conversion of the Arctic Sea to an open-water body provides a new and important source of moisture that is fed into the atmosphere through evaporation and is returned from the atmosphere to the adjacent lands in the form of glacier-building snow. There are other aspects of the theory, such as a suggested mechanism for the initial warming of the Arctic, but the hypothesis is inadequate chiefly because it neither provides for world-wide climatic change nor does it explain how it happened that extensive glaciation occurred simultaneously both in the Northern and Southern Hemispheres. The remarks of J. K. Charlesworth, even though they were made before Ewing and Donn advanced their theory, are pertinent:

> Local causes, such as a temporary diversion of an ocean current which slightly increased the precipitation, a submerged Sahara which provided moisture for the Alpine glaciation, or sudden irruptions of vast masses of floating ice into the North Atlantic . . . are quite inadequate to meet the general situation, as are the opening or closing of sea-connexions or the alterations of ocean currents, for the latter play a much smaller role in transferring heat than does the circulation of the atmosphere. A global phenomenon requires a global cause.

There are only three broad ways to produce, on a global scale, the major climatic changes that are known to have occurred thus far in the Ice Age. One is to alter the atmosphere, as through the introduction of great quantities of dust like that ejected by the eruption of Krakatoa or through varying the amount of carbon dioxide and hence the absorption of sunlight in the atmosphere. A second is to have the poles wander or the continents slip around and change location. A third calls for fluctuations in the amount or character of the energy arriving from the sun. The first two cannot be accepted unless there can be appreciable and, in a geologic-time sense, rapid changes, time after time, in the amount of volcanism, in the amount of carbon dioxide, in the movement of the poles, or in the slippage of continents so as to account for that speedy onset and speedy termination of glaciation that modern radioactive clocks and chemical thermometers have demonstrated once took place. There is no substantial evidence that swift changes of these kinds can occur on anything but a minor and insignificant scale. So attention has now been focused on the third broad possibility: fluctuations in the amount or character of energy from the sun.

The Sun and Climatic Change

The idea that variations in the energy output of the sun may be associated with fluctuations in weather and climate was first propounded by Sir William Herschel in 1801. Thereafter, many investigators attempted to demonstrate that there is a correlation between the amount of solar energy arriving at the outer limits of the atmosphere and climatic fluctuations from one year to another and from decade to decade. This statistical-correlation approach culminated in the work of Sir Gilbert Walker in England and of H. H. Clayton in America, who for almost half a century, beginning in the 1890's, studied a great many possible connections between total solar output, on the one hand, and temperature, precipitation surface air pressure, and other facets of the weather and climate, on the other.

The work of Walker and Clayton, although generally untenable, was highly important. Not only did it tend to show that there was no proved relation between total energy output of the sun and climatic variations; it also, by the very nature of its inconclusiveness, caused them and other investigators to turn with renewed interest to an intriguing possibility that had been suggested long before by the findings of solar astronomers. This was the possibility of correlating climatic variations with sunspot frequencies.

Sunspots had been observed ever since the invention of the telescope. As seen through a telescope or on photographs, they appear in clusters, so that the face of the sun may contain several different sunspot groups in each of which there may be forty or more individual spots. Though each sunspot group occupies only a small part of the surface of the sun, the groups may be large in absolute area. One extraordinarily large group, observed at Mount Wilson Observatory in Pasadena, California, on February 7, 1946, contained a single spot that was 90,000 miles in diameter, and the group as a whole covered a surface area of over sixty billion square miles—more than three hundred times the entire surface area of the earth. Yet even this group occupied less than one-tenth of the surface of the sun.

For more than a century, at solar observatories in Zurich, Switzerland, and elsewhere, careful records have been kept of the frequency of sunspot groups and of individual sunspots within groups. These tabulations have shown that maximum sunspot frequencies occur quite regularly, at intervals of slightly over eleven years. When they turned their attention to sunspots, Clayton and others found a slight but significant correlation between this eleven-year sunspot cycle and variations in air pressure at the earth's surface. In addition, slight but real correlations were found for double-sunspot periods—periods of twenty-two years. Among the more interesting of these was that discovered by C. E. P. Brooks, who found that there was a significantly greater chance of there being low levels at floodtimes on the Nile River every twenty-two years than at years that were intermediate.

Sunspots are areas upon the surface of the sun that are magnetically disturbed. Within these areas there are charged particles that revolve clockwise or counterclockwise, depending on whether the spots are north or south of the sun's equator, and in this respect these electromagnetic swirls are analogous to our hurricanes or typhoons, though they are hundreds or thousands of times greater in diameter. Sunspots migrate across the sun's surface, but to an observer on the earth their apparent motion is dominated by the rotation of the sun, which carries the sunspots and sunspot groups around just as a hurricane is carried by the rotation of the earth.

What is most significant of all, however, is that sunspots produce great bursts of radiation in the very-short-wave-length ultraviolet range. At times of sunspot maximum the ultraviolet radiation is often ten times that at sunspot minimum. There are other effects also, for sunspot maxima are associated with an increase in the output of X rays, radio waves, and charged particles from the sun; and these, together with the surge of ultraviolet light, produce great electromagnetic storms in the upper atmosphere of the earth and are accompanied by auroral flares and lights of spectacular extent and intensity. So far as climatic change is concerned, the crucial question is whether outbursts of this kind can not only influence surface air pressure but can also, with sufficient sunspot activity over a period of thousands of years, create a climatic situation that produces glaciation.

To provide at least a tentative answer to this question, Harry Wexler of the U.S. Weather Bureau decided, a few years ago, to examine the climatology of periods of sunspot maxima. He went to the daily weather maps and, as an independent check, to tabulated weather observations that had not been analyzed in daily-weather-map form. From both these sources he extracted pressure, temperature, and rainfall data for the entire Northern Hemisphere for those three-year periods from 1899 to 1939 that were centered about years of sunspot maxima. These values were then averaged and compared with average conditions for the several three-year periods centered about years of sunspot minima. The purpose of this comparison was to determine what the climatic trend would be if sunspot maxima and accompanying maxima of ultraviolet, X rays, and charged particles should become dominant for any great length of time.

Wexler's results indicated that great sunspot activity, long continued, would tend to produce increased winter snowfall in northeastern North America and northwestern Europe, which are precisely those areas in which the great glaciers of the past originated.

Also, the summers in these areas would tend to be slightly cooler, thus decreasing the loss of glacier-forming snow during the warm season of the year. Wexler states conservatively that his findings are by no means conclusive. But certainly they tend to confirm the general notion that even though variations in over-all sun radiation, measured in total energy, may not produce significant climatic changes, variations in a certain band of the ultraviolet range, together with variations in the emission of X rays and charged particles by the sun, may well produce such changes. This viewpoint appears to be confirmed by many observations, including a spectacular event that was observed at Berlin, Germany, in 1952.

On February 24–25 of that year, the usual observations of conditions in the troposphere and lower stratosphere were taken at Berlin by means of balloons carrying radiosondes that would send back to earth records of temperature and humidity conditions aloft. These upper-air soundings revealed that a sudden increase in temperature of about 70° had occurred in the lower stratosphere. This fantastic rise above the temperature of the previous days and weeks was coincident with a sudden outburst of ultraviolet radiation from the sun. Furthermore, the abrupt heating effect, which had occurred initially at levels above 100,000 feet, was followed by a peak temperature increase of about 21° at a level of only 70,000 feet a few days later. It now seems clear that this marked heating, at both the higher and lower levels, was associated with the rapid sinking of large masses of air that was warmed by compression just as air is warmed in descending a mountain slope. The role of the outburst of ultraviolet radiation may then have been to trigger the sinking of the air, thus producing marked warming, not directly but through a chain of events.

From this event at Berlin, from Wexler's studies, and from other observations and studies by many different solar astronomers, geophysicists, and meteorologists, it appears likely that major climatic changes have been produced and will be produced by long-term variations in the solar output of ultraviolet radiation, X rays, and charged particles.

This view of the importance of special kinds of solar radiation may soon be substantiated through the studies of meteorologists and astronomers, and especially through rocket and satellite observations that will provide more and more information about conditions in the very high atmosphere, where emanations from the sun exert their first full impact upon the ocean of air. This new realm of exploration—the regions hundreds of miles above the surface of the earth—may yield the remaining vital clues that are required to answer at last the question whether and when it will be the fate of mankind to face once more, as it did many thousands of years ago, the advance of gigantic icecaps across much of what is now the inhabited and inhabitable earth.

14 Weathermakers

To know what have been the innermost dreams of mankind, one must look to the mythologies and religious writings of the peoples of all times. From these it is clear that ever since man first came into being, one of his greatest dreams has been to control the forces of nature. Neptune shakes his trident to shatter the calmness of the sea. First Man and First Woman of the Navajo build mountains and tie them down with rainbows and bolts of lightning. Hanuman, the monkey king of India, rips a massive chunk of rock from the Himalayas and with it builds islands that will serve as steppingstones from India to Ceylon. Moses stretches out his hand and the Lord causes the waters of the Red Sea to part. Foremost among these achievements, so graphically presented in myths and religious writings, are those involving control of the weather. Winds, storms, heat, cold, and rain become by proxy the slaves of mankind.

But myths are not enough. When a drought withers the crops upon the field, when a storm threatens the ship at sea, or when extreme heat or cold brings heavy consequences, something active must be done to control the weather. So there have always been weathermakers–magicians, priests, medicine men, sciolists, or scientists, who by rites or incantations, or more rational means, with paraphernalia or without, have practiced weather control.

Early Weathermakers

If somehow all the different kinds of weathermakers, past and present, could be brought together in an arena to practice their skills, the scene would be one of confusion and clamor. In the assemblage would be two Omaha Indians flapping a blanket to make the wind blow; a native of Halmahera in the Moluccas shaking water from a stick to encourage rain; a man-powered Chinese dragon parading back and forth; some villagers from southeastern Europe banging on drums, beating two firebrands together, and pouring water on the ground; Snake Priests of the Hopi Indians stamping their feet in rhythm to the rattle of gourds in the hands of the Antelope Priests; an early American scientist building a bonfire; a Yakut, swinging a stone around his head, shouting for the wind to blow; Ojibway Indians firing flaming arrows at the sun; an airplane flying overhead, dropping silver iodide crystals into clouds; a Wawamba native boiling a stone in water; and a small girl of ancient Greece, adorned with flowers, who, whenever she pauses in her walk, is drenched by water thrown upon her by her companions. And there in a corner would be General Dyrenforth, firing off cannons and mortars, and sending aloft balloons so rigged as to explode in mid-air.

The rain-making efforts of General R. G. Dyrenforth were sponsored by the United States Government. In 1890, Congress appropriated $2,000 to finance experiments to test whether rainfall could be produced by explosions. Later, additional amounts of $7,000 and $10,000 were appropriated. These appropriations were initiated by Senator Charles B. Farwell of Illinois, who had been much impressed by the writings of Edward Powers on the effects of battles upon rainfall. The funds went to the Department of Agriculture, which turned the job of testing over to General Dyrenforth.

In August, 1891, and again in the fall of 1892, the general carried out a series of rain-making tests. Typical of the results he obtained were those at San Antonio, Texas, in late November, 1892.

A few miles from town the general set up his apparatus, the chief feature of which was a stand from which a huge hydrogen- and oxygen-filled balloon was to be released. The balloon carried a slow-match fuse that would cause it to explode two and one-half minutes after release. One mile to the west of this stand was a battery of eight guns and one mortar, to be used simultaneously with the balloon.

The experiments started at noon on November 25. There had been showers in the morning, as forecast by the Weather Bureau, but at noon the skies were cloudless and the sun was glaring bright. The general gave the signal for the tests to begin. The balloon ascended to a height of about 4,000 feet, then exploded with a force that rattled windowpanes and dishes for two miles around. Immediately upon the blast of the exploding balloon came the roar of the artillery to the west. All eyes looked upward, searching the sky for gathering clouds. The sky remained cloudless.

The tests continued at approximately forty-five-minute intervals. Finally at three o'clock the next morning, forty minutes after the last combined barrage, it began to rain beneath the broken clouds which had been gathering for the past hour. The general, who had been stanchly standing by, quickly ordered another salvo. The rain continued, and the general, impressed and triumphant, decided to call it a night.

The tests were repeated at intervals until December 1, without results. Once some clouds gathered momentarily—then dissipated. As successive tests failed to produce results, the general called in more artillery. He added two more mortars to the battery and increased the size of the balloon. But to no avail. The only result was that the people of San Antonio continued to lose sleep; for, as reported in the New Orleans *Picayune* of December 1, for some reason or other the general insisted on making his tests at night despite the protests of the local inhabitants.

The rain-making experiments of General Dyrenforth attracted wide attention. The effectiveness and scientific merit of his methods were debated in newspapers, in magazines, and at scientific gatherings. At first there were many, including a few scientists, who with Dyrenforth held the view that explosions produced rainfall. But in time there was almost unanimous agreement with the remarks that appeared in an article published in *The Nation* in 1891:

> To show how groundless is the notion that there is any relation between cannonading and rain, one need hardly go further than the little book in which Mr. Edward Powers tried to prove the contrary. By painstaking research he showed that during our civil war a great many "battles," "artillery fires," "gunboat firings," one tenth of the whole number perhaps, were followed by more or less rain, either next day, or in two, three, or four days. A farmer who should go out and blow his horn every Monday morning for a year would make a better showing than this, for his tooting would surely be followed by rain in two or three days oftener than one time in ten. . . . The great mass of air which was over the heads of the combatants during a

> battle would, next day, be hundreds of miles away, to be replaced by another mass from an equal distance. If a cannonade brought rain at all, it would do it in a few minutes; if we wait hours, we have a new mass of air coming from a distance of hundreds of miles. . . .
>
> This gentleman [Dyrenforth] had the indisputable qualification of absence of bias, being quite innocent of meteorology . . . and was therefore willing to take hold of the business seriously, instead of laughing at it, as all the scientists of the poor Secretary [of the Department of Agriculture] were suspected to be doing. How good a man he was from this point of view is evinced by the fact that, although he was going to make rain, he did not take a rain-gauge with him to measure it.

Like nearly all rain-making methods, that employed by General Dyrenforth was not based on sound scientific principles. In contrast, there was some real scientific basis for the rain-making method devised by Espy in the early nineteenth century. Espy reasoned that, since precipitation results from the cooling brought about by the upward movement of moist air, the convection produced by the heating of air over a very large bonfire should yield precipitation under favorable circumstances. It seems likely, although it has never been proved, that large forest fires or urban conflagrations may sometimes cause enough extra convection to produce precipitation. The difficulty, as Espy discovered from experiments with bonfires in Florida, is to create sufficient heat over a wide enough area to cause vigorous and widespread convection to great heights. Unless this is done and unless the air is both moist and unstable, there cannot be any appreciable amount of precipitation.

It is significant that despite the presence of extremely moist tropical air during the first nuclear bomb test at Bikini, no rain was produced by the detonation, although tremendous quantities of heat were released by the blast. This does not mean that atomic explosions can never produce precipitation; but rather that if they do, conditions will be such that rainfall through natural processes is about to occur in any event.

Modern Rain Making

In March, 1951, there appeared before the U.S. Senate Committee on Interior and Insular Affairs a throng of expert witnesses called upon to testify with reference to proposed legislation relating to rain making. The meteorologists were there in force. Witnesses were there from the U.S. Forest Service, the Agricultural Research Administration, and the Bureau of Reclamation. The General Electric Company, which had been experimenting with rain making, was represented. Associations concerned with water use sent their agents. Also among those present was Vannevar Bush, president of the Carnegie Institution of Washington and one-time director of the Office of War Research.

The members of the Senate committee had every right to be confused by the testimony of the witnesses. Excerpts are sufficient to indicate the diversity of views:

> . . . a few pounds of silver iodide released into the atmosphere in the form of fine particles can exercise a profound influence over the weather hundreds of miles away.—Bernard Vonnegut of General Electric.

> During the course of our operations, we have analyzed weather patterns throughout the country searching for possible effects of the cloud seeding operations on areas far removed from the operation itself. At no time has it been possible to discern an effect of any kind in the weather conditions occurring well outside of the operational area.—Irving P. Krick, the most famous rain maker of this century.

> There is very little available evidence and no present scientific basis for the belief that we now have the ability to modify or control the large-scale atmospheric processes which are responsible for our general weather and climatic patterns.—Henry G. Houghton of M.I.T.

> . . . man has begun for the first time to affect the weather in which he lives.—Vannevar Bush.

> . . . rainmaking is not only a boon to the farmers, but to industry and all those who are dependent upon electric power for their operations.—Richard D. Searles, president, Salt River Valley Water Users' Association.

> Rainmaking contracts are often cleverly drawn. They guarantee nothing in tangible results. Yet thousands of dollars are being paid commercial rainmakers in advance by drought-panicked farmers and ranchers.—Robert McKinney, chairman, New Mexico Economic Development Commission.

The senators, confronted with this welter of conflicting testimony, took the only step possible. They introduced a bill, which was passed in 1952, establishing a committee to investigate the whole problem of rain making.

The committee labored hard and long at its task. It analyzed statistically, and with the greatest care, the results of the seeding of 427 different storms, and compared the accompanying rainfall patterns with patterns in the same areas in previous years from 5,516 unseeded storms. The test regions were in different areas, not only in the United States but also in France.

In its final report, issued December 31, 1957, the committee concluded that ". . . the seeding of winter-type storm clouds in mountainous areas of the western United States produced an average increase in precipitation of 10 to 15 percent from seeded storms with heavy odds that this increase was not the result of natural variations in the amount of rainfall." In contrast with this, "In nonmountainous areas, the same statistical procedures did not detect any increase in precipitation that could be attributed to cloud seeding."

The conclusions of the committee as regards the positive effects of seeding in mountainous areas were seriously challenged by mathematicians, statisticians, and meteorologists. In addition, the problem was further thrown in doubt by Vannevar Bush, who, on December 2, 1957, seemingly contradicted his statement, made before the committee five years earlier. No longer did Bush take the view that ". . . man has begun for the first time to affect the weather in which he lives." Now it was his view that "We do not know whether it will be practically feasible for man to control the weather, or favorably alter the climate in which he lives." It is possible that in expressing this view Bush was relying upon a group of studies by Petterssen, Spar, and others, the results of which had been published a few months before. The studies, based on field experiments, had failed to reveal significant success in rain making.

Thus it is clear that the matter remains in doubt. Perhaps it is possible to increase the rainfall slightly through cloud seeding in certain preferred areas under certain preferred conditions. Perhaps even this is not possible. In any event, it is questionable that large-scale weather modification is possible today or will be possible at a reasonable economic price in the decades yet to come.

The Prospects for Weather Control

Control of the weather is not an impossibility; it is an impracticability. A few years ago the Weather Bureau received an anonymous letter that suggested a method for regulating the weather. The letter began: "I am not at all pleased with you. While, in the winter, you correctly predict the arrival of violent winds, year after year, you do absolutely nothing about them." It continued with the explanation that the anonymous writer was troubled by the cold winter winds of New York City, which caused him and countless others to have stiff necks, headaches, and other ailments. In conclusion, the suggestion was advanced that a huge wire coil heater be constructed, stretching in a semicircle around New York from Atlantic City on the south to Connecticut on the north. Such a coil would be used to regulate temperature and would, the writer claimed, also have an effect on the winds.

There is no doubt that these claims are true. But the cost of such a project is almost incalculable, and the thought of charging the chief of the Weather Bureau with the responsibility for regulating the temperature to please everyone is unpleasant to contemplate. Nor would the inhabitants of Atlantic City like to be moved out to avoid death through scorching.

Numerous other plans for regulating the weather have been advanced that are failures only in that they are impracticable. It has been suggested that a 100-mile gap be cut in the Sierra Nevada Mountains to permit moist air from the Pacific to enter the Nevada Desert; that mountain ranges be constructed to catch rainfall from winds off the ocean; that the Gulf Stream be dammed at one end to deflect the warm water toward cold parts of the coast; and that nuclear bombs be used to suppress hurricanes.

Regarding the latter, it has been estimated that it would be necessary to drop five middle-sized hydrogen bombs each minute for a period of several hours to suppress a medium-sized hurricane, and that these bombs would have to be detonated above the hurricane with all the energy directed downward and spread over an area of 600,000 square miles.

Although it is not practicable to alter the weather in its broad aspects—to produce rainfall, change temperatures over wide areas, create high winds, or still the winds that are blowing—weather in its minor aspects, adjacent to the ground, can be altered or ameliorated.

The farmer changes the weather when he erects a windbreak, the citrus grower when he burns smudge pots to keep his trees from freezing during a cold wave; and the weather is changed when a city is built, since the heat from hundreds of thousands of buildings and houses makes the winter temperatures slightly higher than they would be were the buildings and houses not there. All of these changes, however, are effected on a very small scale.

A great advance in controlling weather on a small scale was made during the war. American and British planes based in the British Isles were frequently grounded because of fog. It was desirable, therefore, to devise a means of dispersing fog. The method developed was called FIDO, the name representing the first letters of a file entry labeled "Fog, investigations dispersal of." Essentially FIDO consisted in burning large quantities of oil in pots placed along runways, thus raising the temperature of the air and dispersing the fog. FIDO was highly successful when the fog was shallow, clinging close to the ground. With deep fog that had rolled in off the sea, the burning merely dispersed the fog for the first few feet above the ground. However, even under these conditions, it was helpful when planes had to return to their bases, for some visibility near the ground is better than none.

FIDO was a wartime extravagance. It is far too expensive to be utilized in peacetime except, perhaps, in the most extreme emergency. Far more promising in a practical sense is the idea of dispersing fog through seeding; for since fog is cloud, the same seeding techniques that are known to cut holes in cloud will certainly be useful, at least in some instances, in dispersing fog. It is possible that this application of modern cloud-seeding methods may prove to be more important than their application to rain making. It is also barely possible that in time modern rain-making methods will have taken their place alongside General Dyrenforth's experiments as historical curiosities.

Part Three

Man and the Ocean of Air

In the progress of organic advance which has led through inconceivably numerous stages of existence from the primal base of life to the estate of man, the dependence of beings on the conditions which surrounded them has always been very close. The lowliest organism is influenced by the temperature in air or water, by the conditions of the soil or sea-bottom, or the circumstances which serve to bring it the needful food. . . . When the human state is attained, when the progressive desires of man are aroused, the relations of life to the geography and other conditions of environment increase in a wonderfully rapid way.

—N. S. Shaler

15 The Human Body

The human body is an efficient machine. The volume of the average adult body is equivalent to only two and one-half cubic feet. Yet within that space there is such an effective organization of structure and function that the body is capable of assimilating food, discarding waste products, storing energy, maintaining constant temperature, growing, thinking, warding off disease, and providing the means for reproduction. These primary functions involve thousands of diverse regulatory processes that are closely related to one another and to the physical environment of the body itself.

From minute to minute, year after year, the human body reacts and adjusts to the air in which it is immersed so that its internal environment will remain constant despite violent external changes. Sixteen times each minute, it feeds on air—pulling it into the lungs, extracting oxygen from it, and expelling the air with its carbon dioxide waste given off by the blood cells as they pass through the lung capillaries.

Many of the effects of weather upon the body are indirect and difficult to evaluate. Who can say with certainty what part the weather plays in causing tropical neurasthenia—disorders of the nervous system that are thought by some to be significantly high among peoples of the United States and western Europe who move to the tropics? To what degree is this ailment to be attributed to the heat, rain, and humidity of the tropics; to what degree to diet, lack of exercise, mental strain induced by foreign surroundings, and the daily tropical custom of sipping drinks from work's end until bedtime?

Many of the effects of weather are direct, and of these a few can readily be evaluated. Heat and cold evoke definite bodily responses, and there are both high-temperature and low-temperature thresholds beyond which even the most healthy body cannot continue to live. There are also definite effects of sunlight and of low air densities, such as those encountered on high mountains. Less well defined than these are the effects of various aspects of the weather upon disease, to be discussed later in this chapter.

Medical meteorology is a field in which there are far more questions than there are definite answers. It is necessary to distinguish carefully between proved relationships and merely probable or possible ones.

Heat and Cold

Fundamental to an understanding of the relationship between weather and the human body is the knowledge that has been gained by physiologists concerning heat regulation within the bodies of mammals, including man. Hundreds of millions of years ago, in the Mesozoic era, the reptiles were dominant among the larger animals of the land and air. In that time of mild climates, huge reptiles such as dinosaurs and brontosaurs abounded in the sparsely forested grasslands and along the edges of vast marshes choked with thick grasses and interlocking trees. For hundreds of millions of years these creatures ruled the lands. Then, toward the end of this Age of Reptiles, the mammals came into being.

At first the mammals were small animals and they still possessed many reptilian properties. But among the first nonreptilian characteristics that they gained, along with such changes as those in metabolic rate and the blood circulation system, was the ability to regulate somewhat the temperature of their bodies. Perhaps it was this ability that gave them a decided advantage over the reptiles; so that when over periods of hundreds of thousands of years the climate became more and more severe, with extremes of heat and cold over more and more of the world, it was the mammals with their self-heating and self-cooling systems that took over as dominant forms in wider and wider geographical areas, while the reptiles, at the mercy of the weather, died by the thousands each time an unusual cold or heat wave struck or fought the battle of self-extinction through overcrowding in the slowly contracting mild-climate regions of the world.

The heat-regulating system of many mammals has become more and more efficient over the millions of years since Mesozoic times. Though the environmental temperature may vary widely, these animals can maintain constant body temperature. The reptiles, now a rarity in contrast to their former abundance, remain incapable of body-temperature adjustment. A snake, trapped on a rapidly cooling rock as night comes on, will slowly pick its way toward warmer ground. It moves sluggishly because its metabolic rate is lowered in the cold. Its blood is at a temperature almost as low as the rock across which it crawls. Should the rock cool below the freezing point before it finds warmth, the snake will die—frozen to death because it cannot keep warm.

A price is paid by the mammals for their ability to regulate their body temperature. As Carlson and Johnson state:

> . . . through the long ages of later mammalian . . . evolution the body tissues have become so adjusted to this fairly constant temperature that relatively minor fluctuations in temperature, under abnormal circumstances, are now injurious or fatal to cells, tissues, or the organism as a whole. Cold-blooded vertebrates tolerate temperatures well below 80° F. indefinitely, but mammalian tissues cannot long survive if the body temperature should temporarily fall to 80° F. or rise to 110° F. Needless to state, such temperatures would be reached only when serious defects in the temperature-regulating machinery develop.

The internal temperature of the human body is normally maintained at between 98° and 99°. The adult body, completely at rest, produces in seventy minutes about enough heat to bring one quart of ice water to a boil. In the body-heating process, the fuel is the food stored in the body as carbohydrates and fats; the fire is the oxidation of body tissues; and the pipes for heat distribution are the thousands of feet of blood vessels that comprise the arteries, arterioles, capillaries, and veins of the blood circulation system.

If an unclothed man stands motionless in a room where the air temperature is 82°, his body temperature will begin to fall slowly despite the constant production of body heat. The first body reaction to this lowering of temperature is vasoconstriction: the blood vessels near the surface of the skin contract to decrease the amount of heat lost from the skin to the air. The greatest constriction occurs at the extremities, in the fingertips and toes; the man literally gets cold feet. Still the body temperature continues to fall.

Now other mechanisms come into play. There is a change in muscle tone, and this increases the rate of heat production in the body. If the body temperature still continues to fall, shivering may set in, which changes further the muscle tone and speeds up the production of heat. In all of these processes the trigger mechanisms are messages that speed from cold-perceptive sensory nerve endings to the thalamus, in the forebrain, there to be relayed to the muscles of the skin and of the body interior. Through such rapid reactions the body temperature is brought back up before it has had a chance to slip more than a degree or so below normal.

The mechanisms just described are almost wholly automatic. Among them, shivering is the only one that can partly be controlled voluntarily, for it can often be inhibited at the will of the individual. There are in addition major actions that can be taken voluntarily to prevent the body temperature from falling. Exercise, the addition of clothing, or the ingestion of warm food or liquids all serve to raise the body temperature even though the air temperature is not raised.

Despite its efficiency, the heat-regulating system of the body is not able under extreme conditions to protect it against cold. The first parts of the body to suffer on a cold day are extremities such as fingertips, toes, ears, and nose. In its efforts to conserve heat and so to protect vital inner tissues, the body withholds heat from these outer regions through extreme vasoconstriction, which limits the amount of blood that reaches the extremities. The situation is the same as closing the door to an unused outer room in wintertime in order to hold more heat in the central part of the house. Actual freezing of skin tissue requires a skin temperature of 26°–30°. Because considerable heat is supplied to the skin even in areas of extreme vasoconstriction, unprotected extremities do not freeze until the air temperature is 24°, and then only when a strong wind is blowing. In still air, the temperature must fall to 12° to produce such freezing.

The soldiers who in the last war stood, lay, and tramped through the cold mud on Attu Island know what the combined effects of cold and water can be. When feet and socks and shoes are soaking wet and are embedded in cold mud, the water acts as a most effective conductor of heat. Heat is pulled outward from the foot more rapidly than the body supplies added heat. Blood vessels and even relatively hardy skin tissues suffer damage. Swelling occurs. Gangrene may set in, and in extreme instances amputation is necessary. There were over 25,000 soldiers in the Attu invasion. In one two-month period alone, 1,200 of these were hospitalized with cold injuries. Many underwent amputation of one or more toes or of entire feet as a result of freezing of tissues.

There is such a thing as moderate acclimatization to cold. If a person moves from a hot to a cold climate, his blood and plasma volume slowly decrease over several days, a process that necessarily accompanies increased vasoconstriction. The same effect is observed on a lesser scale when a cold wave hits during winter. On the first day of cold the public rest rooms are unusually busy because liquid is diverted from the blood to the kidneys and bladder due to decrease in blood volume. Another change produced by moving from hot to cold climates is in the level of the trigger mechanism for sweating. In a hot climate, sweating begins at a relatively low temperature to protect the body from excessive heat. In a cold climate, it does not begin until the temperature is distinctly higher, even though the individual may be working and so generating extra body heat.

Some investigators believe that there are changes in the metabolic rate with moves from one climate to another. It is possible also that thyroid activity increases in the cold. Certainly this is true for various animals whose reactions to cold have been intensively studied. The thyroid glands of pigeons are functionally enlarged during winter, then slowly decrease in size in late spring and early summer.

With the body at rest in the shade, the air motionless, the air temperature at about 91°, and the relative humidity at about 60 per cent, the skin feels neither warm nor cold. The body is in perfect balance with the surrounding air. It neither gains nor loses heat.

At higher temperatures, however, the body must call upon its heat-regulating mechanism to hold down body temperature. The first response to heat is vasodilation: the blood vessels of the skin dilate so that body heat will more readily be lost to the surrounding air. Then the two million sweat glands of the body come into play. The significance of sweating in holding down body temperature was demonstrated experimentally almost two centuries ago, although at that time the import of the experiment was not understood. Dr. Douglas H. K. Lee has succinctly described the experiments.

> In 1775 Blagden reported to the Royal Society . . . upon experiments carried out by Fordyce in a heated room at 260° F. Men remained in this atmosphere fifteen minutes, without any noteworthy rise in body temperature, while a beefsteak was nicely cooked in thirteen minutes. These observers noted that water kept in a bucket did not boil, even though left in for some time. They failed, however, to draw the conclusion that man's failure to follow the beefsteak was of a kind with the failure of the water to boil; that evaporation provided the means of heat regulation.

Among the major studies that have been made of the heat-loss mechanisms of the body is one that was conducted in the California-Arizona desert in 1943–44, using United States troops as guinea pigs. The program permitted comparison of body behavior under a wide range of heat conditions. With the air temperature 130° and the sunlight scorching in the clear desert air, soldiers carrying full equipment marched at a stiff 3½ m.p.h. pace for hours on end, with few rest periods. For comparison, others lounged around in the shade. Soldiers dug foxholes, working furiously in the stifling heat. They lay relaxed in hammocks swung beneath canopies that shielded them from the sun. Soldiers drove across the desert in open jeeps. They lay motionless on the desert floor, unprotected from the heat and sun of early afternoon. Soldiers were deployed in dozens of different ways so as to study their reactions to heat under widely varying conditions of air temperature, sunlight, and wind while working, riding, running, marching, walking, sitting, and lying still; and under various conditions of food and water intake. And dozens of times each day, to learn how his body was reacting to the heat, each man was measured and tested.

From this thorough study of the effects of heat under desert conditions much was learned. At 100° F. on a bright day, a soldier sitting in the shade sweats water at the rate of one cup per hour; driving in an open car, he sweats three-fourths of a quart per hour; and walking at 3.4 m.p.h., one quart per hour. This enormous drain on body water —a drain that totals over two gallons on many days—must be made up by drinking water.

If a man fails to replace the water lost as sweat, his pulse rate increases, his rectal temperature rises, breathing is accelerated. In time, there is a tingling and numbness as his blood becomes thicker through water loss and the violently throbbing heart becomes less and less able to force the thick blood through the arteries and veins. He is seized with violent cramps and fits of vomiting. He moves with difficulty, as though half-paralyzed. Things seem confused, detached, far away. Visions appear. When the water loss exceeds 12 per cent of the body weight, and if the air temperature remains high, the deep body temperature suddenly becomes explosively high. If immediate relief is not at hand, the man is killed, cooked to death by his internal tissue heat.

In a hot environment there may be, through sweating, an excessive loss of body salt as well as of water. For the unacclimatized man, especially if he is performing manual labor, the daily salt loss may exceed the voluntary dietary salt intake. For an adult, the remedy is to take additional dosages of salt. Otherwise, with continued and accumulating salt deficiency, he will suffer heat exhaustion.

A person moving to a hot environment begins to adjust physiologically within ten days to two weeks. Complete acclimatization requires four to six months. Acclimatized individuals lose less salt through perspiration. They maintain a distinctly lower pulse rate when walking, running, or performing other exercise. However, they lose just as much water through sweating as do the nonacclimatized, and to make up the total loss they must deliberately drink more water than they crave.

The problem of adjustment to hot environments is especially significant today because there are large areas in the tropics, notably in South America and Africa, that are virtually unpopulated and that offer opportunities for settlement by peoples from the cooler, overpopulated regions in Europe and in parts of the Americas. The available evidence supports the view of Dr. Lee that adjustment to tropical environments is largely a psychological matter. Except in rare instances, as when an individual has an abnormally low number of sweat glands or is abnormally obese, he can adjust to living happily and productively in any region of the tropics, provided his psychological outlook favors making the adjustment. If he considers his tropical sojourn to be a temporary assignment to a hell on earth, the prognosis for his doing well physiologically and mentally is not good.

If he has some strong motivation to adapt, as when he brings his family with him and settles down with the determined purpose to remain in the tropics, the prognosis for his success is excellent. The importance of motivation is illustrated by the experience of the naturalist Richard Spruce, who returned to England in far better health than when he had left, after having spent fourteen years in the Amazon Basin in an avid search for new flora and fauna.

In all environments, so far as comfort is concerned, social and psychological factors play a major role in influencing the effects of air temperature on the individual. The Londoner feels uncomfortable in the average United States home in winter. He can barely countenance the dry air, the temperature of 72°. The American is just as unhappy in a London house in winter, where the temperature is apt to be in the mid-sixties and the windows are kept open to admit damp, cool air whenever possible. A Buganda native from central Africa would be more comfortable in an American home in winter than in a British one; but he would wish that the air were moister, more like that of his homeland. These differences in defining comfort are mostly a matter of taste developed throughout the lifetime of the individual. To a much lesser degree they are a matter of physiological adjustment to the climates of the homeland. So far as the most careful experiments can show, they involve at most only slight physiological variations from one race to another.

Largely at the instigation of heating engineers, numerous studies have been made to determine preferred comfort conditions among persons of the United States. One out of two United States residents is perfectly comfortable in an indoor climate of 68°–83° with a relative humidity of 70 to 40 per cent in summer, the higher temperature tolerance existing only at the lower relative humidities. One out of two is comfortable in an indoor climate of 66°–78° with relative humidities of 70 to 40 per cent in winter. The more extreme the temperature, either toward cold or hot, the lower the relative humidity must be for the air temperature to remain comfortable. Wind also has an effect. Extreme temperatures are less tolerable in the wind than they are in still air.

Ellsworth Huntington, Clarence A. Mills, S. F. Markham, and scores of others have studied at length and in devious ways the effects of temperature on mental activity. Unfortunately, definite conclusions in this speculative field are almost impossible to come by. Yet it is equally impossible to discount entirely the effects of temperature on mental activity. To persons raised in areas such as the central or northeast United States, briskly cold weather does seem to be stimulating, while hot, muggy weather is debilitating and tends to inhibit both mental and physical activity. The changeability of the weather in these regions is thought by many inhabitants to be stimulating, while if such persons move to the rainy tropics they find the weather monotonously depressing. The effects of weather on mental activity require further study, which must include consideration of differences in cultural conditioning from one group of people to another.

Sunlight and Air Density

The direct effects of weather upon the human body are not confined to the effects of heat and cold. Sunshine and air density also have direct and important results. Ultraviolet light causes sunburn. It also converts certain fatlike substances in the skin to vitamin D. If the body is deprived of vitamin D, bones become deformed, teeth suffer decay, and bodily health in general is seriously impaired. Vitamin D is obtainable from egg yolk, fish oils, and many other foods as well as from the action of the sun. However, persons exposed to sunlight for appreciable periods of time each week can obtain thereby all the vitamin D required by the body.

There was a time when it was the vogue for fashionable physicians to consult the barometer in order to relate the diseases of their patients to the rise or fall in air pressure. Then it was commonly believed that air pressure had a marked influence on the course of such diseases as gout and consumption. Today the notion that day-to-day variations in air pressure have an influence on health or disease has been discarded. These variations are only sufficient to produce differences of 1 to 2 per cent in the pressure of the air upon the body; and since inward air pressure is balanced by pressure from the body interior outward, the body is always in balance in this respect so long as the individual does not rapidly change his altitude, as when he ascends in an airplane that is not pressurized.

High-altitude effects upon the human body are brought about by oxygen deficiency rather than by the lowering of air pressure. At Denver, one mile above sea level, there is 15 per cent less oxygen in an average lungful of air than there is at New York or some other sea-level location. Most persons adjust automatically to this slight oxygen deficiency through inhaling more frequently and taking slightly deeper breaths. At about 8,000 feet, where the oxygen deficiency is 22 per cent, there is a slowing down of the reaction time of individuals who have not become acclimatized to the altitude. This accounts for the practice of airplane pilots who, when flying a plane whose cabin is not pressurized, don an oxygen mask when the plane reaches 8,000 feet. Few individuals from low altitudes can even survive without an artificial source of oxygen at an altitude of 22,000 feet, where the oxygen supply is only half that at sea level.

The feat of the Mount Everest expedition of 1922 is unmatched. On this expedition, unlike the one that led to the successful assault of 1953, the climbers did not carry oxygen. Toward the end of their ascent, they were in air that was 60 per cent deficient in oxygen supply. Each exertion placed a strain upon their hearts and lungs. Each minute of painful climbing had to be compensated for by many minutes of rest. Mallory, Norton, and Somervell worked their way to 27,000 feet before finally being forced to retreat.

There are some inhabited tableland areas which rival in height the highest mountain peaks in the United States. In Bolivia, near Potosí, such a tableland throughout its extent lies above 13,000 feet. In Tibet there are contiguous areas, larger than the state of Texas, that are over 14,000 feet high. This Tibetan region is inhabited by natives who have lived there successfully decade after decade and century after century. The region even includes inhabited areas that lie above 16,000 feet. But the highest permanently inhabited area known is in southern Peru, where for tens of centuries people have lived at an elevation of 17,400 feet, where the oxygen deficiency is 43 per cent.

More than any other man, Dr. Carlos Monge, director of the Institute of Andean Biology, has studied the effects of altitude upon permanent inhabitants of the highlands of the world. His chief laboratory has been Peru, which affords the greatest range of inhabited altitudes found anywhere in the world. Dr. Monge has studied old Spanish documents. He has conducted experiments with a wide variety of animals. He has studied, measured, and compared the attributes of highland man as contrasted with lowland man. And he has studied particularly the physiological effects induced by changes in habitation from lowlands to highlands and from high areas to low.

When cats, rabbits, goats, men, or other animals move from low to high elevations of 13,000 feet or more, their reproductive organs often are affected so that they become temporarily or even permanently sterile. When male cats were moved from lowland Peru to Morococha, 13,000 feet above sea level, their testicles became smaller and it became impossible to locate spermatozoa in their seminal fluid. Rabbits were similarly afflicted. Geese moved up the mountain produced no eggs. Sheep were temporarily affected at the relatively modest altitude of 9,300 feet.

The human picture is of particular interest. Shortly after the Spaniards arrived in Peru, they settled in Potosí, 13,000 feet above sea level. Young women were among the early settlers; yet for over five decades no Spanish woman at Potosí gave birth to a child that survived. When, in the fifty-third year, a child who survived was finally born, the event was so unusual that it became known as the Miracle of St. Nicholas of Tolentino. The Spaniards were keenly aware of the effects of altitude on reproduction and health; for when they moved their Peruvian capital from Jauja in the highlands to Lima in the lowlands, they wrote in the Act for Founding of Lima: ". . . neither there [Jauja] nor in its surroundings nor anywhere in the upland could pigs be raised, nor mares nor fowls because of the great cold and sterility of the land and because we have seen by experience among the many mares that have dropped colts their offspring usually die."

Yet high altitude does not inhibit reproduction among those whose forebears have long lived in the highlands. The Peruvian census of 1940 gives a birth rate of 164 per 1,000 women between the ages of fifteen and forty-five for persons dwelling above 13,000 feet, as contrasted with a rate of 144 per 1,000 on the coast. Physiologically, the highlanders are at least as capable of reproducing as are the lowlanders. The Incas at the time of the coming of the Spaniards had long since come to recognize the difference in physiological capabilities between the lowland and the highland Indians. They knew—and their conclusions have since been verified—that highlanders moving to the coast were almost immediately seized with respiratory diseases: pneumonia, bronchitis, pulmonary abscesses, tuberculosis, and related illnesses. They knew that lowlanders moved to the high Andes could not perform heavy labor, and suffered from stomach and lung afflictions.

It would seem that they knew also that marked changes in altitude in either direction tended to result in sterility, or at best in a high rate of childbirth deaths. Because of this knowledge, the Incas maintained special groups of slaves for work at high altitudes and other groups for work along the coast, and one of the punishments they sometimes invoked was to sentence a slave to an altitude zone that was foreign to him.

The studies of Dr. Monge and of a few others in the same field have raised some fundamental questions in the fields of physiology and genetics. How is it that a highland people can evolve with physiological characteristics so sharply at variance with those of most people of the world? Is this merely a matter of acclimatization? It would seem not. It would almost seem that here are peoples who are a special subspecies of the human race. As Dr. Monge states it: ". . . the Andean carries in his organism the hereditary soma which permits life at the great altitudes that mark certain large inhabited areas of South America."

Many authorities disagree with Monge's conclusions, but if he proves to be correct it will be necessary to explain how under present evolutionary theory a new subspecies of man could develop through mutation and selection in the relatively few thousand years that man has been in the Americas. Or perhaps the anthropologists will have to push back further the date of coming of man to the New World—a date that now stands at 20,000–60,000 B.C.

Weather and Disease

The lung and stomach ailments produced by changes in altitude and such other ailments as heat cramps, heat stroke, sunburn, frostbite, and snow blindness are all produced directly by weather or climate. Yet the effects of weather and climate in promoting health or inducing disease cannot be summed up merely in these direct terms. There are indirect effects of weather upon health which in the aggregate are of enormous significance. Some of these effects are clearly established and well understood; many are obscured to such an extent that they cannot be defined, even though the weather factor is clearly important.

Weather has a profound influence upon the incidence of disease where it limits the carriers of the disease or the disease organisms themselves. Dampness and warmth are absolute environmental requirements for the malarial mosquito, which breeds in swampy regions or in the stagnant waters along the edges of lakes or rivers. The mosquito is abroad only at night. Unless aided by wind, it can travel no more than twenty-two miles on a single night, so its radius of action is definitely limited. In areas where malarial mosquitoes exist, a small malaria-infested region may in a few days grow tenfold in size as warm weather pushes back the frontier beyond which the mosquito cannot thrive and as warm rains convert each low-lying hollow into a breeding place.

Hookworm is another disease that is limited sharply by weather. There are two worms that produce this disease in human beings. Each is slightly under a half-inch in length and each penetrates the human skin as larvae, which are carried to the lungs in the blood stream, after which the worm casts off its old skin and makes its way to the stomach and intestines. Hookworm is endemic only in warm, damp regions because the larvae, which are hatched in the soil, cannot tolerate drought or low temperatures. In the United States, the disease is common only in the Southeast, the Gulf states, and eastern Texas. Occasionally, however, hookworm epidemics occur in other regions during spells of warm, rainy weather.

Most common diseases, whether or not the disease organism is directly affected by weather, are more common at some seasons than at others. Pulmonary diseases are most common in winter and least common in summer. Infantile paralysis is most common in summer and its incidence declines sharply with the onset of cold autumn weather. Cholera and other types of dysentery are most common in warm, humid weather.

It is difficult to say just what part the weather plays in creating these seasonal variations in disease incidence. The common cold is an excellent example. Some doctors claim that even moderate exposure to wet or chill weather will often bring on a cold. Yet a few years ago a British physician, investigating this hypothesis, obtained negative results. While one group of men, women, boys, and girls remained warm and dry, a second similarly composed group was exposed to damp and cold. Some members of this second group were required to stand unprotected in pelting rain for several hours, so that their shoes, socks, and other clothes became waterlogged. Others moved suddenly from the warmth of a well-heated room to the cold outdoors, where they walked up and down until thoroughly chilled. Two of the group were immersed in cold river waters and then remained exposed on the river bank for three hours. Nevertheless, the members of this second group did not catch colds with any greater frequency than did the members of the control group, which had been kept warm and dry. To conclude the experiments, the two groups were reversed. The results were the same.

Sinusitis, arthritis, and gout are other diseases whose course seems to be influenced by the weather. Yet there is no agreement as to what constitutes a favorable climate for sufferers from these afflictions. Some persons with sinusitis have fewer attacks in a moist climate than in a dry one; others have fewer attacks in a dry climate.

Probably individual differences are highly important in considering the effects of weather upon disease, just as there are marked individual differences in defining comfort in terms of weather. Perhaps psychosomatic considerations have some bearing on the problem.

Despite confusing and conflicting evidence, the conviction remains that weather is an important element in influencing the incidence and the course of most diseases. The body is a closely knit organism. All bodily functions, including the ability to ward off or subdue disease, are interrelated. It is inconceivable, therefore, that the physical environment to which the body must adjust in dozens of ways should have no influence upon the body's ability to ward off disease or to conquer disease once it has been contracted.

The challenge is to determine precisely how and to what degree the weather operates to aid or hinder the body in its attempts to remain free of disease. One promising line of inquiry regarding this problem would be to study further the effects upon the human organism of changes in the weather. Vital statistics show that the death rate rises every time there is a marked change in the weather. Careful examination of these statistics shows that the rise is due to increased deaths among persons who are already ill. Probably the change in weather, from cold to warm or wet to dry, places upon the body just that added strain which is required to tilt the balance in favor of death. It is possible that weather changes operate in the same manner to influence both susceptibility to disease and the course of a disease once it has been contracted.

16 Agriculture

The achievements of science and technology are now commonplace; and to modern man of this modern day, they appear more revolutionary than any achievements of the past. Yet the most far-reaching achievements in the history of man occurred thousands of years ago. These were the miracles of plant and animal domestication: the beginnings of agriculture.

The unknown men who were the first agriculturalists achieved far more than they knew. They made possible the increase of world populations from a million or so to the two and a half billions that now exist on earth. They made possible a level of civilization that in time would yield the scientific and technologic advances of the present day. Also, they tightened the bonds between mankind and the ocean of air, for the weather is a vital determinant of agricultural success or failure.

Agriculture is bound to the weather through a multiplicity of relationships, all of which lead to one critical factor: the health of the individual plant. Whether the plant is a tree, a range grass, a fiber plant, a grain, or a vegetable, it must respond, throughout its growth cycle, to its constantly changing weather environment. The plant is nourished by moderate rains or ripped from the soil by torrential downpours. It thrives in the warmth of the sun and wilts in the glaring heat of drought-stricken days. Cool, cloudy days slow its growth; deep, sudden freezes destroy it. Sunshine and cloud, heat and cold, rain and drought, wind and calm—to all of these the plant responds continuously. Man can do much to alter the weather environment of the plant. He can water it, shade it from the sun, alter the surface soil to minimize water losses, and plant trees to ward off the wind. He can do all this and more; but he cannot prevent the plant from responding to the weather, nor can he shield it from extreme episodes of weather.

The diverse and often complex relationships between agriculture and the weather have long been studied by experts of many different kinds. The fundamental expert is the farmer himself, who, if he is canny, has an expert knowledge of the weather that may affect his crops and plans his schedule and his day-to-day tasks accordingly. The agricultural geographer takes a much broader view. He likes to think in terms of the world-wide distribution of crops as related to the world-wide banding of climatic regions. The agricultural climatologist is apt to view plant-weather relations with reference to the weather odds as a measure of the chances for agricultural success or failure. There are also the viewpoints of the agronomist, the geneticist, the plant pathologist, the conservationist concerned with the well-being of the land, and many others.

Among them these experts have studied intensively such subjects as the influence of length of day and light intensity upon plant growth, the effects of weather upon plant parasites and plant diseases, the problem of adjusting the farm work schedule to the weather, and how soil conservation can best be practiced from one weather region to another. Each of these many approaches is important in the study of the relations between agriculture and the weather. Each contributes significantly to an understanding of the composite nature of the impact of weather upon agriculture.

Weather and the Farmer

Somewhere this year there will be a major drought. It will lay waste hundreds of thousands of acres of crops and grazing lands. There will also be floods that wash out farmland, hail that batters down the crops, winds that uproot trees and scatter dust across the land, searing heat waves, and freezes that disrupt the biochemical balance within the cells of young, green crops and moist, maturing ones. For the farmer, these are the more spectacular and decisive aspects of weather. He fears these rampant weathers, knowing that they may ruin entire crops.

However, the farmer's concern with weather extends far beyond such major weather disasters. A little higher or lower temperature or a little heavier or lighter rain may greatly affect crop yields, even if there are no freezes, extreme heat waves, floods, or droughts. The outlook for a crop may change from good to bad and back again a dozen times a season with the varying weather. And operations in the field—plowing, planting, cultivating, harvesting, and a dozen others—must be geared to the day-to-day and hour-to-hour weather.

Consider the corn crop several years ago on a 150-acre farm in the western corn belt of the United States. The case is a representative, composite one based on actual weather and crop records for a county in eastern Nebraska.

This was a farm on gently rolling land with twenty acres along the bottom lands, about the same amount lying across the smoothly rounded hilltops, and the rest on middle and lower slopes. This farmer had fifty acres in corn. He also had twenty acres in winter wheat—wheat planted in the fall and harvested in early summer—and twelve acres in alfalfa, eight in sorghum, ten in woodlot, one in vegetables. The remainder was pasture and clover, the clover planted in rotation with the corn to help maintain the soil fertility.

The farmer usually plowed in April, turning under the remnants of the clover that had stood beneath the winter snows. But there had been little snow the previous winter and the soil was dry the first part of April, so he waited for rain and for warmth. By the last week in April it was still dry and cool. To wait much longer would be dangerous, since corn takes about four months to mature and there would be the risk of an early autumn freeze. So he plowed during the last week in April. Still no rains came and still it was cool. Not one, but three, harrowings were needed to break up the hard clods, preparing the soil for the hoped-for rains.

On May 8 he decided to start planting. Of the farmers in his area, only a few were planting in the dry soil; but he decided it was better to plant and take a chance on rain soon than to plant much later, delay the crop, and risk an early autumn frost. By the 15th of May the planting was finished. There had been light rains, but the soil was still too dry for rapid germination and early growth. Worst of all, it was too cool. Corn needs an average night temperature of at least 55° after planting; the night temperature had been averaging 51°.

Late May brought sufficient rain. It also brought cloudy skies that shut out the sun and kept the temperature far too low, so that much of the seed rotted in the ground. By June it was obvious that replanting was needed if any kind of corn crop was to be realized. So thirty of the fifty acres were replanted; the twenty acres on the highest slopes were left without replanting because this land had not been exposed to the coldest air that drained downslope at night.

By mid-June, with temperatures reaching the high eighties in the daytime, the crop sprouted throughout all fifty acres. There were a few light rains from the edges of thunderstorms during late June. In early July, the thunderstorms continued intermittently, but with heavy amounts of rain. One thunderstorm brought hail that slashed down the corn in the far north field. Another brought over an inch of rain in one hour. The runoff from this storm carved a gully along the fence line between the corn lands and the pasture. Two days were required to build rock dams, replant along the new-formed gully, and repair the ripped-out fences.

In late July, the rains stopped and temperatures soared. Maximum temperatures hit 105°. The corn began to tassel and 10 per cent was lost through firing: burning out in the drought and heat. In mid-August, abundant rains began and much of the remaining crop was saved. By early September, there was too much rain—if the rains continued and the corn was too moist, an early freeze would seriously cut the yield. Fortunately, there was no hard freeze in late September and a week of drying weather, though not enough, saved at least 80 per cent of the remaining crop. In mid-October, the corn was cut for silage. Later, part of the silage spoiled because its moisture content, owing to the late continued rains, was too high.

For this particular farmer the corn crop had been poor, but not disastrously so. Yields, deducting losses from hail and firing, had been the equivalent of twenty bushels per acre, as compared with a ten-year average for the general area of thirty-one bushels. The wheat crop harvested in July had done well. It had been unharmed by the early cool weather that delayed the corn, and greatly aided by the moist, warm weather of early July. Good firm heads had been obtained and yields were well above average. Over all it was a year when crop returns were slightly below average.

Crop Distributions and Climate

For all crops, the absolute climatic limits vary from variety to variety and from strain to strain. Even for one particular strain, it is virtually impossible to set precise climatic limits because of the complex interaction of the weather elements themselves and the variety of conditions under which plants are actually raised in the field. From laboratory and controlled hothouse experiments, the agronomist can state the heat and moisture needed for a seed to sprout or the heat and moisture most conducive to heading out or to the formation of new shoots. The conversion of these heat and moisture figures into temperature and rainfall figures is another matter.

If a seed is planted at a depth of four inches, it will be less affected by extreme air temperatures than if planted at shallower depths. If planted in dry soil, it will require more rain than if planted in wet. Under any conditions of planting, the rain requirements will depend on the kind of soil and the slope of the ground. They will also depend on how much evaporation and transpiration occur. To cite an extreme example, in 1920 a twenty-four-bushel yield of spring wheat was obtained on a farm in western North Dakota, with practically no rainfall after planting. Fall rains and heavy winter snows had saturated the soil, which held the moisture well. Temperatures and wind velocities were low and the skies were frequently overcast so that water losses through evaporation and transpiration were slight.

Though the interacting factors that determine the climatic limits of various crops defy precise analysis, such limits actually exist and result in a banding of crops across the agricultural areas of the world.

Hot, cold, dry, and wet are the four cardinal directions on the weather-and-crop map. Some crops, such as corn and hemp, spread across many weather areas. Others, such as the date palm or jute, are relatively confined by weather. All crops have certain weather areas in which they thrive and certain general weather limits beyond which they cannot be grown on a large scale, so that as one moves from weather area to weather area there is a gradual shift from one set of crops to another.

In the cool, drier lands the hardy cereals are the principal crops. Wheat, rye, oats, and barley are all capable of growing under temperatures of 32° to 100° and are able to withstand light freezing temperatures in the early periods of their growth. These are the crops of the great plains areas of North America, the Argentine, Russia, central Europe, and northern China. They are also highly important in northwestern Europe and in the cooler parts of South Africa and India. Where the hardy cereals are raised in the subhumid plains regions, the greatest danger is drought; in moister areas, as in France, the greatest danger is too much rain that may bring with it rust and other crop diseases and parasites. With the hardy cereals, and in some areas replacing them, flax is raised. It too thrives in cooler areas, though requiring slightly more rainfall than the cereals.

The hardy cereals, such as wheat, give way to millet and the sorghums in the drier, warmer areas and to corn in the moister, warmer areas. Millet, the sorghums, and corn grow under temperatures of 55° to 122°; but while millet and the sorghums require less rain than wheat, the commonest varieties of corn require more. In the still moister and warmer areas, rice is the chief cereal crop.

The relation of weather to the distribution of the major cereal crops is well illustrated in northern India and Pakistan, a vast plains area centered about the Ganges River and its tributaries in the east and about the Indus River and its tributaries in the west. The rainfall increases steadily west to east across these lands, from less than ten inches in the middle and lower Indus Plains to over 100 inches a year in the lower Ganges Plain and Delta. Temperature increases from north to south as the higher elevations of the submontane region are left behind and the tropics are approached.

In the densely populated regions of the lower Ganges, rice is the chief cereal crop. Here, in the rainy lands well beyond the reach of frost, the Indian farmer floods the lowland fields in spring with the onset of the seasonal monsoon rains. The rice is sown broadcast or is set out in the flooded fields. When the rains slack off in autumn, the fields are drained and the crop is permitted to stand and dry out before being harvested in late November or December. Sometimes another, winter, rice crop is planted; but if this is done, irrigation must be used since here winter is the dry season.

Northwestward from the heart of the ricelands, the rainfall and temperature decrease. Corn then takes its place with rice as a summer crop, and wheat and barley begin to appear as winter crops. In the cooler and drier areas still farther up the Ganges Valley and in the Indus region, wheat is dominant, the rainfall being too low for rice or corn. In the hotter and drier areas south of the wheat belt, millet and the sorghums predominate, crowding against the hot, dry edges of the Thar Desert.

Weather affects the distribution of all groups of crops. Among the fibers, flax requires cool, subhumid land; jute calls for high tempera-

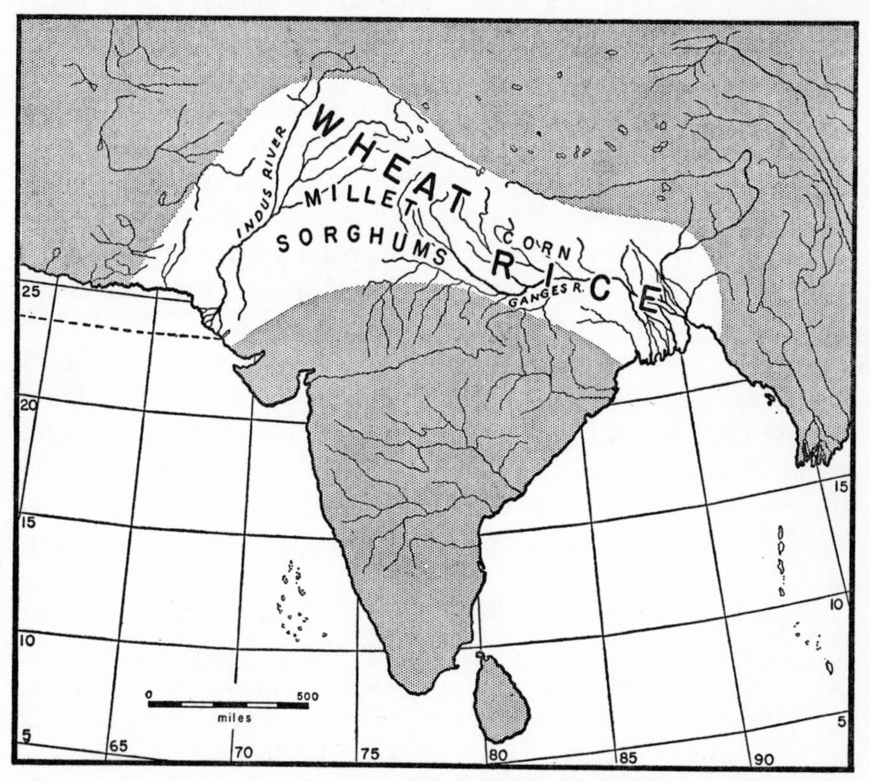

PRINCIPAL CEREAL CROPS OF NORTHERN INDIA AND PAKISTAN

ture and heavy rainfall. Cotton and hemp are intermediate, although hemp, like corn, is found in many climes. The fruits occupy three main weather areas: dates, figs, olives, and citrus in the mild subtropics; the banana, pineapple, coconut, and such fruits as the mango in hot, moist areas; and deciduous fruits, such as the apple, in the cooler and cold humid and subhumid areas.

Vegetable crops too are distributed in patterned form across a wide range of weather areas. Hardy vegetables, such as turnips and beets, are raised in the coldest areas; watermelons, sweet potatoes, and other vegetables that are completely intolerant of cold weather, in the warmest areas. Most vegetables require moderate amounts of rainfall. Only onions, spinach, and certain types of beans can be raised in areas where the rainfall during the growing season is appreciably below twelve inches.

Crops of one kind or another are raised throughout a wide range of weather areas. Winter temperatures in east central Siberia often fall to 60° below zero, and the growing season is scarcely ninety days long. Yet in this region, often called the "icebox of the world," hardy vegetables are grown. In parts of North Africa where the summer temperatures frequently exceed 130°, the date palm is found. In the highlands of the Philippines, rice is abundantly raised, even though the rainfall is over 200 inches a year. At the dry end of the scale, certain sorghums are cultivated without irrigation under as little as eight inches of annual rainfall.

In weather terms, about 42 of the 57 million square miles of land on the earth's surface are suitable today for extensive agriculture. Beyond the limits of extensive agriculture lie 10 million square miles of cold lands, in which the summer temperatures are too low or the growing season is too short to permit the raising of crops. An additional 5 million square miles are too dry for cultivation without irrigation.

These 15 million square miles comprise over one-fourth of the land area of the world. In time, step by step, the scientific studies being conducted in agricultural experiment stations in the Soviet Union, the United States, and many other countries will push back these boundaries of agriculture. Yet progress will be slow. The land regions without agriculture will never shrink to nothing. At best there will come into being a few more narrow zones of specialized agriculture that will emphasize still further the broad climatic basis of crop distributions.

Playing the Weather Odds

Farmers everywhere are playing dice with the weather. If they raise a crop near its weather limits, the dice are loaded in favor of the weather. The weather is favored if cotton is raised where early freezes are frequent, or if corn is raised where late heavy rains are frequent. It is favored if wheat is raised in the semiarid lands, where drought is a constant hazard.

Certainly no snap judgment is ever reliable in estimating the weather potentialities of farmland. An Indiana farmer who came out to western Kansas to see about purchasing some land made such a judgment. Fortunately, he was saved by his own ignorance.

The real-estate agent from Dodge City was afraid he would be unable to sell dry west Kansas farmland to a farmer from rainy Indiana. He was cheered, therefore, when just before the farmer arrived an unusual thunderstorm occurred, flooding the flat fields to a depth of two inches. Proudly he drove the prospective purchaser to the rich, wet fields.

The farmer shook his head. "Too wet to farm out here. I'm going back home."

Less fortunate were the farmers who bought large tracts of land in the western Great Plains in the early and middle twenties. In these years wheat growing was pushed far westward into the semiarid zone where the chances of drought are great. Spurred onward by a series of good rain years and by soaring prices, few farmers stopped to reckon how much the weather dice were loaded against them. In the early and middle thirties the droughts came—droughts which, though they could not have been forecast to the year, were nevertheless sure to come—and millions of acres of land were taken over by the eastward-surging desert. With the droughts came wind, and the powder-dry topsoil from tens of thousands of farms was swept into the air high aloft to be carried eastward beyond the Mississippi and even beyond the eastern shoreline of the United States.

The year-to-year variations in rainfall across northern Oklahoma from 1926 through 1935 illustrate the interplay between desert and humid conditions that characterizes dry marginal lands. On the average, summer rainfall decreases from east to west across Oklahoma, the westernmost part lying in a semiarid zone, the easternmost part in a humid zone. The whole 570-mile stretch from the dry west to the humid east is an area of critical rainfall variation, a condition typical of cross sections of the great plains areas of Canada, the Argentine, Australia, South Africa, and northern India. In 1927, humid conditions extended farther west than in any other summer during the ten years. Across all of northern Oklahoma there were over ten inches of summer rain. Corn yields were excellent.

The year of driest summer was 1935. Only east of Osage County were there over ten inches of summer rain. Corn yields dropped to one bushel per acre in one county, to four to six bushels in others.

Corn requires a minimum of about eight inches of summer rainfall. The chances of getting this rainfall can be readily computed from weather records, and represent the weather odds that the farmer raising corn is fighting against in the long run. In Osage County, Oklahoma, the chances of getting at least eight inches of summer rainfall are approximately five in six; a farmer raising corn in this county runs a one-in-six chance that there will be insufficient summer rainfall. This does not mean that insufficient rainfall will be experienced only once every six years. Two, three, or even more bad years may occur in a row, just as it is possible to roll two, three, or more sevens with two dice, even though the chances of rolling just one seven are one in six.

The odds hold in the long run, but are no guarantee against successive failures in summer rainfall, any more than against successive rolls of the same dice total. In Cimarron County, the odds are only one in five of obtaining at least eight inches of summer rainfall. Obviously the prospects for raising corn are worse there than in Osage County.

Similar agricultural gambling odds can be computed for any area for which there are rainfall records and for any period, even day, of the year. Odds may be found for the date of first heavy frost, high wind velocities, hail, heavy rains, and dozens of other aspects of weather. Through utilizing such odds the farmer cannot free himself of weather, but he can use knowledge of the weather as a sound basis for business calculations.

Photoperiod and Light Intensity

There is one aspect of weather vital to the farmer on which he does not gamble. This is the photoperiod, the period of daylight, which varies regularly with latitude and time of year and has a pronounced effect on the growth of many crops and crop varieties.

The Biloxi soybean is a short-day plant. Grown in the Gulf area of the United States, where summer days are thirteen to fourteen hours long, it thrives and produces abundant seed. Under the fourteen- to fifteen-and-one-half-hour days of more northern states, it matures rapidly but fails to produce seed. The Minsoy soybean is just the opposite; it thrives and produces ample seed in the far northern United States, and is stunted in growth and produces little seed in the South.

Extending agriculture to high latitudes, as to central Alaska, is closely related to the effect of photoperiod on crop growth. In such high latitudes, the early summer days are seventeen to twenty-two hours long, and there is often an abnormal growth of crops indigenous to shorter-day areas. Fruit, stem, or root tends to thrive, one at the expense of the others. Sometimes this is an agricultural asset, as in the case of the strawberry, which grows to giant proportions in Alaska, even though the bush is stunted in growth. More often it is a liability, as with the potato, which grows to abnormal heights but produces unusually small tubers.

In middle and high latitudes, where there is considerable variation in length of day throughout the year, the farmer may time the planting of a crop so that it emerges at a period when length of day will promote the desired growth characteristics. If he wishes to raise a short-day soybean he may do so, even though his farm is in a long summer-day latitude, simply by postponing planting until midsummer. Then, when the plant emerges, it will benefit by the shorter days of late summer.

Light intensity as well as photoperiod has a marked effect on crop growth. Beneath cloudy skies, stems are long and spindly; the seedling plant that germinates and stretches upward rapidly toward the light fails to find sufficient light upon emerging from the soil and continues to grow upward at an abnormal rate. Where sunlight is present on emergence, however, the stem elongates far more slowly and becomes short and stocky. Leaves are affected by light intensity in the same manner as stems, becoming fully expanded in ample sunlight and long and thin when clouds obscure the sun for many days on end. Light also has an indirect effect upon crops since increased light brings increased leaf temperature and transpiration.

Between them, photoperiod and light intensity are climatic factors of primary concern in agriculture. The effects that they produce in the crop plant are not as spectacular as those of severe drought or extreme temperatures. For this reason they are often overlooked in brief inventories of weather-crop relations. But their effects, though often subtle, are nonetheless important. Thus they must be ranked among the principal weather factors that influence the health of agricultural plants.

Plant Pests and Plant Diseases

There are many pests that affect the growth and cultivation of crops. Each has its own weather likes and dislikes, so that weather is an ally or an enemy of the farmer depending on how it affects the pests that endanger his crop. Moist, warm weather favors fungus disease. The fungi develop in small patches on tree bark and plant stems. During moist weather, they swell and exude tiny spores that are carried by the wind to adjacent trees and plants. If the surface on which they land is moist, they multiply rapidly; and if the moist weather persists, the cycle starts once more, with the secondary infections sending out spores to infect the plants of the surrounding area. During rainy weather persisting only a few days, a fungus pest may spread and infect the plants over many hundred square miles.

Most dreaded of the fungus diseases is cereal rust. In the worst year of record, 1916, it cut the spring wheat yield of the United States by 150 million bushels. The crop had done well early in its growth, but July was moist and warm, and across the wheat lands of the Midwest the rust spread, carried by the winds and nurtured by the warm, damp weather. Billions of rust spores were carried by the wind, and each rain brought to earth both spores and the moisture that they needed to reproduce.

Rust epidemics such as that of 1916, and those of 1935, 1937, and 1938, each of which resulted in losses of over 100 million bushels of wheat, are produced not merely by local weather, but by widespread weather situations. Rust spores from late-harvested wheat crops of the northern United States and Canada may be carried by strong north winds far southward into Oklahoma and Texas, there to infect the wheat planted in the fall. With the coming of spring, the rust in the south spreads northward if the weather is damp and warm, moving across the winter wheat fields of Oklahoma and Kansas and into the spring wheat fields of Nebraska, the Dakotas, and Canada. And by fall, if wind and weather are still favorable, the spores may be carried southward and the vast cycle may begin once again.

The effect of weather on plant disease is often complex. Weather affects the plant itself, often making it more susceptible to disease.

It affects the fungus or bacteria, and also the carriers of many diseases. Pear blight thrives in moist weather, but if the weather becomes too moist the insect carriers decrease in number and disease stops spreading.

The plant pathologist searching for the relations between weather and plant disease must often follow a tortuous trail of clues. It was known that drought seemed to stop the spread of curly top, a virus disease that attacks the sugar beet. But neither the virus itself nor the leafhopper that carried it was directly injured by drought. Further investigation showed that there was an indirect effect on the leafhopper: certain plants on which it fed were killed by drought, thus indirectly killing the leafhopper carrier and suppressing the disease.

Insect pestilence, like plant disease, is restricted or spread by the weather. Endemic to every weather region are many insects, some of which are crop enemies. Their weather limits are defined in terms of temperature and moisture. Insects like the San Jose scale, which attacks fruit trees, are limited chiefly by cold weather. Their number and destructiveness vary with minimum temperatures: cold winters wipe out large numbers; warm winters permit their spread into higher latitudes. With the scale, as with other insects limited by cold weather, a succession of mild winters may permit their extension farther and farther into what are normally cold-winter latitudes. Then, with the coming of a cold winter, they disappear from the colder lands and remain confined to their normal weather area until mild winters once more permit their spread.

There is hardly a weather that does not promote the spread of some insect enemy. Warm, moist weather is favorable for the boll weevil, the most damaging of the insect pests that attack cotton. Drought is favorable to the grasshopper and the chinch bug. The chinch bug has a weather problem of its own: when the weather is moist and warm, it itself falls victim to a parasitic fungus.

The complicated connections between weather and crop pests or diseases make it clear why simple, one-factor studies of plant-weather relations do not always apply in actual farming practice. One tenth of one acre of durum wheat raised on an experimental plot of an agricultural college, where fumigation and other treatments suppress plant pests and disease, is not wholly equivalent to 100 acres of the same wheat on a farm in Nebraska. Therefore, to study the yield of such a protected plot in relation to rainfall, temperature, and other weather variables is to arrive at conclusions that will not always hold in practice. The agronomist knows this, but is nonetheless helpless when faced by the necessity to limit his experiments. Though the experimental approach yields results of real benefit, it can never wholly replicate the conditions of actual agricultural practice.

Cultivation and Care of the Land

There is not a major farm operation that cannot best be done under certain specific kinds of weather, and some cannot be carried out at all if the weather is adverse. On heavy soils, plowing must be done a few days after a rain, else the soil will be too sticky, or too dry and full of clods to turn. If the soil hardens under wind and sun, disking is needed. Planting requires a warm, moist seedbed, so the best conditions are found under high temperatures following a light to moderate rain. With some crops, such as tobacco, whose weather needs are well defined, planting may have to be done in dry soil to avoid the risk of early frost later in the season. Then it is necessary to water each hill, a costly process that may cut deeply into the year's profits.

At harvest time particularly, the farmer takes his chances with the weather. Most harvesting, be it of a hay, cereal, or fruit crop, depends on reasonably dry weather. Often the season grows later and later without good harvest weather setting in. Then the difficult decision must be made whether to harvest and garner a poorer-quality crop or to gamble against an early frost and wait for the weather to break.

Spraying and fumigation to eliminate weeds and parasites are effective only in certain kinds of weather. If rain falls immediately after spraying of weeds, the spray solution is washed off and the job must be done again. If it is dry and windy and a sulphate spray is being used, the sulphate will solidify into crystals and be blown away by the wind before it can be wholly effective.

On cool to warm days in southern California, when the wind is not blowing, the citrus orchards are dotted with white tents that cover trees being sprayed. Late winter is the best time for such spraying, since then the chances of rain or very high temperature are slight. Wet tents become sealed, holding in the hydrogen cyanide and causing so great a concentration that the tree is damaged. Temperatures above 80°–85° or relative humidity below 20 per cent cause the spray to vaporize too rapidly. Too much wind causes the tents to sway, permitting the fumes to escape and making it difficult to regulate the amount of spray. The citrus grower, like other farmers, must often wait for the right combination of weather to begin spraying operations.

Nowhere is the mark of the weather upon agricultural land more clearly stamped than in the southeastern United States. There in the cotton lands, the heavy rains of decades have sluiced away the unprotected soil, cutting into the friable underlayer and carving out huge gullies. Many of these are miniature Grand Canyons, 100 to 200 feet deep, with side canyons and "hanging valleys" leading into them. These gullies are the result of the nonattention of farmers of many successive generations who did little to protect their land against the heavy sluicing rains.

For the largest gullies, reclamation is almost impossible. The situation with respect to them is summed up by the comment of a well-known conservationist. He had been called to the Southeast by the Soil Conservation Service to make recommendations for the reclamation of such ruined land. Now he stood with the government men at the edge of a 150-foot gully which, with its tributaries, occupied over 300 acres.

"What would you do with it, Professor?" asked a government man.

"Do?" he said slowly. "I'd make a national monument of the place!"

Not allowing for differences in slope, soil, and method of cultivation, the greatest hazard of erosion through running water exists where rains are most intense. In the United States, this area of maximum hazard is the Gulf states, over which flows warm, moist air from the Gulf and the Atlantic, air within which heavy thunderstorms occur. Too, this is the area most directly affected by hurricanes that move inland, bringing with them torrential and prolonged rain. In this region it is not uncommon to have over three inches of rainfall in one hour, or over eight inches in a day.

Rainfall intensities decrease northward and westward from the Gulf states. They are at a minimum in the desert areas, where more than one inch of rain an hour or three inches a day is uncommon.

Residents of desert areas are apt to overestimate the intensity of rainfalls there, for on the desert there is little or no vegetation to check the rapid runoff and even comparatively light thunderstorms may cause severe local floods. From the deserts westward into California, Oregon, and Washington, rainfall intensities increase slightly; but the West Coast states do not experience as intense rains as do the New England states and the Midwest, much less the southeastern United States.

Wind is the other great destroyer of the agricultural lands. The greatest wind erosion has occurred in the western plains of the United States during periods of major drought. In the Great Plains alone, wind has seriously eroded over 5 million acres of land. One dust storm, that of May 12, 1934, is estimated to have removed over 300 million tons of soil from the plains. The droughts and windstorms of the early and middle thirties and those of the early and middle fifties forced cattlemen and wheat farmers out of vast areas of the Midwest and West. Much of this land has been reclaimed, and the work is going on; but some of it will remain lost to agriculture until the slow healing processes of nature have re-established the grassland and soils.

Microclimates and Farm Geography

Each part of each farm has its own distinctive weather regime, its microclimate. True, the large-scale aspects of weather are expressed quite uniformly throughout even the largest of farms. A general rainstorm brings rain to all of the farm. A cold wave causes the temperature to drop in all fields. But all farms display appreciable variations in weather from one field to another and even within the same field. These variations are not of practical importance so long as the overall weather is favorable. In unfavorable weather, as when there is frost, the variations are often critical.

Where even gentle slopes exist, there are certain preferred areas that will receive the greatest warmth and others that will be most susceptible to heavy frost. Outside the tropics in the Northern Hemisphere, the warmest fields on any farm are those facing southeast or southwest. Southeast slopes are the warmest in areas, such as the Gulf states, where the skies often become cloudy on summer afternoons. There, only the morning sun is unobscured, and the sunlight falls most directly on southeast slopes; the afternoon sun, hidden by cloud, does little to warm the southwest ones. Where afternoon cloudiness is not common, the southwest slopes are warmest, for much of the energy from the morning sun is consumed in evaporating the moisture on soil and crops rather than raising the temperature of the ground and lower air; but by afternoon, when the sunlight falls on slopes facing southwest, a greater part of the energy of the rays goes into raising the temperature and a lesser part into causing further evaporation.

Southeast or southwest slopes are as much as 5° to 10° warmer on summer days than north slopes. They may be as much as 7° to 15° warmer than valley bottoms that are in the shadow much of the day. Even as small a difference as 5° may be critical when a crop such as corn or cotton has just been planted and unseasonably cool weather sets in.

At night the slope relations are also of great importance. On many nights the temperature in valley bottoms is 5° to 15° colder than on middle or upper slopes, a highly critical difference when a frost occurs. And since the temperature differences are greatest beneath clear skies, they are apt to be particularly great when a cold wave occurs, after a cold front has swept through and the cold, cloudless air behind the front is standing over the area.

Not only valley bottoms but any spot that slows down the speed of draining air acts as a cold-air trap at night. Where corn is planted on a slope with pasture above it, the cold air piles up against the upslope side of the corn. If there is hollow or uneven ground that checks the downward flow of air, relatively colder air will collect there. This principle may be used to advantage by the farmer, as in planting a hedge on the upslope side of a vegetable garden to trap the cold air that would otherwise move down into the garden on cold, clear nights. In general, trees, bushes, or tall growing crops will modify appreciably the nocturnal temperature variations on a farm through their effect on air drainage.

The planting of crops affects low temperatures in still another way. As was found in the citrus area of California, interplanting among the trees may increase the danger of frost by lowering the temperature because of radiational effects thus introduced. The plants between the trees have a greater radiating surface than would be afforded by the ground. As a result, cooling occurs more rapidly and lower temperatures are produced than if there was no interplanting.

In certain specialized types of farming, as in the raising of orchard crops, the knowledge of how the weather may vary from one part of a small area to another has been utilized in selecting planting sites. In southern California, slope situations are highly valued as sites for citrus orchards because the importance of the air-drainage effect is fully appreciated. In general farming, there has been less attention paid to these factors. This is partially caused by the necessity of practicing crop rotation, which makes it difficult always to place temperature-sensitive crops on those fields where the most favorable weather odds can be obtained. Nevertheless, even the general farmer can gain appreciably by studying his farm to determine how the weather will vary from place to place and by applying this knowledge in planning crop locations.

Modification of the Weather Environment of the Plant

A master farmer is a weather-control expert. Through shrewd agronomic practices he changes the nature of the weather to which his crops are exposed. He puts in shade plants to protect the growing crop from excessive transpiration. If a high-priced commercial crop is being raised, it may even pay to use cloth canopies for shading, a practice that is followed in raising tobacco in Connecticut. If moisture deficiency is a problem, supplemental irrigation may be used. Or, as in many parts of the West, dry-farming methods may be employed, as when the uppermost portion of the soil is worked into a dry mulch to keep it free of moisture-consuming weeds so that, when rainfall does occur, a maximum amount of water will be retained by the soil.

If it is economically feasible, the character of the plant's weather circumstance can be controlled in even more radical ways. Two farmers near Edinburgh, Scotland, placed a network of steampipes beneath eleven acres of their vegetable farm. Above the crops they placed panes of glass supported by low concrete frames that honeycombed the fields. With this elaborate arrangement, which permitted "weather control" equaled only in a true greenhouse, the farmers obtained phenomenal yields. In one year, 1942, they raised over 300,000 heads of lettuce, 900,000 turnips, 1,000,000 carrots, 46,000 heads of cauliflower, 1,500,000 leek plants, 20,000 bunches of radishes, 250,000 heads of celery, 500 pounds of onions, and large quantities of squash, cucumbers, French beans, mint, tomatoes, rhubarb, and Brussels sprouts.

Such ultramodern means of ameliorating the broad effects of weather are in marked contrast with the method employed by Indian farmers in dry parts of Rajputana. There the Indian farmer plants three grain crops simultaneously: "true" millet, jowar, and bajra, the last two being sorghums. These crops are sown by hand, the seed being mixed and scattered broadcast. Of the three crops, true millet is preferred; but it also requires the most water. Bajra, which requires the least water, is the least preferred. The rainfall of Rajputana is distinctly seasonal. The Indian farmer's chief worry is when the summer monsoon rains will begin. The farmer of Rajputana who sows three grain crops has taken out his own primitive form of insurance. If the rains come early, the preferred millet is left standing and the jowar and bajra are weeded out. If the rains come a little too late for the millet to do well, then the puny millet and the bajra are weeded. Finally, if the rains are very late, there is always the bajra. Insurance against starvation is purchased, but at a high cost in backbreaking human labor.

Between the two extremes represented by laying steampipes and multiple sowing lie numerous other more generally applicable methods of modifying the weather or its effects. In raising crops such as cranberries, flooding may be practiced to guard against freezing weather. Cranberries are raised in low-lying land or swamps, their moisture requirements being exceedingly high. The best-quality fruit is obtained if a long ripening period is allowed in autumn, but to provide this period the cranberry grower runs the risk of heavy frost that may ruin his crop.

Autumn is a time of hard and trying work. The crop must not freeze, but it must be picked, and if picked "wet" it must be set out to dry. The cranberry grower cannot afford to be caught with berries on the drying rack or unflooded in the field when a heavy frost sets in. If a freeze is threatening, the beds must be flooded and drying racks must be moved to sheds in the hope of saving some of the berries. A critical situation develops if rain sets in when the berries are drying. Wetting of berries by the rain may greatly prolong the drying period, thereby exposing them for a longer period to the danger of frost. And wet berries are particularly susceptible to even the lightest frost. So critical is the weather factor during the picking and drying period that the successful cranberry grower must constantly follow the weather forecast and watch the temperature readings at critical spots throughout his bog. His every operation is timed to these forecasts, to what his field thermometers read, and to his own knowledge of what turn the weather will take.

For many other crops, artificial methods of combating freezing weather are employed. Nowhere are freeze-battling techniques more highly developed than in citrus-fruit orchards. In raising high-priced citrus crops, it is feasible to spend considerable money to avoid disastrous freezes, and all kinds of methods for combating frost have been tried out. In one venture a giant fan was used to churn up the air at night, the purpose being to mix the cold air next to the ground with the warmer air lying above. Although the desired result was achieved over a small area, the method proved too expensive to be maintained.

Also tried without notable success have been various methods of changing the rate of radiation and hence of nocturnal cooling by the ground through constructing artificial ground coverings between the trees. These methods succeed only insofar as the new surface radiates heat energy outward during the night at a rate appreciably below that of the natural ground surface, a condition difficult to achieve at reasonable cost. Such metal surfaces as tin cans are not suitable, as was discovered by a vegetable farmer who covered his crops with cans to protect them from a freeze. Only the covered plants were frozen in the morning, the tin cans being far better radiators than the ground and plants.

Of all the frost-fighting methods utilized by citrus growers, the most successful is the use of smudge pots. The pots, which are essentially small oil burners, are distributed throughout the citrus orchard in sufficient number to provide one for each tree. If a frost threatens, smudging is started, the heat from hundreds of small burners acting to raise the temperature of the air near the ground. The fires are lit in a specific order, starting with those in the area where the temperatures are expected to fall the lowest and continuing throughout the orchard until all the pots are burning. Only in rare instances has smudging failed to save an orchard against a freeze when the weather trend was correctly foreseen and smudging was started in ample time.

For most farmers raising general crops, it is economically impossible to purchase weather protection through installing steampipes, flooding, or smudging even where such practices would be suitable for the crops raised. For many farmers it is not even sound economics to take lesser protective steps, such as planting shade crops. But any farmer raising any crop can better his chances of success by knowing the weather odds against which he must fight and the weather needs of his various crops. Armed with this knowledge, he can take steps that will give him maximum protection against adverse weather.

He can plan his farm layout to take advantage of minor weather variations from one place to another. He can plant at those times that promise the best weather chances for success. He can raise those strains and varieties of crops that will best withstand the weather and can practice those methods of cultivation that will protect his land from the erosive forces of rain and wind. In these and in other ways, he can hedge against bad weather. Then, although bad weather brings a poor crop, it may not bring disaster.

17 Industry and Commerce

All forms of agriculture have much in common; all forms of industry and commerce do not. Because of this basic contrast, industry and commerce differ from agriculture in two elemental respects as regards the ways in which they are influenced by the behavior of the air ocean. In agriculture, only the behavior of the lower, tropospheric air is of direct importance; in industry and commerce, that of the high upper air is sometimes directly important. And whereas certain kinds of weather are harmful to all agricultural activities of whatever kind, the weather event that hurts one industrial or commercial enterprise invariably helps some other enterprise. These differences between agriculture and industry and commerce are fundamental.

Agriculture is practiced on the surface of the earth. It is conceivable that in the far distant future a kind of agriculture might be carried out on satellites or space ships, or even Venus. But until that time arrives and until such extraterrestrial agriculture yields vast quantities of food, the only real concern of agriculturalists will be the weather of the troposphere. In contrast, even today there are certain industrial and commercial activities that are directly influenced by conditions far upward in the air ocean. Stratospheric weather already influences airline operations. Magnetic storms of the ionosphere affect radio communication. And tomorrow the weather of the exosphere may influence satellites used as relay stations for radio communication and rockets that carry freight from Lake Michigan to Lake Geneva.

All agricultural enterprises suffer from certain kinds of weather, as from prolonged drought, scouring rains, or sub-zero weather. Yet the drought that overtaxes the reserve of a water company also boosts the sales of soft-drink concerns; the torrential rains that immobilize trucking also fill the dam that provides hydroelectric power; and the sub-zero weather that requires a construction company to stop work on a building in New York is a boon to the tourist trade in Florida and Bermuda. Such opposite responses to any given weather situation are inevitable because the terms industry and commerce embrace a large range of activities.

Since there are many thousand categories and facets of industry and commerce, there are also many thousand unrelated, highly particular relationships between weather and industrial or commercial activities. Considered individually, most of these relationships are not sufficiently critical to determine whether an enterprise will succeed or fail in a particular place at a particular time, even though they are of pressing practical concern.

It is, for example, true that cloudy weather abruptly boosts the consumption of gas and electricity; that weather changes require adjusting the rate of air intake in blast furnaces; that a heat wave sharply decreases consumer demands for breadstuffs; that if it strikes without warning, a hurricane will demolish costly oil-drilling equipment in the offshore fields of the Gulf of Mexico; that an unexpected afternoon shower increases retail sales through causing shoppers to take shelter in nearby stores; and that heavy rains delay the laying of cement.

Yet even though these effects are operationally important, they almost never determine whether a gas or electric system will be installed; where steel mills are constructed; when a wholesale bakery or retail store will fail; what areas will be tapped for oil; or whether a construction project will be undertaken. Though of immediate practical consequence, particular relationships of these limited kinds cannot be said to constitute major themes relating the weather to industry and commerce.

In contrast, there are a few industries in which the weather factor is of great economic consequence. Among these are the lumber, insurance, and fishing industries. The lumber industry is vitally concerned not only with the agricultural problem of raising trees but also with the highly specialized problem of fire hazard and control.

The insurance industry must reckon in practical, money terms the probabilities of natural weather disasters and the influence of more usual kinds of weather upon insurance risks of many kinds. The fishing industry must consider how certain kinds of successive weather conditions will cause whole schools of commercial fish to migrate hundreds of miles. Problems such as these involve highly specific weather relationships. They have led, in recent years, to the development of private meteorological firms and to the establishment of meteorological departments in many industries.

On a broader scale, there are three general themes that relate industry and commerce to the weather. First, the nature and degree of industrial and commercial development in many regions reflect the weather conditions of that region; more particularly, relatively underdeveloped regions are, in fact, precisely those regions in which the weather is a barrier to the flourishing growth of the industry and commerce of western culture. Second, the whole complexion of the industrial life of the future is strongly linked to the weather because in time the wind and the sun will become major sources of power. And third, the character of transport, especially in the air, is partly dictated by weather considerations. These are the themes that require the greatest emphasis; but to achieve a balanced view, it is necessary to consider first one specific example of the weather problems of a single industry.

The Lumber Industry

Lumbering is based on tree culture. This aspect of the lumber industry is agricultural and the weather therefore enters as a prominent economic factor and in much the same ways as in other agricultural enterprises. There is, however, the specialized problem of the weather as it has a bearing on fire hazard and upon the damage done by a fire once it has started. These critical fire-weather relations have been studied intensively for many decades, chiefly by national forest services, but also by state services and private companies. The knowledge gained through these studies has been put to practical use and illustrates the point that industries confronted with a weather problem can help solve that problem through applied scientific research.

One of the great industrial resources of the United States is its 525 million acres of lumber—lumber in the form of spruce, maple, and Norway pines of the Northeast; hardwoods of the middle East; the pines of the Southeast; and the pine, larch, and magnificent Douglas fir of the West. The greatest enemy of these resources is fire. The greatest ally of fire is the weather.

Most feared are long, hot, dry periods in summer when the litter and duff on the forest floor become so dry that the spark from a passing train or the heat from a glowing cigarette is sufficient to start a low brush fire. Then, if the wind is blowing, the fire will run along the forest floor until soon the dry foliage and branches above are also ignited and a major fire is under way.

Lightning too starts fires, striking usually at the tallest trees. If the weather has been hot and dry, one lightning storm may cause numerous fires throughout a large forest tract. The greatest lightning hazard is in the West, particularly in the coastal states, where long, dry summer periods are common, and summer lightning storms frequently occur with little or no accompanying rainfall. In one year, 1926, there were 3,250 lightning fires in California, Oregon, and Washington, constituting 36 per cent of all the fires for that year.

Fire fighting is largely a matter of fighting the wind. With no wind, fire control is relatively simple: ground fires, in shrubs and duff, are fought by spanking out the fire or digging ditches to stop its advance; crown fires are fought by burning out an area ten to fifty feet ahead of the advancing fire. With a wind blowing, the fire spreads more rapidly, at a rate proportional to the square of the wind velocity. This means that the spread is four times as rapid in a ten-mile wind as in a five-mile wind, four times as rapid in a twenty-mile wind as in a ten-mile one. With a stiff wind, fire control is exceedingly difficult and hazardous. Frequently, the only chance of halting the fire is to start a backfire after falling back to a river, plowed field, cleared ridge, or to a belt of barren land especially bulldozed and cleared for the purpose.

Even when a backfire is started, the weather may at the last moment thwart the efforts of exhausted fire-fighting crews. Hundreds of men may have worked around the clock felling trees, pushing bulldozers, hauling fallen timber, digging ditches to construct a fire break. The backfire may have been started to burn out the area ahead of the fire and rob it of its needed fuel. And then the weather may change.

It was a shift in wind from the north to the east and a sudden drop in humidity that caused the great Tillamook fire of 1933 to blaze up and overrun 270,000 acres of fine Oregon timberland after ten days of almost continuous work by hundreds of fire fighters had finally brought the fire under control.

The Tillamook fire burned out over 12 billion feet of lumber. Of this over 10 billion feet, an amount equal to over one-fourth of all the lumber used in the United States in 1957, would probably never have burned had the wind not shifted and the humidity dropped. The weather also played a part in stopping the fire. Twenty-four hours after the blaze got out of hand, the wind shifted again. Where the fire had been racing with the speed of wind along the tree crowns, it now became enveloped in dense, fire-quenching fog borne inland from the adjacent Pacific by light westerly winds. It became a simple ground fire that was readily extinguished.

The role of the weather in the Tillamook fire was not exceptional. The fire started like all major forest fires in weather that was dry and hot and windy. Its control was as always a matter of anticipating what the wind would do. In this instance the wind shifted too rapidly for control measures to be altered accordingly.

Foresters are weathermen of necessity. They have developed special weather-rating methods so that they can remain constantly posted on the degree of fire danger within the forested area they guard. The elements usually used in rating the weather for fire danger are the amount of the last rain, how long ago it occurred, the condition of the vegetation, the wind velocity, and the fuel moisture content of material on the forest floor. The water content of forest floor materials may be as low as 3 per cent by weight or as high as 50 per cent—either powder-dry or so soggy that it cannot possibly burn.

The moisture content is determined indirectly by weighing indicator sticks that have been exposed on the forest floor. When it has been a long time since the last rain and that rain was a light one, when fuel moisture content is low, when the vegetation is cured rather than green, and when the wind is blowing strongly, a major forest fire is in the making. This is an extreme example of what under one rating system is termed a "class 5" condition, one of maximum danger. Under class 5 conditions, fifty-six times as many fires have occurred in the southern Appalachian area as when the weather was class 1, least favorable for fire.

By using historical weather map series, such as those developed by the U.S. Army Air Forces during the war, and employing one of the standard fire-weather rating schemes, it is possible to determine the frequency with which dangerous fire conditions can be expected to occur in any forest area at any time of the year. Such actuarial values permit the scheduling of fire patrols and other preventive measures on a sound yet economical basis throughout the year. This approach is also helpful in making fire weather forecasts by permitting even a novice forecaster to draw upon a knowledge of the hazardous conditions of the past.

Private and Industrial Meteorology

The realization, in recent years, of the practical importance of the weather in industrial and commercial enterprises of many kinds has resulted in the birth of a new type of commercial business, that of the private meteorological consulting firm. The first really successful enterprise of this kind was established by Professor Irving P. Krick in the late 1930's, when he was still on the faculty of the California Institute of Technology. Krick issued special weather forecasts for the motion-picture industry, which had to schedule outdoor shooting in advance, for construction firms, and for many other industrial and commercial interests. He also provided highly useful consulting services. The firm remained the only one of its kind anywhere until the attack on Pearl Harbor, when Krick discontinued his private business and concentrated on teaching and forecasting in support of the prosecution of the war.

After the war, Krick re-entered business, and soon several other competing firms were established in major cities of the United States. Today there are more than twenty. Their numbers are small, but they are growing.

In addition, many industries have established meteorology departments within their organizations. Du Pont, Hartford Life Insurance Company, Pacific Gas and Electric, and others have found that it pays to allow, in a calculated scientific sense, for the influence of weather upon their industries, whether the problem is one of designing smokestacks for a new factory, estimating the frequency of damages caused by storm and wind, or dispatching gas in an economical manner by anticipating how the changing weather will change consumer demands from day to day and even hour to hour.

The Underdeveloped Lands

The deserts, the polar lands, the rainy tropics—these are the underdeveloped lands. Each one possesses a weather personality that is a barrier to the industrial and commercial expansion of the modern world. In the desert, the barrier is lack of water. In the polar lands, the barrier is cold. In the rainy tropics, there is such a luxuriance of intermingled warmth and moisture that it is almost impossibly difficult to wrest from nature and to hold lands that are continually threatened by the resurgent growth of vegetation.

Here and there western man has successfully breached these weather barriers, but he has done so only where the economic rewards were so great as to justify vast investment outlays, or in time of war, when the usual economic considerations do not apply. Some day, tens of years from now, the gates must be lowered to accommodate the influx of peoples from an overcrowded world.

That such a lowering has not yet taken place to any appreciable degree is evident from the staggering size of the underdeveloped lands. Antarctica, Greenland, the barren polar lands of northernmost Canada and Siberia; the Amazon Basin, great reaches of tropical Africa, and the scattered warm and rainy lands of southeast Asia; the Sahara, the Arabian Desert, and other major deserts of the Old World together with those smaller deserts of the New—among them these lands total over 15 million square miles, over one-fourth of the total land area of the earth.

In part, industry and commerce tend to follow agriculture; therefore the linkage between weather and the distribution of industry and commerce rests partly upon the relation between weather and agriculture. The markets for industrial products are the densely populated regions of the world, which either coincide with highly productive agricultural regions, as in much of the Orient, or are embedded in such agricultural regions, as in the Occident. Yet only in a few places, and then only on a local scale, can the polar lands, the rainy tropics, and the deserts support the highly productive agriculture that is necessary for the existence of densely populated market areas.

Where industry attempts to penetrate farther and farther into these inhospitable lands, it is handicapped more and more by the increasing costs of transporting goods over ever-increasing distances to the primary areas of consumption. Nor is increasing distance the only cost factor; in these same weather regions the transportation costs are far higher, mile for mile, than in other parts of the world.

Where land transport is concerned, much of the added cost in

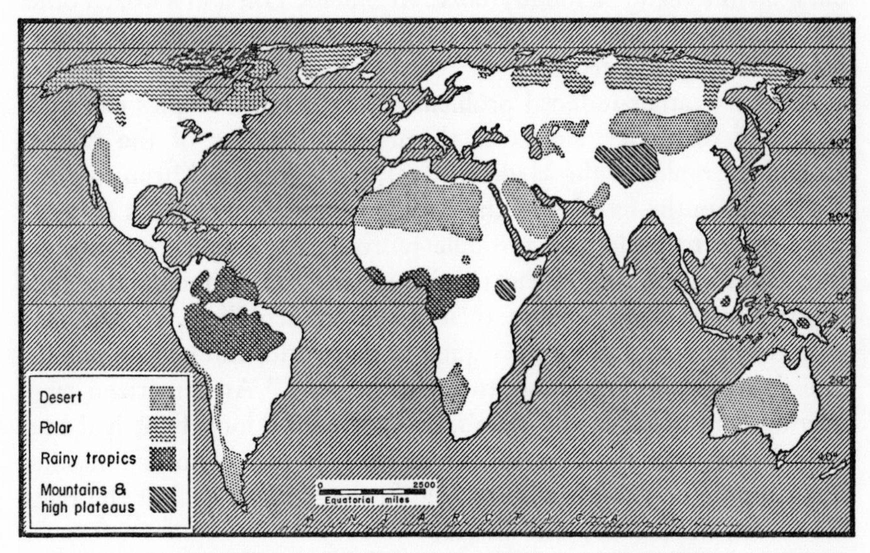

THE MAJOR UNDERDEVELOPED LANDS OF THE WORLD

polar, rainy tropical, and desert regions is the result of the enormous price paid for initial construction. During World War II, the builders of the Alcan Highway, which runs from Edmonton, Canada, northward to the Yukon, then west to Fairbanks, Alaska, had to battle the weather continually, winter and summer. They triumphed only through the greatest ingenuity, and then at a high cost in dollars and in lives. With temperatures running 40° to 60° below zero in the wintertime, they kept fires burning at night beneath idle machines that otherwise would have become frozen in, solid as rock. Unable to wash clean the aggregates used in mixing concrete, they constructed drying plants, baked the aggregates dry, and cleaned them by blowing out the impurities. They designed and installed special heaters to raise the temperature of newly set concrete sufficiently high that it would set.

They blasted out basins along river channels to prevent the ice from crowding in to crush bridges that were under construction and built the bridges unusually high to allow for ice jams when the thaw would arrive. In summertime they fought mud and muskeg and mosquitoes. They employed special wide-webbed tractors that could traverse deep mud without bogging down and could even cross muskeg terrain despite the blisters that, under the weight of tractors, burst open to exude a muddy ooze. At Suicide Hill and a dozen other places many of them died. On a steep, icy road, brakes do not always hold a twenty-ton truck.

All the weather-induced problems that the rainy tropics can yield conspired to hinder, almost to thwart, the building of the railroad around the rapids of the Madeira River, from Guajará Mirim to Pôrto Velho, far in the interior of the Amazon Basin. Three times attempts were made to build this 250-mile railroad. An English engineering firm failed at the task in the 1870's, declaring in its failure that "the country was a charnel-house, their men dying like flies . . . and that, with the command of all the capital in the world, and half its population, it would be impossible to build the road." An American engineering firm failed in the 1880's, but not until a long fight had been waged that took the lives of 221 of the 941 men who had reached San Antonio on the Madeira to help in the struggle against the rains, the forest, the insects, and disease.

With the third attempt, in the early twentieth century, the line was finally completed, despite rains that repeatedly sluiced away the earth from beneath the railroad tracks, converting them to twisted ribbons hanging in mid-air; despite the forest canopy that robbed the sun of its light yet stored its heat in the still, moist air between ground and canopy and held it there, night and day, unceasingly. It was completed—and these were the worst of all opponents to success—despite the insects and disease.

Tomlinson describes visiting one of the many medical stations that were maintained by the construction company that finally completed the job:

> The labourers, halfbreeds, Brazilians, and Bolivian Spaniards, work being over, were giving the doctor a full evening with their ailments. Mostly these were skin troubles. The least abrasion in the tropics may spread to a horrid and persistent wound. The legs of the majority of

> these natives were unpleasant with livid scars. In one case a vampire bat had punctured a man's arm near the elbow while he slept, and that little wound had grown disastrously. We were in a region where the pium flies swarmed, tiny black insects which alight on the hands and face, perhaps a dozen at a time, and gorge themselves, though you may be unconscious of it. Where the pium fly feeds it leaves a dot of extravasated blood which remains for weeks, so that most of us were speckled. Even these minute wounds were liable to become deep and bad. There were larger flies which put their eggs in the human body, where they hatch with dire results. . . . So the doctor was a busy man that evening.

There was also malaria, with chills and fever despite quinine, and with the occasional severe complication known as blackwater fever.

There is no greater contrast than that between the rain forest and the desert, and this contrast is reflected in road building as in other human activities. The desert nearly always provides a good roadbed and there are no major problems of washouts, of the clearing of vegetation, or of insects and disease. These advantages are partly offset by the heat, the savage sunlight, and the shortage of water. To avoid heat and glare, it is best to work at night or in the first few hours after sunrise. Whatever the timing of the work, water must be hauled constantly to meet the needs of men and machines and to permit the mixing of cement. The costs of highway and railroad construction are not nearly as great in desert regions as in polar ones or in the rainy tropics, but mile for mile they are still substantially greater than in the relatively mild and well-watered regions of the world.

The disproportionately high cost of highway and railroad construction and of maintenance also, especially in the rainy tropics and polar areas, has helped to inhibit the development in desert, tropical, and polar areas of those kinds of transport nets that are familiar to those living in the milder regions of the western world. Instead, the transport nets are partly residual, carrying forward into modern times modes of transport whose roots lie deep in history, and partly ultramodern, relying to an even greater degree than elsewhere upon modern air transport. In Alaska, the Amazon, and the Sahara, the traveler flies from place to place. But air transport is expensive. Only rarely can bulk goods be flown from place to place. And so the ancient forms of transport remain.

In the polar areas the sled remains important locally, even though it carries no great tonnage of goods; and in the summer season, the coastwise water transport supports bulk movement of considerable magnitude. In the rainy tropics, the rivers are the transport arteries. The rivers bind the land together, but they also cut it up into long strips that are readily accessible and vast hinterlands that are beyond all reach. It is nothing to move 500 tons of goods from Belém up the Amazon to Manaus, 1,200 miles away; but to move it from Manaus twelve miles into the hinterland is quite another matter.

In the Sahara and elsewhere the camel caravan still moves major quantities of goods, even though a Westerner may take the weekly bus that crosses the Sahara from Touggourt in Algeria to Gao on the Niger River far to the south. As for river transport in the desert, where there is a through-flowing stream like the Nile, the Euphrates, or the Indus, it is thronged with traffic.

The barriers erected by the cold and snow of the polar lands, by the warmth and moisture of the rainy tropics, and by the heat and drought of the desert are not absolute. Though these areas can seldom support either the kinds of agriculture or of industries necessary to the establishment and maintenance of large populations, they do permit specialized industries that support small population clusters. In this sense the barriers are like semipermeable membranes that can be penetrated by some kinds of particles but not by others.

It is chiefly the extractive industries that can successfully invade the lands that are inhospitable to most western industries. Minerals, timber, fish, and furs are garnered wherever the natural and economic situations permit. The factors of natural and economic permissibility result in geographic patterns of industrial location that are distinctive and unique for each of the three major weather regions.

In the icecap provinces that are the heartlands of the polar regions, there is no industrial activity of any kind. The icecaps support no animal life of any economic significance and no forests whatsoever. If they held the richest mineral resources in the world, those resources would still be economically inaccessible. However, toward the margins of the polar regions, as in central Alaska, northern Canada, and Siberia, the pattern becomes a positive one.

First there are the wide areas across which native peoples or hardy individualists from the western world set out their trap lines to tend them and bring to the trading posts the pelts of ermine, mink, marten, fox, and other animals that grow especially luxuriant fur in cold, polar climes.

Second, and far less widespread, are the areas in which there is a harvesting of the forests. The polar forests yield trees that are dwarfs as compared with the trees of the tropics, but they have the advantage of growing in pure stands that frequently include but a single species and usually not more than two or three. This is a situation that favors inexpensive logging, and more and more the edges of these forests that are closest to the major population centers are becoming the supply areas for lumber and especially for the timber used for woodpulp and newsprint.

In terms of the size of the area involved, the third greatest industry is that of fishing, which pervades the subpolar seas and the rivers that pour into those seas. Finally, in a few scattered locations there are mines that tap resources so rich in uranium or gold or copper or some other mineral that mining camps have sprung up and taken root.

Because of these primary industrial occupations, secondary industrial activities have come into being. Sawmills and fish canneries and milling plants lie along the edges of the polar lands, and each such installation attracts and holds a small population cluster. The total pattern for the polar lands is therefore one of icecap core regions, virtually devoid of all activity and all inhabitants; of thinly inhabited regions where trapping and lumbering prevail; and of scattered settlements where there are mines, sawmills, milling plants, or canneries.

In the rainy tropics, mining is carried on wherever the deposits are sufficiently rich to warrant exploitation. There are gold mines toward the headwaters of the River Fly, in New Guinea, only because the ore is so rich as to permit flying ore concentrate to the coast.

There is also lumbering, but on a far more limited scale than in polar lands. To harvest the forests in these areas is to cut down individual trees on a highly selective basis from among the myriad species that comprise the tropical forest. To log off land in such a discriminating manner greatly increases the cost; therefore, the forests of the rainy tropics are harvested only to a limited extent and only in areas close to the few good transport routes.

As for fur and fish, the rainy tropics have little to offer. There are a few pelts to be garnered from tropical lands, such as those of the leopard; but this is a wholly minor, maverick operation. Tropical fish of commercial value abound chiefly away from the continental masses and their harvest imposes a pattern of utilization that is associated chiefly with the open seas and that seldom supports local canneries.

Most unrewarding of all regions are the deserts. Their only industrial asset is minerals, and these must be economically available, so that the deposits must be rich, easy to transport, or inexpensive to mine. In some desert areas, as in the deserts of the Near East, petroleum is profitably mined because the deposits are rich and transport costs, by tanker or pipeline, are not excessive. Still more valuable minerals, like uranium and gold, are mined on a small scale in many scattered desert localities, where the richness of the deposits more than offsets the high cost of water and transport.

Cheap minerals are mined also, but only where they are both abundant and readily accessible. Borax, gypsum, and salt are among the cheap minerals mined on the desert, for often they are found in deep, almost pure deposits, which can be scooped up by steam shovel or pumped up in solution from deep wells at a cost that is trivial as compared with most mining operations.

The pattern, then, for desert, rainy tropics, and polar lands alike is one of industrial poverty—of occasional use of resources here and there, but of far less intensive industrial development than in other regions. And since this pattern matches that of agriculture, which also is little developed throughout these lands, it follows that in the world of today these are the barren lands that fail to support an appreciable proportion of the population of the world.

Yet the world's population is increasing rapidly. In 1850, the world population was about a billion. In 1950, it was 2½ billion. Barring a third world war or famines of unimaginable proportions, by 2050 the population pressure will be so great that, merely to gain living space if for no other reason, the polar lands and rainy tropics and deserts will have to be invaded on an unprecedented scale despite their weather barriers.

Tomorrow these lands will witness greater and greater inroads of industry, commerce, agriculture, and people. These inroads will be of two kinds. In many instances it will become not merely economically feasible but absolutely necessary to accept the weather penalties that these lands exact. In a few particular instances, technology may overcome these weather disadvantages and make it economically desirable to invade what are now the inhospitable lands. But whatever the future decades may bring, the weather characteristics that identify these areas will continue to be reflected in the distribution of industrial activities and in the forms whereby those activities find expression.

Wind, Sun, and Energy

Man has always utilized the energy provided by the wind and the sun. The earliest men drew upon the energy of the wind to cool themselves when they were hot, to help them to dry when they were wet, and to carry away the scent of the hunter and so permit him to stalk game on the downwind side without detection. After man became the master of fire, the wind became his ally for driving game, through his setting the grasslands ablaze. And through the thousands of years that followed, the wind was utilized for such varied purposes as to winnow grain, to power ships, and to turn windmills that lifted water, ground grain, or recharged electric batteries.

The uses of solar energy have been even more extensive than those of the wind. In a basic sense, the sun is the source of virtually all the energy that exists upon the earth. Sunlight permits photosynthesis in plants, and so is the source of the energy that man himself draws both from plant foods and from the food he obtains from animals, all of which directly or indirectly depend upon plants for their existence. Also through photosynthesis, the sun is the fundamental energy source for the secondary energy stored in wood, peat, coal, petroleum, and natural gas.

Most of these and many other relationships that have in the past linked the activities of man to the energies of wind and sun will retain their fundamental importance so long as man exists. But in addition, because of recent technologic advances, the wind and sun are certain to become direct energy sources of great importance to the industries and commerce of the future. And this is true despite the advent of nuclear power.

Nuclear energy will certainly become a power source of great importance to industry and commerce, but it will never become the sole source of energy. Ever since he learned to control fire, man has relied directly upon multiple sources of energy. Fire released the energy stored in wood and added this energy source to that residing in the muscles of man himself. Later such animals as the horse and ass and ox were domesticated and their energy came to be used for many purposes, from carrying man and his belongings to turning a water wheel or plowing a field. Later still, yet long before the Christian era, asphalt, petroleum, and peat were burned to release the latent energy that provided heat and warmth.

Today there are many sources of energy: the muscles of man and of domesticated animals; wood, peat, coal, petroleum, and natural gas; the running water that provides hydroelectric power; atomic fission; and the wind and the sun. Each has a place not only in different cultures but also within the most sophisticated western cultures. Coal is an excellent energy source for smelting, but is certainly not economical for propelling automobiles. The electricity derived from the energy of running water is ideal for driving many kinds of industrial motors, but is hardly appropriate for moving a ship across an ocean. Similarly, nuclear energy will be useful for many purposes, but not for all, or even for half of all. There will remain the familiar energy sources, and in addition, more and more, the energy available from the wind and the sun will come to play directly important roles in many industrial and commercial situations.

For the wind, the possibilities for the future were underscored by the development of a wind-driven electric generator that was in actual use for a period of almost four years in the early 1940's.

The idea of constructing a true, full-scale electric generator to be driven by the wind was born in 1934. In that year Palmer Crosslett Putnam, a young engineer, pondered the problem of how to obtain electricity cheaply. That wind power was going to waste there could be no doubt. Nor did Putnam need to be told about windmills. Having lived for some time in the Midwest, he was well aware that windmills are commonly used not only to draw water from wells but also to charge storage batteries during times of high wind speed. But storage batteries and generators are two different things. Even when the wind is blowing, a windmill cannot be used to run a full-scale generator. A generator has to turn at a constant rate, and with variable windmill speeds it would be impossible to control its output.

After three years' work, Putnam at last felt certain that he had a fundamentally sound design. Its basic feature was a system whereby the blades of the wind-driven turbine would change pitch automatically to maintain a constant speed so long as the wind speed was at least 17 m.p.h. He then sought out Dr. Vannevar Bush to obtain support for his project. Bush studied the plans. He liked them. Then things began to happen. Bush phoned Beauchamp Smith, president of the S. Morgan Smith Company, of York, Pennsylvania. Would he be interested in this project? He certainly would. His company made water wheels and here was something new and promising, right in his line. Within a few months a plan emerged, a plan for co-ordinated action.

The key company in the plan was Central Vermont Public Service. They would foot the bill and would install the generator as part of their power system. The wind generator would be thrown into the line whenever extra power was needed and the wind was blowing at sufficient speed. Thus they would save just that much precious water, which otherwise would have to be discharged over the dam to provide an equivalent amount of electricity.

The Smith Company would build the turbine; the Budd Company, the stainless-steel parts; General Electric would provide the electrical equipment. The Guggenheim Aeronautical Laboratory at Akron would run the wind-tunnel tests and the results would be reviewed by von Kármán of the California Institute of Technology. Other consultants would be Dr. Griggs of George Washington University on ecologic problems, Newell of M.I.T. on structural analysis of the turbine blades, Petterssen of M.I.T. on weather problems. Professor Hurd C. Willett, a top-notch meteorologist and an excellent skier, was to scout the countryside, even though it was the dead of winter, to find a suitable generator site.

There were delays and difficulties and shortages of critical materials. Finally, on Sunday, October 19, 1941, atop a hill known locally as Grandpa's Nob, overlooking the Champlain Valley, the Smith-Putnam wind turbine was ready to start operation.

Over 200 people were there to witness this first capturing of the wind for the large-scale production of electric power. The group gathered in the control room at the base of the tower could hear, above the voices of the speechmakers, the whine of the wind about the tower, the steady whir of the generator overhead, and the deep, throaty hum of the two turbine blades, swinging round and round, tracing enormous circles in the air. Finally the time had come. Putnam threw a switch and 1,250 kilowatts of power, enough to light a town, surged from the generator, sped downhill through the high-tension wire, and raced into the main transmission lines of the Central Vermont Public Service Company.

Except for a minor interruption when a bearing failed, the Smith-Putnam turbine remained in operation for almost four years. During that time it was operated in conjunction with hydroelectric and steam generators of the Vermont system and was thrown into the line whenever needed, provided the wind speed was high enough. Then on March 3, 1945, just before dawn, one of the blades snapped and hurtled downslope. Quickly the operator in the control room cut off the power and feathered the remaining blade. Though he did not know it, the test program had ended.

The Central Vermont Public Service Company seriously considered ordering and installing a new turbine. But the damage had been great and they had spent far more than originally planned for the initial installation. Furthermore, they had hoped to obtain power at the foot of the generator at a cost of $.0025 per kilowatt hour. Their actual cost had been slightly higher. Regretfully they closed down the project. As their president explained, they were a small company without large sums of reserve capital, and they were responsible to their stockholders.

In a broad sense, the wind generator experiment was not a failure. In the field of engineering, pioneer projects are often uneconomic. Beauchamp Smith, whose company built the Smith-Putnam turbine, has this to say about what was learned from the experiment: "We think we could now design, with confidence, 2,000-kilowatt wind-turbines incorporating important improvements leading to smoother operation, simpler maintenance, and lower cost." Putnam believes that wind turbines may become a highly important source of power in many parts of the world. Most meteorologists who have studied the question agree with him.

That wind-driven generators will become more and more important in the future seems certain despite three limitations imposed by this kind of power source. The first limitation is that, within or near an area requiring electricity, there are not always sites where wind speeds are high enough a sufficient percentage of the time to permit the economic harnessing of wind energy. Because of this, the wind is actually a potential source of electric power only over 10 to 20 per cent of the land area of the world.

Second, there is no site on earth where the wind speed is invariably, night and day, year in and year out, sufficiently high to guarantee the generation of electricity at an acceptable minimum rate. For this reason, wind generators must always be supplemented by secondary stand-by generators that can automatically assume the generation burden when the winds slack off. At the present stage of technologic advance, such stand-by generators might best be diesel-powered since coal-burning or nuclear-powered steam generators cannot be brought quickly into line because of the time required to build up pressure in the boilers.

Finally, wind generators probably will never be able to generate, economically, more than a few thousand kilowatts of electricity. Therefore, their primary use will be to supply electricity only to relatively small population clusters.

In part, the use of the sun's energy as a source of power will override that of the wind. Solar power is certain to arrive eventually because it is, unlike man's present power sources, inexhaustible and because the basic technologic problems necessary to the utilization of solar power have already been solved.

There are three kinds of energy resources. Nonrenewable resources are those that cannot be replaced, such as coal, petroleum, and uranium. With continued usage, these resources must eventually be depleted. Renewable resources are those that can be replenished at a price. Timber resources can be replenished if time and money are spent to replant trees and to await their becoming full grown before harvesting them. Inexhaustible resources cannot be depleted and require no effort for their maintenance.

The sun's energy is inexhaustible, at least on any time scale that lies within human comprehension. The sun has been pouring out energy for at least three billion years and will certainly continue to do so for ages to come. Furthermore, the contrast between the amount of energy available from the sun and that from all other energy sources is far greater than that between the energy in the little finger of a baby of three and the potential of all the electric generators in the world.

The superabundance of solar energy is strikingly evident from the comparison made by Ayres and Scarlott:

> Suppose all the earth's coal, lignite, peat, tar sands, crude petroleum, natural gas, and oil shale that we are ever likely to produce in the

future (according to the more optimistic forecasts) were collected and that all our timber were cut into cordwood. Suppose we segregate all the uranium and thorium that we are likely to produce in the future (based on estimates by Lawrence R. Hafstad) and that it is all purified for nuclear fission. Thus we have at hand for immediate use all the earth's stock of fuel. Then, suddenly, we extinguish the sun. We ignite our fuel in such fashion as to give us energy at the rate at which we are accustomed to receive it from the sun. In about three days our entire supply of combustible fuel would be gone. Then we would get the nuclear reactors under way. This would last us less than an hour if the "breeder principle" could be applied—otherwise only a few seconds. At the end of a few days the earth with its load of ashes and radio-active wastes would begin its descent toward some temperature only slightly above absolute zero.

The virtually limitless energy of the sun is today being tapped in new ways that are certain to be employed on a wider and wider scale in the years to come. In addition, experiments are going forward that will enlarge still further the realms within which solar energy will in time replace other energy forms.

The most important new use of solar energy in recent years has been for space heating. Of course, in a general manner the warmth of the sun has always been used to heat houses and other buildings; but the new heating methods are so much more efficient than the haphazard methods of the past, and so different from them too, that the contrast is as great as that between the wood-burning fireplace that served to heat the cabins of the early American pioneers and the automatically controlled oil- or gas-burning furnaces that in the winters of today heat a high percentage of the houses in the cities of the northern United States.

The modern solar-heating plant evolved from the ordinary glass window that for half a century or more has been a characteristic feature of virtually all the houses and industrial buildings of the western world. Ordinary glass, like the moisture in the atmosphere, transmits nearly all of the incoming sunlight that falls upon it, but blocks the outward passage of the longer-wave-length radiation emitted by bodies behind or beneath the glass which are warmed by the incoming sunlight. In greenhouses, this principle is deliberately utilized to keep interior temperatures high even on cold days. In ordinary houses or industrial buildings, the principle is made use of only indifferently because in the architectural designs the glass windows are primarily thought of as transparent vents that provide daytime illumination and permit those within to view the outdoor scene. Any heat that accrues is fortuitous bounty.

The first step toward modern solar heating was to consider the glass window as the architect of a greenhouse considers it—as a device for trapping heat—and accordingly to design buildings with many windows so oriented as to catch the maximum amount of sunlight, especially in the winter months. The second step was to improve the design of glass windows to minimize heat loss. Ordinary windows are highly effective in stopping the outward flow of heat in the form of radiation, but nonetheless permit appreciable outward flow by conduction through the glass. This defect was corrected by constructing windows that consisted of two panes of glass containing between them a thin, sealed-in air space to act as an insulating layer. The final step was the development of flat-plate heat collectors to be used in conjunction with a system for the chemical storage of the collected heat.

The flat-plate collector is a double-pane glass window backed by a copper sheet. Since the copper sheet is opaque, it is a window only for heat, not for light. The copper sheet absorbs the heat of the sun, and this heat is passed on to air or water which is circulated through the house or building, usually in conduits beneath the floors. At an early stage, after being warmed by the sun, the air or water is circulated through substances that have melting points of around 80° to 110°. If the fluid air or water is warmer than these substances, heat passes from the circulating fluid to the substance and melts it if it is in a solid state. If the circulating fluid is colder than the substance, heat passes from the substance to the fluid and part or all of the substance freezes solid, at a temperature of 80° to 110°, if it is in a liquid state.

By extracting heat from the circulating air or water, the substance stores heat; by discharging heat to it, the substance returns the stored heat to the water or air. And because melting is a process that absorbs great quantities of heat and freezing is one that emits great quantities, the system is effective for heat storage and for the maintenance of uniform temperatures in the circulating fluid and therefore in the building as well. The substances actually used for this heat regulation are various salts, such as hydrated sodium carbonate. Usually these salts are placed either in a single large tank or else in small sealed containers distributed throughout the vents that are the passageways for the circulating air or water.

Solar-heating systems of the kind just described are presently in use on a limited basis in New England, where winter temperatures often fall below 15°. Even in such cold areas they can provide the majority of the heat needed in winter and all of the heat needed in the cool months of fall and spring. In somewhat milder climates, as in eastern North Carolina, western Oklahoma, and central France, they can provide all the space heating necessary at all times of the year.

According to Eugene Ayres, "more energy is required for warmth in homes and places of work than for motor cars, for industrial power, or for lighting." Therefore, even though solar energy will never meet the heating needs of all regions of the world, the sun can be drawn upon to provide one-sixth or more of all the energy requirements of the entire world, and all this just through space heating.

In addition to space heating, there is a second major use to which solar energy can be put. Sunlight can be used to provide the heat that changes water to steam in the boilers of engines that generate electricity. From experiments that have been conducted in France, the United States, the Soviet Union, and elsewhere, it has been clearly demonstrated that such sun-derived electricity can be produced successfully, and in quantities of any desired magnitude.

Either flat-plate collectors or mirrors may be used in solar-driven steam generators. The mirrors are parabolic and in experiments thus far conducted have sometimes been as large as thirty feet in maximum dimension. In some of the experiments conducted, the mirror has been mounted on wheels to permit it to move back and forth on a track. Through this device it was possible to maintain constant heating, since the mirror could be moved farther away from the coils, somewhat out of focus, when the sun was shining brightly and could be moved closer in, sharply in focus, when the sun was partly obscured.

In an area like Arizona, solar-driven steam generators could supply thirty-five kilowatts of electricity for each acre of harvested sunlight. One square mile would supply all the electricity required by a town of 2,500. At the present time it is not economical to install and use solar-driven steam generators on a wide scale, even in desert areas where their output would be highest. There is every indication, however, that in time this particular mode of utilization of solar energy will, like the employment of modern solar space heating, supply an appreciable percentage of the total energy used by man for domestic, industrial, and commercial purposes.

There are still other modern uses of solar energy. The Bell Telephone Laboratories have developed a low-voltage battery that draws its energy from sunlight. Batteries of this kind are being used to provide power for rural telephone services as well as for earth satellites. French, American, and other engineers have constructed and successfully tested solar furnaces to be employed for metallurgical purposes. Illumination engineers have experimented with the storing of solar energy in the form of light, which will be given off when the sun is no longer shining. In this application, special paints have been made that contain phosphors, which have the property of glowing for long periods after they have been exposed to sunlight.

Finally, experiments indicate that it is possible and may even prove economical to use solar energy to obtain gasoline, through employing the mechanism of photosynthesis in algae. Experiments in Japan and Israel have shown that when algae are raised in tanks under controlled conditions, the yield may be "as high as 15 dry tons per acre per annum, about five times the yield of the *best* land growth." The Japanese and Israelis have been interested in algae primarily as a possible food source; but with yields of this magnitude the algae could be converted to alcohol, which in turn could be converted to gasoline at a cost of less than 25 cents per gallon. By the time the petroleum resources of the world are depleted, a century or two from now at the present rate of consumption, algae may well be a major source of gasoline, especially with improved techniques for raising the algae and for converting them to gasoline. And many kinds of solar stills have been developed, for the sun is the cheapest possible source of energy for the distillation of sea water.

What new uses of solar energy will be discovered in the coming decades it is impossible even to guess. However, with the passage of the years solar energy will be utilized more and more, especially for space heating and for the production of electricity. Solar space heating will be widely used everywhere except in those tropical areas where there is no requirement for such heating and in the sun-poor lands of high and high middle latitudes. Generators will be used at scattered localities throughout low and middle latitudes, but by far their greatest usefulness will be in the desert areas that are the homelands of the sun.

Transport

The movement of goods and people knits together the regions and the peoples of the earth. All cultures of the earth, civilized and primitive alike, have long depended on transport over the seas, across the lands, or through the air; and the members of these cultures have long known that the weather may be propitious, speeding the movement of the vehicles of transport from place to place, or else may be adverse, slowing that movement even to the point of throttling it.

At some particular instant in the Sahara a desert caravan is camped in an oasis, waiting out a sandstorm that blocks its forward movement, while at the same time an Arab merchantman is sailing down the coast from Bombay to Mangalore, with favoring winds that help her on her way. There are great commercial airfields where the skies are cloudless and the aircraft are landing one after the other at brief intervals, and other airfields where within the snow-filled clouds the planes are stacked to great heights at several different holding points, some moving away to divert to alternate fields. Near Novosibirsk, on the Trans-Siberian Railway, there is a train stalled dead still by snowdrifts that block the tracks; in the Argentine, another train is stopped before a bridge that has been washed out by floods; and along the coast of California the Lark, a crack Southern Pacific train, is running swiftly through the clear night.

If all of this could be encompassed, it would include automobiles and oxcarts, 25,000-ton tankers and sampans, railroad trains and pack trains, modern jet aircraft and old Ford trimotored planes, some moving smoothly and swiftly along their way, others making only troubled progress through thick and heavy weather, and still others waiting out the weather or even meeting weather-borne disaster.

Comprehended in this manner, an instantaneous view of all the transport over all the world would yield most properly the generalizations that weather may hasten or slow or stop the transport of goods and people. This would be true. But still there would be two other generalizations of the greatest importance that could never be garnered from an instantaneous, panoramic scene. One would concern geographical contrasts in the frequency of propitious or adverse weather circumstances; the other, the differences from one mode of transport to another in the degree of freedom from the weather.

There are regions of the sea, like those off Antarctica or to the north of North America, that even in the summer can be navigated only with the greatest difficulty. In these high-latitude seas, aircraft, looking for breaks in the ice floes, must scout ahead of the icebreakers to make safe and sure the path of the cargo ships that trail behind.

Quite different is the equatorial mid-Pacific, which for steamships is as benign as any sea, being free both of the heavy winter storms that plague the oceans of middle latitudes and of the typhoons that churn their way across both the eastern and western reaches of the tropical Pacific Ocean. Yet these same equatorial waters were among the worst for the sailing ships of a century and more ago, which often lay becalmed for days and even weeks.

Upon the land and in the air there are weather contrasts of these same kinds. There are lands of blizzards and lands of floods; lands where the sand and dust blow furiously and lands where a sudden freeze, deep and hard, converts the highway to a jagged strip of rubble. There also are lands where it is unusual to have much more than a little fog or an occasional heavy rain to interrupt the flow of traffic on highways and on the railway lines. For air transport there are places like the Aleutian Islands, where to wait for anything approaching clear weather before landing or take-offs might mean waiting half a year; and there are places like Honolulu, where the airport is closed not more than two or three times a year, and then only for an hour or so. So from region to region and place to place, it is possible to distinguish among varying weather conditions, some of which act often and harshly to constrict the flow of transport and some of which favor that flow in the freest possible manner.

The degree of influence of the weather upon transport is related not only to geographic variations in weather conditions but to differences in the modes of transport as well. A Coast Guard cutter can heel far over and still recover in hurricane seas that would capsize many merchantmen. An oxcart can traverse a mud-covered road on which an automobile would bog down hub-deep.

The greatest contrast of all is that between the vehicles of sea or land transport and those of the air. On the land, there is at least a firm underpinning of solid ground. On the sea, the substance on which the transport vehicle rides is mobile and so may heave and twist, but at least it sticks to the earth. In the air, the buoyant substance of the atmosphere is itself the unrestricted playground of the weather, so that the vehicles of the air are inevitably bound to the weather, without the slightest underpinning.

As aircraft speeds increase, as cruising altitudes become greater and greater, and as propeller-driven craft give way to jets and then to rocket-propelled craft, the weather factor both during flight and in terminal operations becomes not less critical, but even more so. This intensification of the effects of weather upon aircraft is due partly to increased flight speeds, partly to the nature of the new propulsion mechanisms, and partly to increased flight altitudes which require the vehicles of ultramodern air transport to run the gantlet not only of the familiar weather hazards of the troposphere but also of new dangers that are encountered in the high stratosphere, the ionosphere, and beyond.

Anyone who has driven an automobile on an exceptionally windy day knows through experience that the faster he drives, the greater the chance that a sudden gust will make the car swerve. With aircraft the effect is precisely the same, but on a magnified scale because the craft may swerve up or down as well as sidewise, there is no stabilizing friction with the ground, and the speeds are from three to twenty times greater than those of an automobile. If a high-speed aircraft suddenly swerves in flight, the danger lies not so much in its spinning out of control as in the plane suffering structural weakening or even immediate damage. If it swerves sharply and suddenly in landing, it may crash before the pilot can bring it under control, a feat that is far more difficult in a hot-landing jet than in a propeller-driven plane.

High speed makes the plane more vulnerable in another manner also. A plane flying through a cloud at 350 m.p.h. merely picks up and then sheds the water droplets without any ill effects. The same water droplets can easily punch holes in the weaker portions of the fabric of a plane flying at 2,000 m.p.h., for the effect is precisely the same as if the water droplets were high-speed projectiles, fired from a gun at supersonic speeds.

The relation of aircraft flight to weather depends in part upon the propulsion mechanism of the aircraft. In a basic physical sense, all aircraft are propelled in the same manner. All achieve forward thrust through the application of Newton's third law of motion, which states that whenever one body exerts a force upon a second, the second body must exert an equal force upon the first, but in an opposite direction. The propellers of a conventional aircraft force the air backward with the result that the propellers themselves, and the air frame to which they are attached, are forced forward. In jet and rocket aircraft, hot gases are thrust backward through an aperture and the aircraft is accordingly thrust forward. The difference between the jet and the rocket is that the jet takes in air, which is compressed and expelled backward to propel the craft; whereas a rocket engine requires no air since it expels gases generated from the fuel, without any air intake.

Because air of a certain density is required for the flight of both propeller craft and jets and because the air density decreases with height, there is a practical limit to the heights to which propeller craft and jets will be able to fly. For propeller-driven craft, the practical height limit is about 45,000 feet, at which level the air density is not quite one-fifth the sea-level density. For jet aircraft, the practical height limit is about 100,000 feet, at which level the air density is about .15 that at sea level. Above 100,000 feet, only rocket aircraft are capable of practical performance, and these can fly thousands of miles upward to the top of the ocean of air and then out into interplanetary space, though to free themselves of the earth they must achieve a speed of over 25,000 miles per hour.

It will probably not be useful for manned commercial aircraft to fly at heights above 100,000 feet. It is, however, likely that unmanned rockets and satellites will find at least minor commercial uses at much greater altitudes. Unmanned rockets might be used for the transport of express cargoes, the rockets being radio controlled at their destination so as to land in lakes or in specially designated target areas in offshore ocean water. Such a rocket, launched from New York, could deliver a cargo to Tokyo within an hour. Unmanned satellites, circling the earth at heights of several hundred miles, might well be used commercially as navigation aids for high-flying manned aircraft and as stations for the automatic relay of radio messages from place to place upon the earth.

Thus as the decades pass and as satellites and rockets provide more and more information on the nature of the high upper atmosphere, there will come into view more and more clearly what the weather problems of very high altitude transport will be. These problems cannot be defined now, but this much can be said: there are certain to be special problems of design and actual performance that in new and often surprising ways will demonstrate the continued close dependence of air transport upon the behavior of the ocean of air.

18 War

Total modern war engulfs the warring nations. It intensifies and forcibly distorts all agricultural, industrial, and commercial activities. It thrusts into being a precarious situation in which failure anywhere may mean disaster.

In such circumstances, the impact of weather upon the fate of peoples and of nations is multiplied tenfold. The drought that in peacetime requires only the importation of grain may with wartime blockades mean near starvation. The storm that in peacetime requires only the delay of a dozen commercial aircraft flights across the Pacific may in wartime postpone the ferrying of 200 heavy bombers. The rainfall that renews the supply of water in a major river basin will in wartime assure continued drafts of water to cool the machinery at fifty industrial plants that produce guns, bombs, tanks, missiles, and other weapons of war.

Because of the importance of basic logistics, all the concepts that in peacetime relate the weather to agriculture, industry, and commerce have their wartime counterparts that operate with maximum force. But the encroachment of weather events is felt not only in this basic stratum of the military pyramid but also throughout the entire structure. In immediate logistic problems, as in supply and resupply, in strategic planning, in the development and execution of military tactics, and in the design and employment of weapons, the weather factor can rarely be ignored and may sometimes be decisive.

Weather has always been a factor in the prosecution of wars, but in the last few decades its importance has increased notably. As military technology has advanced and become more and more complex, military operations have become more and more weather-sensitive. Through his own technical achievements man has bound himself more closely to the weather environment. This is exemplified by the changes in weather-dependence that have accompanied changes in ordnance.

When Neanderthal man raised a spear to kill an enemy, his thrust could not be parried by the weather. Fifty thousand years later, when a Swiss lake dweller shot an arrow at an enemy, he necessarily allowed for the effect of windage. When the arrow became the Minié gun, with internal rifling that would spin the bullet straight, it became necessary to consider not only windage but also air density and deflection caused by the earth's rotation. When the Minié gun became the atomic cannon, there were added the further factors of wind at the target, which might spread a lethal dust across a distance of 100 or 10,000 yards, and rainfall that might wash the dust to earth in lethal concentrations.

Thus far, the quintessence of modern technologic advance in the military realm is in the fields of air warfare and nuclear weapons. Aircraft, rockets, missiles, and earth satellites are all strongly weather-dependent, for all operate within the atmosphere which is the theater of the weather. As for nuclear weapons, their employment will often depend upon the weather, especially upon the winds that spread radioactive dust. There is also the distinct possibility that nuclear bombs, detonated in too great numbers, may so increase the amount of atmospheric dust as to change the weather on a world-wide scale or may through action of the wind endanger all the peoples of the earth. This raises scientific questions the answers to which are of such unparalleled significance to mankind everywhere that they demand separate consideration. Therefore the topic of weather in connection with nuclear devices is reserved for the following chaper.

Technologic advances have necessitated that more and more attention be devoted to the weather aspects of the military art, as well as advances in forecasting, and have led inevitably to the development of military meteorology as a special technology. Most major nations have military weather services and all conduct intensive applied research in military meteorology. The nature and the modes of operation of military weather services are in themselves essential aspects of the broad theme of weather and war in the modern world.

Though the weather factor has increased sharply in importance during the past few decades, it has throughout history strongly influenced the course of military events.

The Historical Perspective

History demonstrates that even a single weather event may determine the outcome of a battle. The cloud-filled weather front that in June, 1942, rolled eastward through the Aleutians served as a shield for the invading Japanese and permitted them to take over Attu without opposition. Following its defeat by the English fleet in 1588, an intense storm off the Hebrides demolished the bulk of the Invincible Spanish Armada and shattered the might of Spanish sea power.

Two thousand years earlier, 2,200 miles away, off the coast of Greece, another storm had brought disaster to the Persian fleet of Xerxes, bent upon the invasion of the Greek city-states. The Persian fleet, over 1,200 ships in all, lay off the west coast of the Magnesian Peninsula, anchored off shore, "row upon row, eight deep." Then, in the words of Herodotus:

> . . . calm and stillness gave place to a raging sea, and a violent storm, which fell upon them with a strong gale from the east—a wind which the people in those parts call Hellespontias. Such of them as perceived the wind rising, and were so moored as to allow it, forestalled the tempest by dragging their ships up on the beach. . . . But the ships which the storm caught out at sea were driven ashore . . . at the lowest . . . 400 of their ships were destroyed . . . a countless multitude of men were slain, and a vast treasure engulfed.

Less dramatic than the single decisive weather event, but in the aggregate even more important in military history, has been the influence of weather situations which endure for days or weeks. Such situations have many times controlled the pace of military operations and often dictated the nature of the warfare. This kind of influence is illustrated by the situation that arose in North Africa in late November, 1942. Then the Allied strike eastward to Bizerte and Tunis had to be delayed in large part because the weather throttled American air power. As General Eisenhower wrote:

> Unseasonable rains soon overtook us, and since none of the scattered air strips that we had hoped to use boasted of a paved runway, our

small air forces were handicapped and for days at a stretch were rendered almost completely helpless. The enemy was far better situated, since his large fields at Bizerte and Tunis were suitable for operations in all kinds of weather.

Another illustration of the influence of weather on the pace of operations is seen in the Ypres campaign in 1917, when with repeated heavy rains the British offensive was submerged for three months in the mud of Passchendaele. In contrast was the swift advance of the Germans into Poland during the clear, crisp days of September, 1939, when German tanks raced eastward over firm, dry terrain and German planes by the hundreds flew precision missions through unobstructed skies.

The British and American troops pushing northward up the Italian Peninsula in the winter of 1943-44 fought against the weather as much as against the Germans. This is how Ernie Pyle stated it:

> The war in Italy was tough. . . . It rained and rained. Vehicles bogged down and temporary bridges washed out. . . . Our troops were living in almost inconceivable misery. The fertile black valleys were knee-deep in mud. Thousands of the men had not been dry for weeks. Other thousands lay at night in the high mountains with the temperature below freezing and the thin snow sifting over them. They dug into the stones and slept in little chasms and behind rocks and in half-caves. They lived like men of prehistoric times, and a club would have become them more than a machine gun. How they survived the dreadful winter at all was beyond us who had the opportunity of drier beds in the warmer valleys.

Commanders in the field and upon the sea have nearly always taken into account the weather factor whenever they could. However, until the last half of the nineteenth century, when military weather forecasting came into being, about all a commander could do, like Hannibal anticipating the fall of the Alpine snows, was to anticipate the nature of the impending weather on a general seasonal basis, meanwhile adjusting his operations to the specific weather situation as that situation unfolded.

For many centuries it was commonplace in Europe for armies to retire to winter quarters during late October and to remain there inactive until June. The usual procedure was to conclude a formal armistice, calling off the war until a given date in spring. Similarly, it was common for the outbreak of wars to be postponed until late summer or early fall, by which time the crops would be harvested, the worst heat of summer would be over, and there would be the prospect of two months of excellent fighting weather.

As for the adjustment of operations to the particular weather situation, if fog set in a commander might attempt a sneak attack. If an attack was planned and there were torrential rains, it was simply postponed. If a sudden flood converted a small, easily fordable stream into a major river, a commander would take this into account by reducing the number of defensive troops along the stream and moving the men thus freed to some other point on his defensive line.

The commander at sea also improvised. Since his force was comprised of sailing ships, he was constantly changing position to take advantage of the winds. If a naval commander had no thought of retreat, he attempted to "gain the weather gauge," to get to windward of the enemy so that he could approach him at will and could also send down fire ships upon him. If, however, retreat was a definite possibility, the canny commander stayed to leeward so that if necessary he could turn and run without passing through the enemy's line.

A fatalism regarding the weather is reflected in the writings of such classical military theorists as Frederick the Great, Jomini, and Clausewitz. In his famous treatise *On War,* General von Clausewitz states as a major dictum:

> Everything is very simple in war, but the simplest thing is difficult. . . . Activity in war is movement in a resistant medium. Just as a man immersed in water is unable to perform with ease and regularity the most natural and simple movement, that of walking, so in war one cannot, with ordinary powers, keep even the line of mediocrity.

He then goes on to state that what renders the simplest things difficult may well be called "friction," of which chance is a major component. Specifically:

> One such instance of chance . . . is the weather. Here, fog prevents the enemy from being discovered in time, a gun from firing at the right moment, a report from reaching the general; there, rain prevents one battalion from arriving at all, and another from arriving at the right time, because it has had to march perhaps eight hours instead of three, the cavalry from charging effectively because it is stuck fast in heavy ground.

In the latter half of the nineteenth century there was a marked change in the orientation of military thinking about the weather. Within a few decades it became clear that good weather intelligence was essential to proper military planning and that military weather forecasts were both practicable and useful. It also became clear that the weather factor was becoming even more important than before because the new and improved weapons were far more weather-dependent in their employment than the old ones had ever been. These new views were in part an outgrowth of the experience of the British and French in the Crimean War.

On June 29, 1854, at the beginning of the war, the British Cabinet sent a dispatch to Lord Raglan, commander of the British troops, cautioning him to select favorable weather for his operations. This advice was excellent, but meaningless. There was no system set up to permit the rapid collection, from many localities, of the wide-spread observations necessary for forecasting the weather. In addition, weather intelligence for the Crimea was so poor that neither Lord Raglan nor any other British commander had the vaguest notion that a Crimean winter could be as severe as was the one encountered in 1854–55. As a result the British lost a fleet of supply ships in an unexpected storm in the Black Sea during November and the troops suffered miseries in the bitter winter weather.

The disastrous November storm attracted wide attention in London and Paris. It was a topic of discussion not only in clubs and salons but in scientific circles. The French astronomer, Leverrier, became interested in the storm as a natural phenomenon worthy of study. From Athens, Rome, Padua, and other places in southern Europe where weather observations were regularly taken, he collected the weather records for the period preceding the storm. Then on a series of maps he plotted the observations day by day up to the date of the Black Sea storm. The results were unmistakably clear. On the successive maps Leverrier could trace the progress of the storm as it moved eastward across southern Europe into the Black Sea. Had a system for collecting simultaneous weather observations been in effect, it would have been a simple matter to anticipate the storm sufficiently far in advance for the supply ships to seek safety in a sheltered port.

Leverrier drew up a plan for using the newly installed telegraph system to collect weather observations for military forecasting. He submitted the plan to the Emperor, Napoleon III, who fully endorsed it and soon put it into operation. Simultaneously, the British and French military leaders were being forced to review their systems for collecting and applying weather intelligence for the planning of military operations. Because there had been no weather forecasting system and because weather intelligence had been grossly inaccurate, British and French troops had died by the thousands. In the decades to come there would be other serious miscalculations; but from the Crimean War onward, the weather factor would never again be viewed with mere helpless fatalism.

Logistics, Strategy, and Tactics

There are three elemental aspects of warfare: logistics, strategy, and tactics. Logistics provide the materials of warfare and move them to the points where they are needed at the times when they are needed. Strategy determines where and when to strike or to defend and with what kinds and numbers of forces. In the words of Clausewitz, "It maps out . . . the war . . . it makes the plans for separate campaigns and arranges the engagements to be fought in each of them." Tactics determine precisely how to attack or to defend; how to deploy tanks, arrange artillery, or hunt and kill an enemy submarine. If striking power is likened to a sword, then logistics forge the sword and assure that its edge remains keen; strategy dictates where and when the sword will strike; and tactics dictate whether the sword will thrust or slash or parry.

In many phases of logistics, strategy, and tactics, the role of weather is crucial. Thus in problems of logistic supply the weather often asserts itself through its influence upon mobility. In such problems, an ordinary map is utterly misleading, for it shows distances as if all routes of equal length could somehow be traversed with equal ease despite weather barriers. From the Suez Canal across the Arabian Desert to the oil fields of Dhahran on the Persian Gulf is a distance of 1,200 miles, about the same distance as from New York to New Orleans. But to the logistics officer charged with supporting the transport of 100,000 men and 5,000 vehicles overland from one terminal point to the other, the distance from Suez to Dhahran is effectively four times that from New York to New Orleans, even supposing that the march to New Orleans had to be undertaken without using existing highways and railroads.

Napoleon's judgment applies today as it did a century and a half ago, when he wrote, "Of all . . . obstacles to the march of an army the most difficult to overcome is the desert." Napoleon was thinking of the heat and sandstorms of the desert, and especially of the almost insurmountable difficulties of keeping an army supplied with water on a long desert march. Identical problems afflict the generals of today. Mechanization is no great help. Air temperatures inside tanks exposed for many hours to glaring desert sunshine often exceed 180°. Sandstorms blast the paint from vehicles and clog engines and fuel lines. And machines consume much water.

At sea the maximum weather barrier to transport is ice. Here also the ordinary map conceals the truth. From Point Barrow, Alaska, across the Arctic Sea to Murmansk is a distance of 2,700 miles. But in summertime, with the need for icebreakers, this distance might just as well be 27,000 miles when the problem is that of transporting huge quantities of supplies by sea; while in wintertime, such transport is impossible.

Air transport also has its weather barriers. During a storm, a guided missile can punch through to its target. Even a manned bombing plane can reach the target and drop its bomb load through undercast with at least that rough degree of accuracy made possible by radar sighting. A transport plane, however, must land, and so is subject to the barriers of fog, low ceilings, and severe storms. These barriers cannot be surmounted by the parachuting of men and supplies, for, as World War II demonstrated, such a form of delivery is unreliable when there are strong winds or when drops must be made through an undercast. Men and supplies scattered in disarray across enemy territory are not a military asset.

For land, sea, and air transport the lines of supply are lengthened or shortened by the weather. Therefore in logistic planning it is imperative to calculate the weather odds and, in effect, to modify simple geographical maps accordingly. Where land transport is concerned, desert areas grow enormously in size; icecap regions in Greenland and Antarctica grow equally; the polar tundra also expands, though in lesser measure; and mild, well-watered regions, as in the southeastern United States or England, contract.

Where sea transport is concerned, the cold, ice-filled seas are enlarged ten times and more; the north Atlantic becomes a region that grows in the season of winter storms and shrinks in summertime; and the oceans of the tropics and subtropics are of wholly modest size except in those brief intervals when hurricanes distort the transport map.

Military air transport to a point where there is no secure major airport is difficult when there is fog or low cloud or high gusty winds. The bulk movement of men and matériel into the area around Moscow would be impossible on half the days of wintertime, unless there already had been established a secure major airport complete with radar beacons and landing aids, tower control facilities, FIDO or other fog-dispersing equipment, and all the variety of other landing and navigational aids needed to permit terminal operations during marginal weather conditions.

Even so, as was demonstrated by the Berlin airlift of 1948–49, traffic will not flow at a fixed, dependable rate. On good-weather days a steady stream of incoming and outgoing planes will throng the airways to capacity and tax the facilities of the airport to the limit. On bad-weather days the planes will trickle in, with long intervals between arrivals.

The fact that weather throttles mobility is of paramount concern in strategic planning and tactics, just as in logistics. An army embedded in mud, naval ships wallowing in a typhoon, or an air fleet scattered through half the cloud-filled sky and searching for an invisible target has zero striking power. Add to these weather circumstances such others as the sudden thaw that converts an ice-covered river into a water raceway five miles wide, a blizzard that lays four feet of snow upon the ground, or the gale-force winds that hold the aircraft on the deck of the carrier, and it is evident that within a day, or even within the hour, weather alone may immobilize an entire striking force. When these concepts of the influence of weather upon mobility are applied to different regions of the world, the results are of primary strategic significance.

Not including the smaller indentations, the coastline of the United States is 4,840 miles long. That of the Soviet Union is almost twice as long, 7,000 to 8,000 miles; but Russia's vulnerable coastline is only 60 per cent that of the United States, since 5,000 miles of the Soviet coasts are effectively guarded by ice, even in the summer months, and for seven months of the year these 5,000 miles are absolutely sealed off from the sea.

As for the land entries to the Soviet Union, to the south are the deserts of Mongolia, Dzungaria, and Kara Kum. To the north is the tundra. To the west Russia lies open in the summertime, but the winters are so bitter that to maintain long supply lines is a feat of such magnitude that it has been effectively carried out only once in all history and then only for a single winter season.

In the winter of 1941–42, brilliant logistics permitted the Germans to support without impairment their forward area strength in the Ukraine and central Russia. However, with the onset of the next winter, German supply lines broke and their forces in the east began to crumple. Aided immeasurably by ice and snow and cold, the Red Army began its steady drive toward Berlin.

Should there be another war, the influence of weather upon the ability to detect enemy forces or targets and, conversely, upon the ability to remain concealed will be significant. But in modern warfare, fog and cloud and blizzard do not provide the solid shields against detection that they once did, for radar and sonar can probe these weather screens. Nonetheless, visual detection is for many purposes vastly superior to electronic detection, as is evident from comparison of a clear, sharp aerial photograph of New York with the fuzzy assemblage of white and gray and black masses obtained from photographing the airborne radar screen that shows the city beneath. Furthermore, again there is the situation that in partially surmounting one weather limitation science has encountered other limitations, for both radar and sonar are themselves weather-dependent in their effectiveness of operation.

When there is a shallow layer of moist air overlain by dry air aloft, radar can detect objects far beyond the horizon, at distances of 100 or even 1,000 miles and more. When the air is uniformly dry or moist to great heights and there is considerable vertical air movement, ranges may not even extend to the visible horizon.

Sonar ranges too are influenced by the weather, through its effect upon the temperature of the ocean water. If warm water overlies colder water at depth, the sound waves sent out by the sonar transmitter travel many miles to the target and are reflected from it to return to the sonar receiver, which then indicates the distance and direction of the target. If, in contrast, the surface water is about the same temperature as the water beneath, the sound waves readily reach the surface of the sea and so dissipate their energy, with the result that ranges are short and may in extreme instances not even extend to the limits of the visual horizon.

It is impossible even to list all the diverse activities of warfare that are influenced by the weather. For as Churchill has observed, in times of total warfare there is no drawing a line between military and nonmilitary problems, and the list would, with categories and subcategories, become a catalogue of a high percentage of the activities of the human race. Who can say with certainty that the magnetic storm in the ionosphere which delays a vital radio message may not have serious military repercussions, or that the unseasonably good weather which speeds the loading of tanks upon a merchantman may not prove thirty days later to be a critical factor for military success at a point 5,000 miles away?

It is, however, possible to list a few of the many immediate military activities in which weather plays a direct and convincing role. The behavior of a smoke screen is determined by the weather. The screen may lie in place and hide from sight the landing craft heading for the beach, or it may be ripped apart by the wind, baring the craft to the fire of enemy guns. Poisonous gas is similarly slave to the wind, which may even shift suddenly and turn the gas back upon the attacking forces, as it did in World War I when first used by the Germans.

There are also the cold of 50° below that cuts the efficiency of an army by a factor of two; the variations in air density that guide an artillery shell along a true path upon a target or cause it to miss by a wide margin; the humid, salt-filled air of the tropics that of itself wrecks radar equipment; and the sudden freeze that turns to ice the water along the margins of a river and permits the army engineers to saw off a block of ice, swing it across the river, refreeze it at both ends, and thus effect a rapid river crossing, just as the Russian engineers did in World War II.

The many weather variables influence different military operations in different ways, so that in the planning of a campaign it is necessary to consider all weather requirements, strike the most reasonable balance, and then define the minimum weather requirements on a total operational basis. In all but the simplest operations, this analytical procedure is a difficult one that calls for judgment of the highest order. In no type is the analysis more difficult than in an amphibious operation, which involves the co-ordinate activities of sea, land, and air forces.

Allowing for the weather factor in the strategic planning for amphibious landings is illustrated by two examples from World War II: planning of Operation Overlord, which was the code name for the Normandy invasion; and Operation Coronet, the invasion of the Tokyo Plain, which never had to be carried out.

For Overlord the invasion area itself—the Normandy beaches—was initially established, in part, on the basis of weather considerations. Thereafter, intensive studies were made of the preinvasion weather probabilities as they would influence such factors as the logistic build-up of strength based in Great Britain, the obtaining of the necessary photo-reconnaissance information over France, and a variety of other aspects of the multitudinous elements of preinvasion operations. Finally, the staff of SHAEF (Supreme Headquarters, Allied Expeditionary Forces) formulated, together with the British, the minimum weather requirements for the invasion:

NAVAL: In the days preceding D-Day, there should be no prolonged periods of high winds of such direction and in such Atlantic areas as to produce substantial swell in the Channel; surface winds should not exceed force 3 onshore or force 4 offshore in the assault area during the days D to D plus 2. Winds could be force 5 [27 m.p.h.] over the open sea, but only for short periods.

AIR FORCE: Airborne Transport: Ceiling at least 2,500 feet along the route and over target; visibility at least 3 miles.

Heavy Bombers: Not more than 5/10 cloud cover below 5,000 feet and ceiling not lower than 11,000 feet.

Medium and Fighter Bombers: Ceiling not less than 4,500 feet; visibility not less than 3 miles over target area.

Fighters: Ceiling not below 1,000 feet.

Base Areas: Ceiling not below 1,000 feet and visibility not less than one mile except for heavy bombers, for which low cloud tops must be less than 5,000 feet and middle clouds no more than fragmentary.

ARMY: Airborne Troop Landings: For paratroops, the surface wind over the target area should not exceed 20 m.p.h., should not be gusty and, for gliders, should not be over 30–35 m.p.h.; the intensity of ground illumination should not be less than half moon at 30° altitude or the equivalent in diffuse twilight.

Through analysis of past weather records it was found that the odds were twenty-four to one against realizing the required conditions during May, thirteen to one against realizing them in June, and fifty to one against July. June offered the best hope, though only a dim one for the meeting of all minimum requirements. These odds correctly predicted what actually came to be: that the best that could be done was to accept marginal conditions, a risk that on June 6, 1944, was taken knowingly and with success.

In Operation Coronet the problems were much the same as in Overlord, but the weather odds were much better. The general war plan called for the invasion of the Kagoshima beaches on Kyushu in the latter part of 1945. After this invasion (code name Olympic) had been completed, with the subsequent establishment of airfields and the build-up of logistic resources on this southernmost of the main Japanese islands, it was planned to begin Coronet, the invasion of the Tokyo Plain. Coronet was scheduled for the spring of 1946. Five beaches were to be hit, covering the coast from Mito, 100 miles northeast of Tokyo, to Iro Cape, 100 miles to the southwest. Because of the curvature of the shoreline, among them the contiguous beaches covered a coastal stretch of almost 400 miles.

On all five beaches all of the spring months, March through May, gave odds of better than three to one that minimum weather conditions would be met both in the sea phase of the actual amphibious operation and the land phase of the operation upon the beaches. However, the chances were only about one in three that simultaneously minimum conditions would be met for effective operation of carrier-based aircraft. Here a major problem was low ceilings and poor visibility either at the beaches or on the decks of the carriers, factors that were not so critical for the amphibious assault itself.

As had been anticipated, the weather was bad for Overlord, the Normandy invasion, but it was "possible." Because it was bad, at the time the press implied that the weather forecasters had made a blunder. In fact, the forecast was excellent, for it called for precisely the conditions that came to exist; and there was even some benefit from the fact that the weather was so nearly marginal because the still worse weather in eastern France and Germany held German planes on the ground.

Meanwhile, the meteorological advisers to the German high command were having their difficulties. Major Lettau, chief German meteorologist, who was captured by the American forces while on his way from Paris to Rennes, stated later that he had advised his superiors to the effect that an Allied invasion in the days immediately following June 4 was impossible because of bad weather moving in from the North Atlantic. As a result of this forecast, the Germans were taken by surprise when the invasion started. In fact, many German division officers in Normandy were on leave or on maneuvers at the time of the landings.

Had Overlord been postponed until the period between June 17 and 21, the next possible time to meet tide and moon conditions, the weather would have been the worst in twenty years. On the weatherman's memo containing this information, General Eisenhower wrote in longhand: "Thanks, and thank the gods of war we went when we did!"

Modern Weapons

New wars reveal new military weapons. World War I brought poison gas, tanks, airplanes, zeppelins, and submarines. World War II brought radar, jet aircraft, buzz bombs, A-bombs, and the proximity fuse. Should there be a World War III, a host of new weapons will be used, especially in air warfare. For this reason and because the air phase may well prove critical, it is necessary to consider the relations between weather and the air warfare of the future.

Any discussion of future air war must be based on certain assumptions about the nature and performance characteristics of the weapons that will be used. These assumptions cannot be precisely correct because detailed official information of weapon performance is not available even for weapons now in mass production, such as the B-52 and the Matador guided missile, and because the arsenal of air weapons is constantly changing, so that the weapon array will be one thing if a war is fought tomorrow and quite a different thing if it is fought two decades from now. Despite these limitations, from information that has been officially released and from carefully reasoned estimates and calculations made by engineers, scientists, and military specialists, it is possible to describe at least in general terms the characteristics of the weapons of a future air war.

Here the air weapons that can be expected to be utilized if an all-out war is fought after 1961 will be discussed. By then at the latest, guided missiles, intercontinental ballistic missiles, and earth satellites should all be standard military weapons of the major powers.

Air missiles may be considered according to their mission, whether offensive or defensive and whether killers in themselves or special-purpose missiles, as for control of other missiles or for reconnaissance. They may be classified as to range or speed. They may be classed as high-precision missiles, armed with relatively small explosive charges and designed to knock out small targets; or as area missiles, armed with nuclear bombs and designed to devastate such wide areas that precise delivery is not necessary. Missiles may also conveniently be classed according to mode of guidance.

The preset missile is the most simple guidance type, for it is essentially an artillery shell that is aimed in a certain direction and that after firing makes only those flight corrections that have been calculated in advance and rigidly incorporated in the missile mechanism.

In contrast, the flight of the slave missile is controlled from the ground or from some manned or unmanned vehicle such as a ship, airplane, or earth satellite.

The auto-navigation missile is still more advanced. It controls its own flight, through celestial navigation or through use of an inertial system that automatically corrects for deviations from a predetermined flight path that has been incorporated in the gyroscopic and electronic memory system of the missile.

Finally, there is the homing missile, which identifies its target and then alters its course as necessary to close upon the target along a true collision path.

Some missiles incorporate two or more of these guidance methods. Thus the intercontinental ballistic missile is probably a slave from time of take-off until flight altitude is reached; then it will cruise as an auto-navigator and will home on a specified target.

In the new air warfare there will be missiles of all ranges and types, performing defensive, offensive, and special missions; flying at supersonic speeds from air-to-air, air-to-surface, surface-to-air, and from beneath the ocean to the air and then to a ground target, as when missiles are launched by submerged submarines. So long as they remain within the atmosphere, their performance will, like that of manned aircraft, be influenced by the weather. The weather influence will, however, assert itself differently for missiles than for manned aircraft.

A missile is the only true all-weather air vehicle, for unlike manned aircraft it can take off despite fog, cloud, storm, and wind; and since it is intended to explode on its target, it does not face a weather landing problem. But a missile, unlike a manned aircraft, is at best piloted by a Simple Simon brain. It cannot correct for unexpected circumstances, for radar beams that bend, for stratospheric clouds that blot the stars from sight, for unusual changes in air density, or for dummy alternate targets that to the human eye would be at once distinguished from the real thing. To quote Warren Amster, "Lots of hustle and not much sense describes the way missiles will do the jobs they will one day inherit."

From a weather point of view, a sharp distinction must be made between high-precision missiles armed with conventional warheads or relatively weak nuclear charges and imprecise area missiles armed with H-bombs. Whatever its guidance mechanism, a high-precision missile may be critically thrown off course by a sudden, unexpected weather event.

In contrast, an area missile, which has only to detonate within twenty to fifty miles of its target, will seldom if ever be critically thrown off course by weather. Its effectiveness will nonetheless be strongly weather-determined since the presence of clouds at the target may cut almost in half the flash-burn kill generated by explosion of its H-bomb warhead, and the radioactive dust that the explosion will hurl into the atmosphere may be scavenged from the air by rain to poison all living things below or else will form a path of death whose length and width and orientation will be determined by the wind.

If there should be all-out nuclear war, involving the unrestricted use of area missiles with H-bomb warheads, then, according to the testimony of General Gavin before a congressional committee, in June, 1956, "several hundred million people" in the Soviet Union and surrounding areas would be killed through "massive retaliation," the exact pattern of death depending upon wind conditions.

With one set of wind conditions, the map of death would embrace not only the Soviet Union with its 200 million persons but also added tens of millions in Finland, Sweden, Poland, Germany, and elsewhere in Europe. With another set of winds, there would be only a few millions killed to the west of Russia; instead, the winds would blanket and extinguish 100 million in China and 10 or 20 million in Japan. The General failed to remark on the effects of all-out nuclear war upon the United States, Canada, and other parts of the world, a subject that is discussed in the next chapter.

In a limited war, not involving the use of nuclear weapons, the high-precision, low-charge missile would come into its own. There would be missiles, like the Matador, firing over distances of a few hundred miles, at speeds of 1,500–2,500 m.p.h., Mach 2 to 3, that is, twice to three times the speed of sound. The present subsonic Matador is a slave missile, guided by radar from the ground. The new supersonic Matador will doubtless also be a slave, and so will travel out along a radar beam to that point where the dive mechanism is tripped by a special radar impulse. The missile will then plunge earthward along a path that has been calculated in advance, making allowance for wind and air density as necessary.

In missiles of this type, which include the Navy's Regulus, designed for firing from the deck of a ship, weather will influence accuracy whenever there are electrical storms in the troposphere or ionosphere to interfere with radar guidance or when there are unusual atmospheric conditions, such as pronounced moisture stratification, that will bend the controlling radar beams. These weather effects will be felt only 5 to 10 per cent of the time in most regions of the world; but when they do influence flight, they may cause a missile to miss its target by five to ten miles, which is a wide miss for a warhead with a low charge.

Many of the new missiles will perform their own navigation and carry homing devices, especially if they are to travel over distances of 1,000 miles or more, when ground control will not be feasible. They will be guided by signals emitted by earth satellites or will steer their own way by celestial navigation or through inertial guidance. If they are jet-propelled, they will travel within the stratosphere at heights no greater than forty miles, where the air is still sufficiently dense to permit combustion within the jet engines. Probably these air-breathing missiles will travel at Mach 2 to 3, a speed sufficient to fly 5,000 miles in two or three hours, yet not so fast as to prohibit effective self-navigation.

Unfortunately from the viewpoint of the attacker, a missile traveling at Mach 3 may be thrown off course by stratospheric winds in the last few minutes before homing, without there being sufficient time for the missile to correct for such deflection. Stratospheric winds are often above 150 m.p.h. and sometimes above 400. In four minutes a wind of 150 m.p.h. may cause a missile to swerve ten miles off course. All that is required for such deflection is a relatively steady high-speed wind on the beam of the missile over a distance of 150 miles, which is the distance traveled by a Mach 3 missile in four minutes. Such winds are common in the stratosphere, and it is doubtful whether much, if any, of the deflection could be corrected for adequately in such a brief time either by celestial or inertial controls. At best, even with winds of only 150 m.p.h., the missile would be three to five miles off course when it started to dive on its target. With very high-speed winds, it would be ten to twenty miles off and ineffective as a precision weapon unless its homing device carried it true to the target.

Missiles launched against an enemy ship at sea can close most surely upon their targets if a radar homing device is used. A ship against the background of the sea will produce a sharply defined "pip" on the radar screen of a missile, which can then be self-controlled to dive unswervingly upon its target. When this occurs, the ship's only chance will be either to jam the radar of the invading missile or to launch a countermissile that will explode the invader while it is still miles away.

Radar homing is excellent against ship targets but poor against industrial ones, since to a missile with a low I.Q. the radar pattern produced by the buildings of an industrial plant or a city is clear and incisive only if these buildings stand in bold relief upon a plain. Against most industrial targets it is more efficient for the missile to home by infrared, which takes advantage of the fact that industrial buildings emit heat in the form of invisible infrared light that is distinctly more intense at very long wave lengths than the infrared emitted by the surrounding terrain, which is at a temperature that is from 5° to 20° lower than that of the buildings. With this type of homing system the defender will, however, be wholly vulnerable only in clear weather; for if there are clouds, the water droplets that form the cloud mass will absorb 50 to 75 per cent of the emitted infrared in the critical wave-length bands and so will seriously impair the "sight" of the homing missile.

As in World War II, when clouds obstructed the vision of bombardiers, there will be cities like Moscow and Boston that are shielded by cloud a high percentage of the time and those like Stalingrad and

Phoenix that usually stand bare and clear as targets that are quickly and precisely "seen" from great heights above the earth.

Of the many kinds of missiles, only the true ballistic missile will, through its fantastic speed, be virtually free of the weather during flight. Hanson W. Baldwin, the military expert of *The New York Times*, estimates that when it is perfected the intercontinental ballistic missile will weigh about 100 tons and have initial and terminal speeds of 20 Mach, or 15,000 m.p.h. It will move from launching site to target in an hour or less, flying a preset course that arches high into the atmosphere, far above the levels accessible to air-breathing missiles.

Though it will move at speeds of but a few Mach through the ionosphere and exosphere, it will nonetheless traverse these regions in thirty or forty minutes and so will be exposed to meteor showers for such a brief time that the chances of its being struck by a meteor will surely be less than one in 100,000. And in its upward and downward flight through the thick layers of the stratosphere and troposphere, it will be traveling at such high speeds that no wind of a few hundred miles per hour can possibly deflect it significantly from its path.

The intercontinental ballistic missile with a nuclear warhead is a nonprecision area missile that has been called the ultimate weapon. Certainly the weather cannot turn it aside. Possibly no effective countermissile can be developed for a good many years. Indeed, there may never be a wholly effective countermissile because even if the nuclear warhead is detonated by a counterattack at heights of a hundred miles, the deadly dust of the explosion will drift downward into the lower atmosphere and will through action of the winds be spread here or there, depending upon the weather situation, just as its spread is determined by the weather when detonation takes place upon striking the ground or at a low preset altitude. In flight the intercontinental ballistic missile is free of the weather, but its effects, like those of all nuclear weapons, are closely determined by the weather.

Missiles are the major weapons of the air warfare of the future, but they are not the only ones. There will also be unmanned balloons that fly over enemy territory, manned aircraft that mount to heights of twenty miles, and earth satellites that circle the earth at heights of 200 to 2,000 miles. The balloons and satellites, insofar as they are used for reconnaissance, will prove more or less effective depending upon conditions of cloud cover. The manned aircraft will, like their commercial counterparts, be subject to severe limitations because weather can bind them to the ground or to the deck of an aircraft carrier just as certainly as it can ground more conventional aircraft.

So should air warfare come in 1961 or beyond, the weather will continue as in the past to add immeasurably at times to that friction of which Clausewitz wrote. In theory everything is possible in the new air warfare. In practice the weather will be a major frictional factor that may determine whether a blow is thrust home with precision, whether it is successfully parried, or whether, as in the use of nuclear bombs, it is deflected to fall upon friendly allies as well as upon the enemy.

Military Weather Services

"War is a practical business. It demands practical answers to practical questions." These words by General D. N. Yates, former chief of the USAF Weather Service, give the reason why every major military organization of every major country has its corps of weather scientists and technicians to provide forecasts for military operations and to conduct special weather studies for logistic, strategic, and tactical planning.

In the United States, Great Britain, the Soviet Union, and other countries, these technical organizations are busy today as they were in World War II. They are training weather forecasters and developing new forecast techniques applicable to all parts of the world, including those far reaches of the atmosphere that only a few years ago were of no direct military concern. They are providing the weather specifications necessary to the design of new weapons. They are also calculating the weather probabilities that must be admitted as factors in hundreds of each of the operational elements of different war plans.

Even a brief view of the problems that confront these corps and how these problems are solved provides an understanding of weather-war relations. Such a view also illustrates what can be achieved when men trained as theoretical scientists join together with engineers and technicians to find practical answers to practical military questions.

The two major phases of the operations of a military weather service are weather forecasting and the carrying out of applied research. These phases are often more closely related than might be supposed. Examples are provided by the planning and execution of major bombing raids during World War II, such as that on Ploesti.

In 1943 the AAF decided to attempt an all-out bombing raid on Ploesti, the oil center in Rumania from which the Nazi war machine was drawing much of its greatly needed power. The nearest bases from which an attack could be mounted were in North Africa. To strike from those bases would mean operating at close to the maximum ranges attainable by the B-24's, the longest-range bombers available at the time.

This immediately defined one essential weather requirement: there could be no strong head winds either going to or returning from the target, else the planes would not be able to return to Allied territory. Additional weather requirements were also fixed by circumstance. Protective cloud would be desirable en route since there were no fighter craft of sufficient range to accompany the bombers throughout their flight. Weather at the target must also be just right: clear, to permit visual bombing; and southerly winds, so that the bombers could move directly in on the target along their line of approach and drop their fire-spreading incendiary bombs on the windward side without having to circle the heavily defended target. Could all these weather requirements be met simultaneously? And when?

To their file of daily weather maps covering forty years of records went the AAF weathermen for their answers. By studying these maps they could estimate the weather odds. They found that all four required conditions—no strong head winds, cloud en route, clear target, and southerly winds at the target—would be almost certain to occur in March or August, but not in any other month. March was too soon, not allowing sufficient time for preparations; so August was planned as the month to lay on the attack.

AAF weather forecasters at the North African bases were alerted to be on the lookout for the required weather situation. They were told the conditions to watch for. Aircraft and crews were directed to stand by on the first of August and to continue to stand by until the weather was right.

As luck would have it, the weather map for July 31, 1943, showed that the required weather would exist on the following day. At dawn the planes took off. There were no strong headwinds. Protective cloud cover was good much of the way. The target was clear. And as the planes swept in from the south before a tail wind, they were able to unload their fire bombs on the target at Ploesti without taking life-endangering time to circle for an approach.

The losses in this Ploesti raid were heavy. Many planes failed to return. But the losses would have been far greater and the raid might well have been unsuccessful had the requisite weather not been carefully selected and properly forecast in advance.

The Ploesti study was, like many others that are carried out by military weather services, closely geared to a single specific military operation. But applied studies in the field of military meteorology must meet a wide range of needs.

For example, during the last war the AAF Weather Service conducted studies that were applied in locating and constructing an airfield in Australia, building a dam in Africa, constructing the Alcan Highway, designing buildings for Iceland, determining fuel specifications for the North African invasion, designing tractor treads for Italian mud, and planning air traffic flow across the North Atlantic.

In the fields of naval warfare and logistics, the aerologists of the U.S. Navy carried out an equally great diversity of studies. In addition every campaign, whether it involved the Army, the Navy, the AAF, or all three, was backed by a weather study whose purpose it was to maximize the chances of success.

Campaigns were timed and planned with weather considerations clearly in mind. Sometimes there were other factors of such overwhelming importance that it was necessary to go ahead at all costs and to risk fighting the weather as well as the enemy; but when this was done, it was seldom through ignorance of the adverse weather odds, and its effects were minimized in every way possible.

More often it was possible to plan a campaign from the outset so as to gain the weather advantage, as through propitious timing or through striking across terrain that would in heavy rains afford far better going than the terrain available to the enemy. The significant aspect of all these strategic studies was that they permitted the military commanders to reckon with the weather as a ponderable factor.

Applied studies in the field of military meteorology are carried out today as they were during the war. Now, however, the emphasis is upon problems of weapon design and the constant modification and improvement of detailed war plans. In the United States these studies are carried out by the two primary military weather services, those of the Air Force and the Navy; and by smaller groups of weather specialists attached to research and development laboratories, to organizations concerned with operations analysis, to major commands of the Army, Navy, and Air Force, and to the General Staff itself. Should war come, the activities of these groups would be greatly intensified. At the same time there would be an expansion of military weather forecasting activities throughout the world. The nucleus for such an expansion would be the forecasting systems and personnel that are now meeting the peacetime requirements of the armed forces.

Today the USAF Air Weather Service has weather forecasters stationed at all Air Force fields, both at home and abroad, to provide the weather predictions necessary to the operation of military aircraft and of major Army and AF installations. The forecasting services of the Navy are centered at its Fleet Weather Centrals at Norfolk, Boston, San Diego, Honolulu, Guam, and other places. At the same time it maintains forecast staffs aboard the flagships of all major fleet units. Both services maintain weather observing stations at remote localities beyond the continental limits of the United States; and when there are maneuvers or weapons tests, as of nuclear devices at Eniwetok, one or the other or both provide the required weather predictions.

In all these forecasting operations, the Air Force and Navy, like the U.S. Weather Bureau, use reasonably standard forecast techniques and depend upon the reports of weather observers throughout the world, reports that are sent by radio or teletypewriter to official weather forecasters everywhere. So in peacetime, the forecasting activities of the armed services are not much different from those of civilian weather agencies. In wartime there is a sudden change.

When war starts, current weather information is transformed within the minute to valuable military intelligence. International radio-teletypewriter circuits carrying weather data suddenly go dead. The radio signals that formerly relayed intelligible weather messages within a dozen foreign countries are silent for a few hours, then fill the air with the gibberish of scrambled or enciphered messages. Almost at once, half of the weather map that is the primary working tool of all weather forecasters is wiped clean of weather information. The military forecaster is then in the position of a doctor who must diagnose the condition of a patient whose pulse he cannot take, whose heart he cannot hear, and whose body he cannot see. He is faced abruptly with the problem of silent-area forecasting.

There are two ways to remedy the handicaps of silent-area forecasting. One is to make silent areas vocal. The other is to devise techniques that will permit some reasonable estimate of weather conditions despite the absence of data from many parts of the earth. In World War II, both methods were used.

There were those who went into enemy territory, who were put ashore from submarines on black, cloudy nights, and who crawled across beaches with radio transmitters on their backs and sought refuge. There were also those who were the countrymen of nations that had suffered from invasion, as in France. They risked their lives by concealing radio transmitters given them by the Underground and by sending out weather messages at preassigned times and at preassigned radio frequencies.

A quite different approach to the problem of silent-area forecasting involves the application of special skills and techniques developed for just such a contingency. One of the techniques used by American forces in the last war was that of single-station forecasting. Forecasters were trained to predict the weather from a succession of comprehensive observations taken at the single station where they were located, rather than from hundreds of widely scattered stations as is possible in times of peace. The single-station technique yielded fair results in the middle latitudes, where weather tends to move from west to east and where such weather events as the passage of a cold front are usually well defined. However, the technique did not apply at all in the tropics, and since it required an unusual amount of skill and perception in weather observing and in interpretation of the successive weather scenes, it was a dismal failure, so far as many forecasters were concerned, even in middle latitudes.

Far better success was achieved by the weather service of the Soviet Union, which had anticipated the possibility of war with Germany and had started preparations for silent-area forecasting many years before the war broke out.

The success of Soviet forecasters was due in part to the nature of their meteorological organization as well as to their anticipation of the forthcoming war. In times of peace the single major weather service of the Soviet Union is the Main Administration of the Hydro-Meteorological Service. The Service is equivalent to the U.S. Weather Bureau, but is a far larger organization with much broader responsibilities; it embraces most of the functions that in the United States are assigned to the military weather services and, as regards the basic aspects of flood and sea forecasting, to such civilian agencies as the U.S. Geological Survey and the Hydrographic Office. In the Soviet Union there are weather officers attached to the armed services, to the Secret Police, to the railroads, to the Forest Service, and to other governmental organizations; but all of these are technically, though not administratively, under the single Hydro-Meteorological Service, which is far larger than all other subsidiary services combined.

In times of peace, every top administrator in the Hydro-Meteorological Service is a reserve officer in the Red Army. As soon as war breaks out, every member of the Service automatically becomes a member of the army, directly answerable to army discipline. Even in peacetime, the discipline is strict; and since the Service is commanded by high-ranking army reservists, it is a simple matter at any time to take what steps are deemed necessary to prepare for wartime operation, including silent-area forecasting.

The Soviet scheme for silent-area forecasting in World War II is known as the Troitsky Plan. Troitsky was a Soviet meteorologist. His name is not nearly as well known in the West as are the names of Pagava, Multanowski, Chromov, Dubuk, and dozens of other Soviet meteorologists, all of whom have done brilliant work in applied meteorology. Yet in a practical military sense none of their work compares with that of Troitsky, who long before the start of World War II designed and put into operation a plan that was so farsighted that when the German armies at last invaded the Soviet Union, causing a sudden blackout of weather information from the West, Soviet meteorologists continued to turn out excellent forecasts for military operations. Historically and operationally, the Troitsky Plan consisted of four phases.

Phase I involved the development of a method for effective weather forecasting in the case of a silent area to the west. This in itself was difficult to achieve since the great storm systems that invade Eurasia move chiefly from west to east.

Phase II consisted of training all principal weather forecasters in the Hydro-Meteorological Service. This training started on a regular basis no later than 1936. By that year, all weather forecasters at all principal forecast stations in European Russia were being required once each week to make their forecasts without using the data to the west of Russia, and in so doing to apply the new techniques. The second phase not only provided training; it also permitted constant review and improvement of silent-area techniques for a continuous period of five and one-half years prior to the German invasion.

Phase III appears to have been a brilliant afterthought. Though accurate information is lacking, it seems likely that it was not initiated until the outbreak of the European war, in September, 1939, and possibly not until somewhat later. This phase consisted of the setting up of teams of forecasters, probably within the Central Organization of the Hydro-Meteorological Service. Team A was required to develop forecasting techniques and to make practice forecasts on the assumption that the silent area had been pushed somewhat eastward through a German advance. Team B carried out the same task for a still more easterly location of the battle line. Teams C and D practiced forecasting for still greater eastward expansions of the silent area. The exact number of teams is not known, nor is it known what were taken as the successive positions of the moving military front. What is known is that in its full form the Troitsky Plan was an integral part of the general war plan and provided a most realistic answer to the problem of silent-area forecasting.

The final phase of the Troitsky Plan was the operational one. When the German invasion began at dawn on June 22, 1941, the weather officials in charge at Moscow, Leningrad, Kharkov, Kiev, Odessa, Minsk, Smolensk, and other major forecast centers opened the safes in their offices, broke the seals on the top-secret war-plan envelopes, and were ready at once for wartime operations. Instructions in these envelopes advised each man of his army assignment, gave the wartime codes to be used in transmitting weather information, and called for the Troitsky Plan to take effect at once. For several weeks key weather predictions were issued at all forecast centers. Thereafter, as the German wave surged eastward, the most critical key predictions were issued by Teams A, B, C, and D in succession.

Perhaps one reason why the Soviet war plan for weather worked so smoothly in 1941 was that it had been tried out previously at the time of the Finnish War, in 1939. There was great confusion then, and the occurrences at Kharkov were typical. There, when word was received that war had been declared, the official in charge of the weather station opened the safe and removed the war-plan envelope. On it, however, were stamped instructions that it was to be opened only by a member of the Communist party.

Since no one attached to the weather office was a Communist, one of the younger men raced into town to find a party member. He returned with a man who, though neither a meteorologist nor a technical man, was nonetheless able to present his party credentials. The party member opened the envelope, but would not let any non-party man look at the contents. Instead, he sat for hours studying and restudying the new codes with their references to weather terms that to him were meaningless. Finally he got up, announced that he could not tell anyone except another party member what the new codes were, resealed the envelope, returned it to the safe, and, after solemnly ordering no one except another Communist to break the new seal, left the office.

For over twenty-four hours the map plotters and weather forecasters at the Kharkov Forecast Center tried desperately without success to find a way out of their dilemma. They sent frantic messages to Moscow without reply. Meanwhile, the teletypewriter was turning out undecipherable weather messages in the new war code. Finally there appeared in the office a meteorologist who had been flown in from Moscow. He was both a meteorologist and a Communist. Quickly he opened the envelope, scanned the contents, issued the necessary orders, and explained the new code to the meteorologist in charge and his assistants. Then he dashed out to continue his rounds among the stations unequipped with a Communist party meteorologist.

There is evidence that, during the many years that have passed since the war-plan episode at Kharkov, the Main Administration of the Hydro-Meteorological Service of the U.S.S.R. has done much to improve both its peacetime operations and its procedural and technical plans for war. It is also possible that there has been a decline in the influence of the Communist party upon the operation of weather services. Before the war, this influence was expressed through awarding many key technical and administrative positions to Communist party members who were not well qualified to carry out their work. Probably the harsh demands of war and the constant improvement of the universities and technical institutes have brought about a modification of this policy.

The Hydro-Meteorological Service is an effective organization that includes among its members many able meteorologists. And in the Hydro-Meteorological Service, as in the weather services of the United States, applied military studies of great diversity and importance are most certainly being carried out.

There is one special group of new military problems that are now demanding the concentrated attention of meteorologists both in the Soviet Union and the United States. These relate to the use of nuclear weapons. In what kind of weather situation can a ten-megaton bomb be detonated three miles above Moscow without endangering Poland? How many megatons of H-bombs can be detonated over the United States before the atmosphere will become so saturated with radioactive dust that even the Soviet Union, 5,000 miles downwind, will suffer from the consequences? Questions of this kind are so vital that today, more than ever before, the calculations, estimates, and predictions of the meteorologist are granted serious consideration in the highest councils.

19 Nuclear Weapons

Only twice in history has the wind created episodes that commanded world-wide public attention, and both of these times the winds were of modest force.

The first episode began in August, 1883, with the eruption of Krakatoa. For long afterward, all over the world, people watched the gray dust settle downward and the red sunsets that marked the arrival of the wind-borne ash from Krakatoa. Millions of people came to realize that the air which streams with the wind across some far-off region of the land or sea will sooner or later be spread throughout the entire world.

The second episode began on March 1, 1954. On that date a great nuclear bomb was exploded at Bikini atoll in the Pacific. Except within a limited area of a few thousand square miles, there was no visible gray dust, no reddish sunsets. Yet because of a Japanese fishing boat, *Lucky Dragon Number 5*, the attention of people everywhere was once again focused upon the world-wide nature of the winds.

For many years prior to the episode of the *Lucky Dragon*, government scientists of the United States, the Soviet Union, and many other countries had known that radioactive dust from bomb tests was being spread throughout the world by the winds, and they had, accordingly, been monitoring dust fallout on an extensive scale. However, except for the Japanese, whose wartime experience of bomb effects had made them highly sensitive to the danger of fallout contamination, there was no really widespread public knowledge of this hazard until the tragic *Lucky Dragon* episode.

Lucky Dragon was a tuna trawler out of Japan. On March 1, 1954, with her crew of twenty-three, she lay about 100 miles to the east of Bikini atoll. She was not within the forbidden zone defined by the U.S. Atomic Energy Commission; but on the other hand, neither was her presence known, because search aircraft monitoring a far larger area had failed to spot the small vessel.

Before dawn on March 1, the Japanese fishermen had witnessed the sudden rising of a brilliant sun—far to the west. Yet, as Schubert and Lapp describe it, a few hours later, when "whitish talc-like ash swirled down from the Pacific sky . . . they never suspected they were being bombarded with radioactivity. . . . Untouched by blast and heat, they were none the less touched by the bomb debris, for it coated the boat decks and the men themselves with a mantle of grayish-white flakes. It was an irritating substance, causing the crew to complain of smarting eyes, painful lips, and inflamed nostrils. That night . . . some of the men became nauseated as through seasickness. In three days some were suffering from swelling and reddening. . . ."

Because of expert medical treatment, some of it provided by specialists rushed to Japan from the United States, all but one of the crewmen of *Lucky Dragon* made fairly good recoveries over the next two to three years. One died on September 23, 1954, "from causes diagnosed as liver disorder." Whether the recoveries of the others have been really complete can be told for certain only with the passage of years.

The *Lucky Dragon* episode was front-page news throughout the world. It raised the question whether there was not real danger from radioactive fallout not only a hundred miles or so from the point of detonation of a nuclear weapon but even throughout the world because of repeated nuclear weapons tests and the repeated spreading of radioactive dust by the winds. Even more, it led to a far more vital question: What would be the fallout effects from a major nuclear war? Government administrators and scientists are gravely concerned with the answer.

Among them are the members and one-time members of official atomic energy groups, like former Commissioner Thomas E. Murray of the United States Atomic Energy Commission, who, in referring to unrestricted atomic warfare, stated that "words are inadequate to convey a real appreciation of the horrendous nature of this threat to our existence."

Among them also are those members of the armed services who are familiar with current war plans, like Lieutenant General James M. Gavin of the U.S. Army, who testified in a congressional hearing that "current planning estimates run on the order of several hundred million deaths" in Eurasia in the event of an all-out war, with the wind determining the distribution of deaths.

A third group includes those who are concerned because throughout the inhabited world all the people have, from tests of nuclear weapons alone, incorporated within their body cells at least a slight amount of radioactive strontium-90, and many have also been temporarily subjected to gamma rays from cesium-137 within their muscle tissues.

Then there is the fourth group, the geneticists. Even the most conservative of these agree with Westergaard, who in writing of radioactive fallout said: "Hitherto geneticists have felt rather comfortable about the old prophecy that the sins of the fathers should be visited upon the children unto the third and fourth generation, because they knew that acquired characteristics were not inherited. . . . But, on the threshold of the atomic age, they are no longer so sure."

If there was no wind, a 20-megaton H-bomb, 1,300 times more powerful than the Hiroshima bomb and equivalent in blast effect to 20 million tons of TNT, would kill or injure its victims only through the effects of blast, burn, and strictly local radioactivity. If the H-bomb was of the kind tested at Bikini on March 1, 1954, and if it was detonated at such a height that the fireball just touched the ground, the blast would destroy all structures over an area of at least seventy-five square miles, would produce burns fatal to more than half the remaining population throughout an area of at least 200 square miles, and would lay down a cloak of radioactive contaminants that for a period of at least one decade would render uninhabitable for normal, unprotected living a core area of at least twenty-five square miles.

There were 140,000 casualties at Hiroshima. In a larger city, with, however, the same population density as Hiroshima, the casualties from a 20-megaton bomb would with no wind factor exceed

2,500,000 and those dead within a month would exceed 1,000,000. The million or so survivors would have their lives shortened by a few years, would develop an abnormally high percentage of cataracts and cancer of the white blood cells, and would, if they produced offspring, pass on to their children and their children's children from three to ten times the number of genetic disabilities that they themselves had received upon birth. These damage values are based on the analyses of physicists and geneticists and upon calculations that stem from the official statements of the U.S. Atomic Energy Commission.

Without the wind, fifty well-placed 20-megaton bombs could within an hour yield 40 million casualties in the United States or 30 million in the Soviet Union, where the concentration of population in urban centers is lower than in the United States.

The effects of the wind must also be reckoned; they operate both quantitatively, to magnify the casualties, and qualitatively, to introduce pathologic and genetic problems of importance throughout the world.

The H-bomb detonated at Bikini on March 1, 1954, yielded radioactive fallout that through wind action over an area of 7,000 square miles would have been lethal to at least half the men remaining in the area had they failed to take cover or otherwise protect themselves through vigorous decontamination measures. There is evidence that this bomb was distinctly weaker than 20 megatons. Also, according to Dr. Libby, the AEC Commissioner, with different wind conditions the area of lethal contamination might have been several times larger.

Suppose, however, that the bomb was 20 megatons and the winds no more destructive than were those at Bikini on March 1. Then fifty 20-megaton bombs could lethally infest an area of 350,000 square miles. This represents something over 11 per cent of the area of the United States or over 4 per cent of the area of the Soviet Union. Should the bombs be placed with maximum precision upon the most densely populated areas, the resulting casualties could easily exceed 60 million in the United States or 50 million in the Soviet Union if the elaborate and expensive civilian defense measures necessary to avoid the effects of lethal contamination in marginal locations were not put into operation.

Even with such measures, the wind would increase the resulting casualties by a factor of one-fifth or more above the "no wind" value.

And in addition to this still rather local effect, there would be the further one of pathologic and genetic damage throughout millions of square miles outside the immediately afflicted countries.

As regards an estimate of the genetic effects of wind-borne radioactive debris, it is unfortunate that nuclear weapons came into being at such an early stage in the development of the science of human genetics. Geneticists agree unanimously that in any quantities whatsoever the radiations emitted by bomb debris are genetically harmful to the human race. They disagree over just how much radiation is required to cripple genetically the descendants of one-tenth or one-half of the exposed population or, for that matter, to injure an entire population so mortally as to assure its elimination in future generations.

It appears reasonable to accept tentatively the estimates of those geneticists who assign an intermediate, rather than an extreme, value to the amount of damage inflicted by a standard dosage of radiation. However, in accepting and applying these estimates, it should be borne in mind that the geneticists who made them admit that their estimates of radiation effects might easily be appreciably in error, and that the damage produced might be distinctly higher than they think it would be.

When the intermediate estimates of the geneticists are coupled with the findings of Dr. Ralph E. Lapp, the physicist, the results are of considerable interest. The detonation of 1,500 20-megaton bombs of the March 1 type would not genetically damage the human race beyond repair. Nor would the bombs damage so very severely that portion of it in the Northern Hemisphere—even assuming the winds did not cross the equator, so that the concentration of radioactive particles remained a maximum.

However, the situation would be dire in the countries where hundreds of bombs fell. Unless they had spent many weeks in thick shelters, the survivors would produce in future generations offspring so damaged genetically that they would constitute a new, handicapped subgroup. The more pessimistic geneticists believe that effects of this kind might extend throughout the world, though in much lesser measure. The human race would not be obliterated, but it would be altered, negatively. At the same time, because of the spread of strontium-90 throughout the world, no peoples anywhere would entirely escape such pathologic effects as an increased incidence of bone cancer. Thus with nuclear war on a major scale, the wind becomes a factor of great interest.

The foregoing comparison between "no wind" and "wind" conditions has been phrased in simple terms to make clear the nature of wind-borne fallout hazard. However, the problem is complex. Also, there are weather factors other than the wind that limit or extend, intensify or weaken, the effects of nuclear weapons. To understand more precisely the connection between weather and nuclear weapons effects, it is necessary to discuss separately how wind conditions are related to problems of civilian defense, how the weather influences strategic planning in this atomic age, the nature of the pathologic effects of strontium-90 and cesium-137, and what the reasoning is that lies behind the concern of geneticists for future generations. The influence that a nuclear war might have upon the weather itself must also be considered. First, however, it may be helpful to review the general nature and behavior of nuclear weapons.

The Nature of Nuclear Weapons

Nuclear weapons are of two kinds. There are fission weapons that derive their power from the energy released when heavy chemical elements, such as uranium, are converted to lighter elements. There also are fusion weapons whose power is derived from the energy released when lighter elements, such as certain forms of hydrogen, are converted to heavier elements, such as helium. In all chemical transformations there is the conversion of chemical matter into physical energy; but in almost all such transformations the amount of matter lost and the amount of energy gained are both so small as to be undetectable. In a fission or fusion bomb the conversion is so abrupt and embraces so much more matter that there is an enormous release of energy.

The detonation of a fission bomb triggers the instantaneous outburst of energetic gamma rays, of beta particles and neutrons, and of other rays and fast particles. Simultaneously, it creates a gigantic metallurgical furnace that in a fraction of an instant yields scores of different kinds of fission products. These products comprise the bomb fragments, both large and microscopically small; and if the bomb has been detonated at a low enough height, they will also include debris blasted from the earth's surface.

Each of the trillions of fragments in this initial churning mass is unstable. Each therefore begins at once to pass through a chain of nuclear transformations that in time will reduce it to some stable form. The gamma rays and the beta particles and neutrons that burst outward directly from the explosion are killers only over an area of several square miles at most, in the immediate vicinity of the exploding bomb. In contrast, with the help of the wind the unstable fission products, being themselves radioactive, provide for death at a distance. It is therefore pertinent to examine briefly how these fission products behave.

Consider the behavior of krypton-90, which is one of the many kinds of immediate fission products and is of special interest because it yields strontium-90. Ordinary krypton is a harmless, inert gas that existed in small traces within the atmosphere long before the first fission bomb was exploded. Ordinary krypton has an atomic weight of about 84, or about 84 times the weight of an hydrogen atom. Krypton-90 is heavier than ordinary krypton since, as its designation shows, it has an atomic weight of 90. It is unstable and changes to rubidium-90, which in turn is unstable and changes to strontium-90, which changes to yttrium-90, which changes to zirconium-90, which is the terminal, stable form. This transformation decay chain may be written:

> krypton-90 *with a half-life of 33 seconds* changes to
> rubidium-90 *with a half-life of 2.7 minutes* changes to
> strontium-90 *with a half-life of 28 years* changes to
> yttrium-90 *with a half-life of 61 hours* changes to
> zirconium-90 (stable).

Many decay chains are even longer than this one, involving six, or even ten, intermediate radioactive substances before a stable end product is reached.

The half-life entries in all chain formulas are important because they define the average length of time during which each of the successive radioactive elements will continue to exist. Since strontium-90 has a half-life of twenty-eight years, half of it will have been converted to yttrium-90 at the end of twenty-eight years, half of the remaining will have been converted in the next twenty-eight years, and so on. After ten successive half-life periods, or 280 years, there will be less than one one-thousandth of the original strontium-90 left because virtually all of it will have decayed to form first yttrium-90 and then, in turn, the stable zirconium-90. Compared with strontium-90, yttrium-90 has a short half-life, one of only about two and one-half days. Therefore, as strontium-90 changes to yttrium-90, it is changed quite quickly to zirconium-90. Thus only 10 x 2½, or 25, days will have to elapse before all but one one-thousandth of the yttrium-90 existing at a given, initial moment has been converted to zirconium-90.

Most of the many kinds of primary fission products formed upon detonation of a fission bomb, and most of the two hundred additional elements formed as part of subsequent decay chains, have very short half-lives, of the order of a few seconds or less. However, this still leaves many products that have long half-lives. Of these the most extreme is technetium-99, with a half-life of one million years. It forms from the initial fission product molybdenum-99, as part of the following chain:

> molybdenum-99 *with a half-life of 67 hours* changes to
> technetium-99 *with a half-life of 1,000,000 years* changes to
> ruthenium-99 (stable).

Fortunately, the longer the half-life of a radioactive substance, the less intense its radioactivity, though any radioactive substance can be lethal in sufficient concentration and with sufficient exposure time of the individual.

The atoms of unstable fission products do not change smoothly and uniformly from one element in their decay chain to another. Rather, they change by a series of spasmodic, energetic jumps, which are always accompanied by the violent ejection of beta particles and usually also by the emission of gamma rays. Taken together, these ejections and emissions give the substances their radioactive character. In terms of human hazard, the gamma rays are the most worrisome emissions; but the beta particles are also unpleasant.

Gamma rays are intense electromagnetic radiations with great penetrating power, which permits them readily to transfix the human body. In the usual terminology of nuclear physics, they include both X rays and rays of still shorter wave length. Like X rays, they cannot be seen; but their intensity can be measured in various ways. The danger of gamma rays in too great quantities is that they can produce direct and fatal burns and can pierce the body cells to disrupt cell nuclei.

If they enter well-developed germ cells in the testes or ovaries, they may produce cell changes that are deleterious to offspring.

Beta rays are electrons that are not bound to any atom and that move at highly energetic speeds, some of them at over nine-tenths the speed of light. They do not have the penetrating power of gamma rays and therefore usually influence only the surface tissues of an organism. However, if products that emit beta rays, such as strontium-90, are ingested and incorporated in the body, the beta emissions may cause serious physiological difficulties.

Neutrons are hydrogen atoms without the electrical charge that characterizes the ordinary hydrogen atom. Like beta rays, they penetrate deeply into tissue; but because of their far larger mass, they may be even more disruptive. Neutrons are produced in quantity by the initial explosion of a nuclear bomb, especially by the explosion of an H-bomb.

The term "H-bomb" has come to mean a bomb in which much of the energy is derived from fusion. There is no such thing as a "pure" fusion bomb because of the problem of starting the fusion process. This problem has been described by Bacher in the following terms: " 'How do you get it going?' . . . This problem is a little bit like the job of making a fire at 20 degrees below zero in the mountains with green wood covered with ice and with very little kindling. . . . Once you get the fire going, of course, you can pile on the wood and make a very sizable conflagration."

This analogy brings out two characteristics of the H-bomb: it must contain a fission bomb to yield the very high temperatures required to inaugurate fusion, and the bomb can be made as large as is practicable from the viewpoint of delivering it to the target. Because it is partly a fission bomb, the H-bomb also must yield radioactive particles that emit gamma rays, and the yield of such radioactive particles will chiefly depend upon the amount of matter involved in the fission portion of the explosion.

Rotblat, Lapp, and other nuclear physicists have analyzed the radioactive fallout figures released by the Atomic Energy Commission and have deduced that the bomb of March 1, 1954, at Bikini, was not simply a fission-fusion H-bomb, with just enough fission to get things started, but a fission-fusion-fission bomb. Such a weapon could be economically constructed through placing around the H-bomb a shell of the relatively cheap and abundant uranium-238.

Then, when initial fission started the fusion reaction, the resulting energy would be ample to produce secondary, but far more extensive, fission in the shell. All three phases of the reaction would occur in such rapid succession as to be complete within a few millionths of a second.

On July 19, 1956, Chairman Lewis L. Strauss of the AEC said that the United States had made "real progress" toward development of nuclear weapons that could destroy military targets with a "minimum" danger of radioactive fallout over nearby civilian areas. This statement may indicate that fusion bombs have by now been developed that have a minimum amount of initial fission and no secondary fission of the shell. These would be fission-fusion bombs.

It has been pointed out since 1956, however, that even if there could be a fusion bomb without any fission whatsoever, considerable fallout hazard would result because of the production of radioactive carbon (C-14) through the action of neutrons upon the nitrogen of the atmosphere. One of the first scientists to stress this fact publicly was O. I. Leipunsky of the Soviet Union. He estimated that detonation of a 10-megaton hydrogen bomb would eventually produce defective genes in 1,400,000 people. Libby of the AEC believes Leipunsky's values are too high by a factor of four. Even with Libby's lower value, a major nuclear conflict that involved the detonation of the equivalent of 700 20-megaton H-bombs would produce defective genes in an appreciable percentage of the survivors, the exact value depending on how many persons were killed by blast, burn, and other effects, since the dead could have no future progeny and hence could not pass on genetic defects to future generations.

For all fission and fusion weapons effects, there are three basic physical rules that help describe the relation between the size of the nuclear charge and the size of the afflicted area. The area afflicted by blast is a function of the cube root of the size of the charge. This means that to double the blast area it is necessary to increase eightfold the mass of the effective nuclear charge. In contrast, the area afflicted by flash-burn effects is a function of the square root of the size of the charge. To double the flash-burn area it is necessary only to increase the mass of the effective charge by a factor of four.

Thirdly, in a general way and with stated wind conditions, the area of lethal radioactive fallout is a function of the square root of that portion of the charge that yields fission products; so that, with the same wind, to double the area of lethal fallout it is necessary to increase by four times the mass of the fission part of the bomb. However, the wind is such a critical factor that it may yield a larger lethal radioactive area for a small fission mass than for one twice as great. This underscores the importance of a fourth physical relationship, which concerns the rate of decay of the radioactivity emitted by the bomb products.

As stated by Libby, the general rule is that with the passage of each seven units of time, the radioactivity of the bomb products decreases to one-tenth its intensity during the first of the seven time units. At the end of seven hours, the intensity is one-tenth what it was during the first hour; at the end of 7 x 7, or 49, hours, the intensity is 1/10 x 1/10, or 1/100, or what it was during the first hour; at the end of 7 x 7 x 7 hours, or about two weeks, the intensity is 1/10 x 1/10 x 1/10, or 1/1000 of what it was the first hour; and so on.

This explains in large part why the wind is so vital in determining the size of the radioactively lethal area. For example, with winds of 50 m.p.h., the radioactive debris will be spread across a large oval area in the first few hours, while the fission products are still extremely hot; but if the same area is blanketed five times more slowly, with winds of only 10 m.p.h., then most of the area, representing that part most remote from the explosion, will receive only radioactive debris that has decayed appreciably.

The physical relations just presented define in a general way the size of the area of effectiveness of nuclear weapons, even though, as will be seen, various local conditions can somewhat modify the effect of a weapon, either positively or negatively. Therefore, the size of a bomb and the amount of fission are dominant primary factors in determining the nature and extent of the damage during the first few hours, weeks, or months in the general area of bomb detonation. If world-wide effects are considered, then the fusion portion of the bomb must be allowed for as well as the fission portion, because of the production of C-14.

Bomb sizes are commonly reckoned in megatons or kilotons. The Hiroshima bomb was 15 kilotons. This means that its blast power was equivalent to 15,000 tons of TNT. In this discussion, the largest bomb size that has been mentioned is the 20-megaton bomb, equivalent to 20 million tons of TNT and just twice as large as the bomb mentioned by Libby in his release of June 3, 1955. Information released regarding the weapons tests at the Nevada Proving Ground make it clear that the United States possesses many nuclear weapons that are much smaller than the 15-kiloton Hiroshima bomb. No official information has been released to indicate whether the United States, the Soviet Union, or Great Britain possesses bombs larger than 20 megatons or, for that matter, any larger than 14–16 megatons. Nonetheless, it is certain that present nuclear weapons cover a wide power range.

From a weather viewpoint, there is one additional point that must be stressed. The higher the altitude at which a bomb is detonated, the less intense will be the local radioactive contamination and the greater will be the percentage of radioactive debris spread by the winds over wide distances. At the two extremes the bomb might be detonated beneath the ground or at an altitude of hundreds of miles, as was done during Project Argus, carried out by the AEC over the South Atlantic in August–September, 1958. In the first instance there would be tremendous local contamination and virtually no spread beyond the blast area.

In the second instance the local radioactive effects, immediately beneath the bomb, would for two reasons be much less than had the bomb been exploded hundreds of miles away at a two-mile height downwind. First, a low-level burst in which the fireball intercepts or almost intercepts the ground yields fallout of the most severe type since the ground and objects on it are blasted out and add their own radioactive dust to that of the bomb itself. Second, virtually all of the radioactive dust yielded by the high burst would travel long distances before settling downward to effective heights. Project Argus did, however, produce a belt of artificial radiation that was comparable to the natural radiation belts of the exosphere. It surrounded the entire earth shortly after bomb detonation and disrupted radio communications on a world-wide scale. One possible military application of creating such belts would be to disrupt the electronic guidance systems of intercontinental ballistic missiles.

The Wind and Civilian Defense

Many people believe that there will never be unrestricted nuclear warfare. Yet all agree that civilian populations must be prepared for nuclear attack. Civilian defense measures are the concern of countries like the United States and the Soviet Union, which would almost certainly be participants were there a major nuclear war. They are the concern also of traditionally neutral countries like Sweden, whose military and civilian leaders fully realize that winds carrying radioactive debris do not discriminate between belligerent and non-belligerent nations.

Any realistic plan for civilian defense must concern itself with patterns of destruction that are weather-controlled. Chiefly, these patterns are related to the wind, which on a large scale determines the shape and orientation of the lethal fallout area, and on a small scale determines whether, for example, a family of five will barely survive because they chose to eat and sleep and live at the north end of the basement of their house or will die because they chose the south end. Partly, however, the patterns of destruction are related also to weather factors other than the wind, such as rainfall and fog.

Suppose that on the evening of July 21, 1953, fifty nuclear bombs had been dropped simultaneously, one on each of the fifty most populous urban areas in the United States. Suppose, further, that each was a 20-megaton bomb of the fission-fusion-fission type, with a shell of uranium-238. What patterns of destruction would have been created?

Before analyzing this problem, it is necessary to elaborate briefly. July 21, 1953, was selected as the date for this example because at the time the analysis was made comprehensive weather data were not readily available for any later year, and because then the winds over the United States were light even for the summertime, which is a season of light winds. In this respect, therefore, the example is conservative, for it is based on a weather situation that provides far less rapid spread of "hot" radioactive debris than would be afforded in the wintertime or even in many summer situations. The analysis assumes that the lethal fallout areas will not extend beyond the distance covered by the winds in five hours' time, that the bombs are no more radioactive than was the March 1, 1954, burst at Bikini Proving Ground, that in each instance the fireball is five miles in diameter, and that the base of the fireball is at an altitude of about 1,000 feet.

In the solution of this problem the techniques employed were those developed by members of the U.S. Weather Bureau and issued by the Atomic Energy Commission in the excellent publication

Meteorology and Atomic Energy. The reasoning and arithmetic computations that led to the results presented here are given in the notes for this chapter. However, one particular aspect of the problem requires specific mention.

The intensity of radioactivity is commonly expressed in roentgen units. According to Atomic Energy Commission standards, a dosage of 400 roentgen units, or 400 r, will kill half of the exposed population if the dosage is received within a relatively brief time, not more than a day or two. Actually, there is evidence that the half-kill dosage is somewhat more than this, perhaps 550 r. With increased dosages, however, the mortality rate increases sharply: 700 r will kill 90 per cent of those exposed; 800 r will certainly kill 99 per cent.

These kill rates do not take into account any genetic effect. They represent immediate kill by radioactivity or reasonably prompt kill through death after a brief period of "radiation sickness." The example considered here is concerned only with kill rates resulting from short, intense radiation dosage; however, it should be mentioned that if exposure occurs over a period of many weeks, the half-kill dose rises to about 1,100 r.

Had an attack of the kind described occurred against the United States on the evening of July 21, 1953, the lethal fallout patterns would have been as shown on the map on page 362. Several aspects of this map are of interest. The bomb that fell on Minneapolis-St. Paul yielded lethal radioactive fallout over a distance of 350 miles, across not only Minnesota but also Wisconsin and even into northeastern Illinois. This was due to the presence of forty- to fifty-knot winds, from the northwest, aloft.

The area covered by this fallout was 15,000 square miles, larger than that embraced by lethal fallout from any of the other forty-nine bombs; yet despite this thinning out of the radioactive debris during the initial five-hour period, the dosage at the extremities of this fallout area was 400 r during the period extending from the fifth to the twenty-fourth hours after time of detonation; and closer in, in western Wisconsin and in Minnesota itself, the dosage was 1,500 to 6,000 r and more in the first twenty-four hours.

At the other extreme, in terms of area covered, was San Antonio, Texas. There the fallout in the five hours after detonation covered only 1,000 square miles. The lower-level winds were from the south and the upper-level winds were from the north, so that the debris was spread first northward across the area as the lowest-level dust fell out and then southward back across the same area as the dust settled downward from higher levels. With this concentration of dust in a restricted area, the contamination was fifteen times more intensive than in the fallout area originating at Minneapolis-St. Paul. The minimum twenty-four-hour dosage within the San Antonio fallout oval was 6,000 r.

The area covered by all five-hour fallout equals 203,000 square miles. However, part of the fallout was over the ocean, off Virginia and Oregon. In addition, there was an overlap of lethal fallout along the shores of Lake Ontario, in the Baltimore-Washington area, in New England, New York, and elsewhere. Subtracting the ocean-area fallouts and overlap areas, the net total for areas of lethal contamination becomes 190,000 square miles. On a different day, with different winds, this area might have been 350,000 square miles, even with all the conservative assumptions made in this example. With less conservative assumptions, the total might well exceed half a million square miles.

When the fifty lethal fallout areas for July 21 are tabulated by size categories, it is found that sixteen cover an area of from 1,000 to 2,500 square miles, eighteen extend from 3,000 to 4,000 square miles, and the remaining sixteen cover a large area range, from 4,500 to 15,000 square miles. This size variability is typical, for at any one time the winds that blow across a region as large as the United States will be strong in some areas and weak in others.

On July 21, the winds happened to be strongest in the Far West and in the region of the northern plains and prairies: in the Dakotas, Minnesota, Nebraska, Iowa, Kansas, Missouri, Wisconsin, and Illinois. They happened to be weakest in Texas and in the region extending eastward from central Ohio across Pennsylvania and New Jersey to the Atlantic coast. On some other day the distribution of strongest and weakest winds might be entirely different.

On July 21 there was also considerable variation in the shape and orientation of the wind-determined fallout areas. The Syracuse bomb produced an area that formed an almost perfect circle. The San Francisco and Los Angeles bombs produced long, cigar-shaped areas; the Allentown bomb, a kidney-shaped area. And there were other shapes of many kinds, many quite regular and oval, a few highly irregular.

The fallout areas were oriented in all directions. At Los Angeles

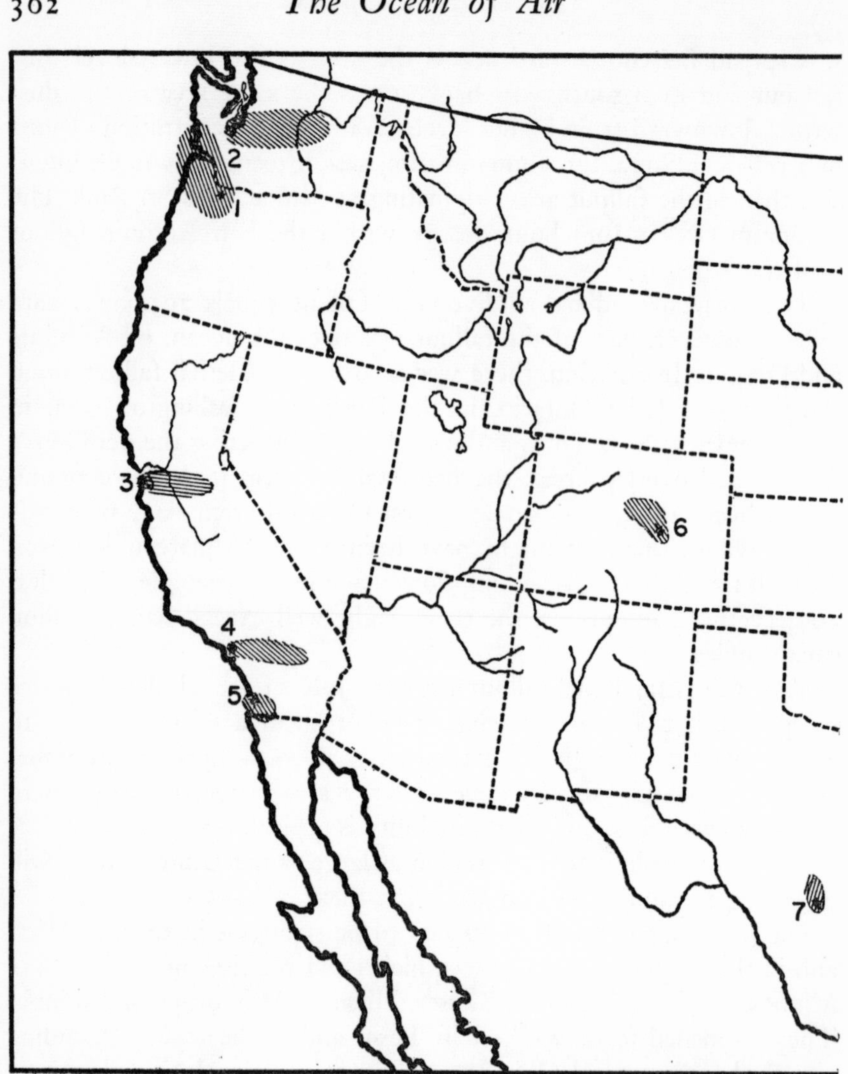

FALLOUT PATTERNS FOR FIFTY

(Based on observed winds and on standard methods

1. Portland, Ore.
2. Seattle
3. San Francisco
4. Los Angeles
5. San Diego
6. Denver
7. San Antonio
8. Omaha
9. Kansas City
10. Fort Worth
11. Dallas
12. Houston
13. Minneapolis
14. St. Louis
15. Memphis
16. New Orleans
17. Milwaukee
18. Chicago
19. Indianapolis
20. Louisville
21. Birmingham
22. Detroit
23. Toledo
24. Cincinnati
25. Dayton
26. Columbus
27. Knoxville

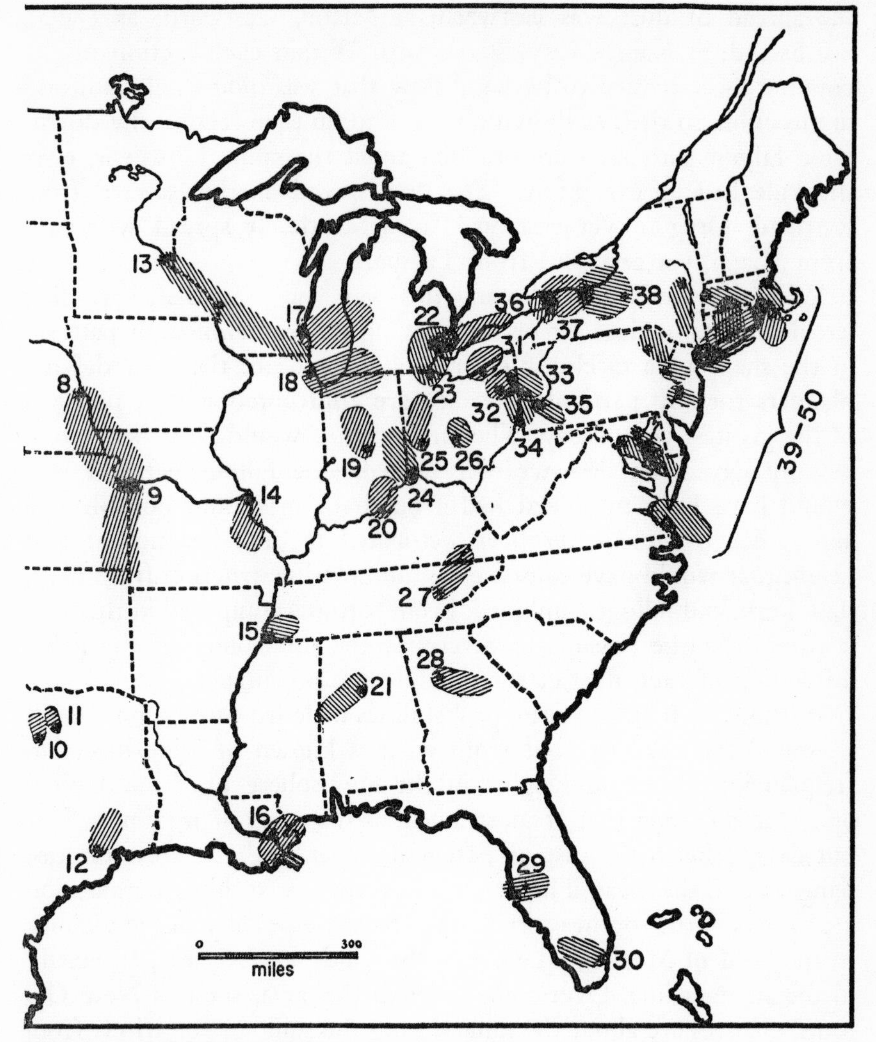

MAJOR CITIES, JULY 21, 1953

for the calculation of the effects of wind on fallout)

28. Atlanta
29. Tampa
30. Miami
31. Cleveland
32. Akron
33. Youngstown
34. Wheeling
35. Pittsburgh
36. Buffalo
37. Rochester
38. Syracuse
39. Albany
40. Springfield
41. Hartford
42. Boston
43. Providence
44. New York
45. Wilkes-Barre
46. Allentown
47. Philadelphia
48. Baltimore
49. Washington
50. Newport News-Norfolk

the spread of dust was eastward; at Miami, westward; at Dallas, northward; at Kansas City, southward. Within each section of the country there tended to be wind flow that was moderately uniform in direction, so that, as shown on the map, in each section the downwind fallout patterns were oriented about the same. However, even this rule had its exceptions. The dust spread northwestward from Portland, Oregon, yet eastward from Seattle. It spread westward from Miami, yet eastward from Tampa.

With the winds now blowing this way and now that, spreading lethal dosages of dust far or near, laying out contamination patterns in the shape of a circle or cigar or kidney bean, the civil defense planners for any particular locality are confronted with a problem of the greatest complexity. The safest course would be to work out, day by day from past weather records, the fallout patterns that would have been produced had a bomb of maximum possible size and radioactive character been detonated in each instance at that height that would have caused maximum total destruction from blast, flash burn, and fallout combined. From patterns computed in this way it would then be possible to determine the probability of the lethal infestation of each district surrounding the potential target.

Without such analyses the probabilities of lethal infestation cannot be stated for any city; but from what is known of wind-direction frequencies at various heights in the atmosphere over the United States, it is certain that at most localities the areas of maximum fallout danger lie to the east of potential targets and the areas of least danger lie to the west. The principal exceptions to this generalization are targets in the southeastern United States, especially in the vicinity of the Gulf of Mexico, where easterly winds are frequent, especially in the summertime. Over some cities in this area, such as New Orleans, chances are about the same during the summer for winds from any direction, so that the fallout hazard is equally great to east or west or north or south.

The problems of civilian defense become still more difficult when the fallout from multiple bursts is considered. The chances are ten to one that the debris from a bomb exploded over Boston will move in a general easterly direction. It would seem, therefore, that with sufficient warning it would be advisable to evacuate Bostonians westward to a town like Oxford, thirty-five miles away. Yet this would place the évacuées in an area that probably would receive lethal fallout if Springfield should be bombed. Therefore it might be better to move them northward to Dover, New Hampshire. Yet if Manchester was bombed, Dover would be an even worse locality than Oxford. Reasoning in this manner, it soon becomes clear that in areas like the northeastern United States, with a mass nuclear attack, there would be no safe place of refuge.

The only true solution may be to prepare for fallout in lethal doses over wide regions of the United States, a million square miles or more in total area. This requires the construction of shelters or, at the least, the establishment of well-provisioned "shelter spots" in basements. In locating shelters, knowledge of wind behavior on a small scale may prove to be of vital importance.

The action of the wind in depositing radioactive debris is somewhat similar to that of a stream in laying down rock debris of assorted sizes. If a truck drove out to the middle of the Chain of Rocks Bridge, which spans the Mississippi just above St. Louis, and dumped into the river a mixture of debris, including rocks and gravel, sand and silt, and extremely fine clay, the largest and densest rocks would sink quickly to the bottom of the river, after having moved only a hundred yards or so downstream. Next to settle out would be the gravel, with the largest and densest particles reaching the bottom first. If the current was swift, these might travel a half-mile or more downstream before reaching the bottom. Then the sand would settle out, and next the particles of silt, each in turn being deposited farther downstream from the bridge, but with some overlapping so that the less dense sand grains would be intermingled with those particles of silt that were unusually dense.

Still farther downstream, as far away as Vicksburg, Mississippi, and beyond, particles of fine silt or clay would still be settling out. They would drift slowly to the bottom in backwash areas, along the banks of the stream or the margins of a swamp, wherever the water was so still as to suppress even those tiny internal motions that are sufficient to buoy up a speck of silt. Beyond this, there would be the very finest of the clay particles, and these would travel past New Orleans and out into the Gulf, across the Atlantic Ocean, north and south and east, before some especially propitious situation enabled them to be deposited.

So in this way the broad pattern of deposition would be determined, whereby particles were sorted out in overlapping fashion, like shingles on a roof, running from large and dense to small and least dense. But upon this broad pattern there would be superimposed a finer pattern of deposition.

Viewed in detail, the deposition on the floor of the river would be far from uniform. Because of the topographic roughness of the river floor and because the water of a river does not flow smoothly but includes both evanescent and persistent eddies, there would be areas of high deposition intermingled with areas of intermediate and low deposition. Yet despite these irregularities, the broad pattern would be there, just as there is a broad pattern of plowed fields upon the countryside even though some fields are deeply furrowed and others are not.

The winds treat atomic debris in much the same way. Close in, under the fireball and the rising doughnut-shaped cloud that it produces, the rock- and gravel-size particles fall out with relatively little downwind displacement. At the other extreme, the smallest and lightest particles may circle the earth in the high atmosphere for months or years before they settle out. In addition, there are all kinds of variations in detail in the thickness of deposits laid down upon the earth.

There is, however, a factor that governs deposition within the atmosphere, though not within a river. This factor is precipitation, in the form of rain, snow, sleet, or hail.

For the first day or two after detonation of a bomb, the fallout distribution is chiefly determined by the wind rather than by precipitation. It is during this period that the larger and denser particles settle out. With winds of 10 to 50 m.p.h., the initial two-day fallout from a single bomb would cover an area of from 50,000 to one million square miles, the exact size depending upon the exact wind speeds and directions at different levels and upon the height of the burst. After about the end of the second day, only fine particles would be left in the atmosphere. The largest and heaviest of these would settle out at a slow and fairly uniform rate over a period of several weeks, during which time they would be spread over distances of thousands of miles by the winds unless they were washed out by precipitation.

Therefore, beyond the area of two-day fallout a map showing the concentration of deposition would show about the same order of intensities over millions of square miles except that in places there would be patches of much heavier concentrations where precipitation had washed the dust from the air. These precipitation areas would be of different shapes and sizes. The larger ones would embrace 100,000 to 200,000 square miles. The smallest ones of all, where local showers occurred, would cover areas of only a few square miles or even less.

Washout may still take place several months after the time of an explosion, but the concentration of dust laid down by the precipitation would by that time have been greatly reduced, since after several months nearly all the radioactive dust remaining in the atmosphere would have settled out except for the ultrafine particles carried by the stratospheric winds, high aloft, above the levels from which precipitation occurs. This last remaining increment of dust would settle out over a period of many years and over the entire world, though not, as will be seen, in even measure.

From these considerations, it is clear that if there should be a single 20-megaton bomb burst over San Francisco, the people in Reno, Nevada, 200 miles away, would almost certainly lie within the two-day fallout area and therefore would receive direct wind-borne fallout. In contrast, the people in Springfield, Illinois, 2,000 miles away, would probably lie beyond the two-day fallout area, and so would be seriously afflicted only if there was washout as the dust moved overhead.

Since in several weeks the winds would carry the dust many thousands of miles, the people in London and Moscow might also receive washout from a San Francisco bomb, though the dosages washed down would be hundreds of times less than at Springfield because of the marked thinning out of the dust as it spread to greater and greater distances, because of decreases in the total amount of dust resulting from settling out and washout during the long journey, and because of the marked cooling off of radioactivity with the passage of time.

Within the inner two-day fallout oval, the dust would tend to accumulate upon the ground in certain preferred locations, depending upon the speed and direction of the surface winds. Radioactive dust tends to "stick" to objects that it strikes. The windward sides of trees and buildings therefore collect more dust than do the leeward sides, even though in back of obstructions, where there are eddies, a certain amount of dust may settle out where the wind speed falls off sharply.

Any kind of shelter affords some protection against radioactive atomic debris. Best of all is an earthen or concrete shelter, with the walls and roof eighteen to thirty-six inches thick. Next best is an improvised shelter inside the basement of a building. A large basement affords considerable protection. Far less effective is the first story of a house or barn or other building. For the person trapped in the open, away from buildings, a foxhole will provide even better protection than the first story of a building; but the foxhole should if possible be roofed and should be on level terrain, where only a little dust will collect.

Wind and snow and rain will not be the only significant weather factors in the event of a nuclear attack. Fog and haze particles may hold within them radioactive dust that drifts with the wind and permeates all spaces invaded by the moving air. However, fog and haze have one advantage. They appreciably reduce the kill of the flash-burn wave from a nuclear explosion through cutting down the transmission of the wave, just as fog cuts down the transmission of sunlight.

With reference to the example discussed earlier, on July 21, 1953, a dense smog lay across the Los Angeles Basin. Had there been an actual burst of a nuclear bomb on that date, about 40 per cent fewer people would have been killed outright by flash burn than had it been a perfectly clear, smogless evening. Thus the "bad" weather conditions that help to produce smog would in this instance prove to be "good."

The Wind and Military Strategy

There is a military principle so obvious that it has never been necessary to state it explicitly as a tenet of military strategy. It is that the less the distance between the warring forces, the greater the chance for either side to strike a quick, decisive blow. Now, with nuclear warfare and intercontinental ballistic missiles, the principle must be restated in totally different form: the greater the distance between warring nations, the greater the chance for either to strike a quick, decisive blow; and, as a corollary, the nation that is surrounded by friendly countries is more vulnerable than that surrounded by enemy countries.

Ever since it became a sovereign nation, the United States has relied upon the application of the old principle. In times now past, the Atlantic and Pacific Oceans protected the United States against invasion.

In contrast, the nations of continental Europe have in every century since Roman times been subjected to attacks from neighbors close at hand who could never have struck effectively against them over distances of many thousands of miles. Sweden has struck against Russia, France against Spain, Prussia against France, and Russia against Poland. Today, Russia can strike more quickly and decisively against the United States, 5,000 miles away, than against West Germany, whose eastern borders lie along the edge of Soviet-dominated territory. For if Russia wished to keep her hold on East Germany, she could not use massive nuclear weapons for fear of the backlash from wind-borne radioactive dust.

Under the new principle, the United States and Russia would be equally vulnerable, one as against the other, were it not for the highly important corollary: the nation that is surrounded by friendly countries is more vulnerable than that surrounded by enemy countries.

The United States is surrounded by friendly countries. The Soviet Union can drop fifty or five hundred 20-megaton bombs on the United States without caring in the slightest that Canada and Mexico and Cuba would probably be lethally contaminated by radioactive fallout. The Soviet Union is surrounded by countries most of whose peoples hate the Soviet Union. These include such countries as Hungary and Poland, which have been coerced into joining the Soviet bloc; Finland, which is economically linked to the Soviet Union as a matter of geography, but whose people are dominantly anti-Soviet; Japan and Iran, both of which are if anything enemies of the Soviet Union and friends of the United States; and at not too great a distance, Greece and West Germany and France, and even Great Britain.

A total nuclear attack delivered by the United States against the Soviet Union would also be an attack against people who are enemies of the U.S.S.R. and friends of the United States. Indeed, even a partial attack against such important industrial targets as Leningrad,

Minsk, Smolensk, Kiev, Odessa, and other cities near the western borders of European Russia would produce at least some lethal wind-borne fallout in parts of Finland, Poland, Greece, and perhaps other countries as well; and an attack against important targets in the eastern maritime province of the U.S.S.R., on Sakhalin and at Vladivostok and northward, would yield some lethal fallout over Japan.

The new strategic principle makes it clear that should Russia deliver a nuclear attack upon the United States, full retaliation in kind would at best leave the remnants of the population of the United States as victors, but as victors whose popularity throughout much of Europe, Japan, and perhaps the Philippines and Iran would not be especially high.

Perhaps it was thinking of this kind as well as concern over the world-wide contamination from weapons testing that led the U.S. Atomic Energy Commission to attempt to develop "cleaner" H-bombs, ones that would yield a smaller burden of radioactive debris. Without information on the amount of fission products yielded by the new "cleaner" bombs, it is difficult to assess the danger they would pose to countries adjacent to Russia were several hundred of them delivered upon the U.S.S.R. simultaneously. However, with the wind patterns that engulf the Soviet Union, it would seem impossible even with the new weapons to avoid entirely the contamination of contiguous regions in the event of massive retaliation.

It is customary to think, in the utmost simplified form, of the belt of the westerlies in middle latitudes as if the wind at all levels at all times blew from west to east. This motion is valid if only the most frequent wind directions are considered. In this sense, it is true that the chances favor the movement of radioactive dust from European Russia eastward to Siberia and from easternmost maritime Russia eastward and southeastward to China and Korea and Japan; and these chances would be likely to deter the U.S.S.R. from launching a massive nuclear attack against continental western Europe. Unfortunately, so far as U.S. attacks on the Soviet Union are concerned, there are many weather situations in which the winds do not blow from west to east over European Russia; and furthermore, the winds at heights of five miles often blow in directions that are quite different from those at the half-mile or mile height.

Both in winter and summer, European Russia is frequently invaded by deep storm systems around which the winds circle counterclockwise. Fairly often, especially in winter, these systems move into Russia along paths that place northern Russia on the northern rim of the cyclone, with resulting easterly winds which would carry bomb debris west and south across Europe. It is dubious whether it would be possible to forecast these and similar weather situations, even supposing that strikes against targets in the Soviet Union could be postponed until there were deep westerly currents across most of European Russia.

In the Far Eastern part of the U.S.S.R. the situation is considerably worse. In winter the chances are somewhat better than even that ten to twenty 20-megaton bomb bursts over Soviet territory in the Pacific Far East would cause serious fallout in Japan, assuming the bursts took place with the base of the fireball at one-half to two miles above the surface of the earth. Higher-level bursts would not yield so much debris destined to move across Japan; but they would lose some of their blast and flash-burn effects through being detonated too high in the atmosphere.

In summertime, serious contamination of Japan would be just as much of a problem. However, whereas in winter the debris would move chiefly at lower levels in the offshore monsoon winds, during the summer it would move chiefly at high levels, from the upper part of the blast and from the rising cloud. Therefore, if the object was to minimize fallout in Japan, in attacking the Soviet Far East the detonation fuses would probably be set for higher levels in the winter and for lower levels in the summer. This would decrease, but would not eliminate, the hazard to the Japanese.

Though the United States may possess relatively clean H-bombs and might even sacrifice striking power through using them in an all-out war, the Soviet Union is still under no obligation to use such bombs against the United States. On the contrary, it would be to her advantage to use moderate-sized but dirty bombs that would be especially radioactive. This could be done without the hazard of too great fallout over the U.S.S.R. itself, provided too many bombs were not used. Further, there would be no need for the Soviet Union to be bothered with wind forecasts at the target, since contamination of countries adjacent to the United States would be of no concern.

Against such Soviet weapons there may be at least a partial defense. The indications are that the United States may develop missiles with nuclear warheads that will explode high in the stratosphere and so detonate the warheads carried by invading planes or missiles.

Should this speculation be correct, many of the nuclear bombs directed against the United States might be exploded in the stratosphere at such heights as to diminish the toll in terms of blast, flash burn, and quick fallout. However, a whole series of such explosions would release to the stratosphere such a mass of radioactive debris as to cause eventual "settle out" in almost as great concentrations throughout the world as if only low-level offensive bombs had been detonated. As a result, there would certainly be serious physiological damage through the effects of strontium-90 and cesium-137 as well as serious genetic consequences in widespread areas.

These fundamental problems demand separate discussion; for should there be effects of such consequence, it would be necessary once more to amend the principle that in times past expressed the relation between distance and striking power. It would then be necessary to state that because of the world-wide winds he who strikes at the enemy, whatever his distance, strikes alike at all belligerent nations, all neutral nations, all friendly nations, and at himself.

Radioactive Strontium and Cesium

From the viewpoint of direct physiological hazard, strontium-90 and cesium-137 are the most problematic of the radioactive elements that are carried by the wind to all parts of the earth. Strontium-90 has a half-life of twenty-eight years and cesium-137 has a half-life of thirty-three years. Both therefore would constitute a major hazard for many decades after a nuclear war was fought, and there are many pathologists and physiologists who believe that both constitute a real, though relatively minor, threat today because of the effects of nuclear weapons tests.

Traces of strontium-90 have been found everywhere that scientists have looked for it, even at the South Pole. Its greatest concentration is in the middle latitudes of the Northern Hemisphere, in areas of highest rainfall where washout has been greatest. To take an intermediate rainfall area, "AEC officials estimate that when all the strontium ejected into the atmosphere from all bomb tests to date falls out, the total will amount to 22 millicuries per square mile in the Midwest of the United States." This estimate, made a few years ago, covered bomb tests to the end of 1956 and included the settling out of strontium from the stratosphere, a process that takes several years. As will be discussed later, by the end of 1957 this figure had already been exceeded markedly in many parts of the United States. As to its significance, the value 22 millicuries must be referred to what is considered to be the maximum permissible concentration of strontium-90 in the bones of an individual.

A curie is a standard unit of radioactivity that is numerically equal to 37 billion disintegrations per second. A millicurie is one-thousandth of a curie, and a microcurie is one-millionth of a curie. Since strontium tends to take its place alongside calcium in the process of bone formation, the maximum permissible concentration has been defined with reference to the ratio between strontium and calcium in the bone tissues. In June, 1957, following the recommendations of a special committee of the National Academy of Sciences, the AEC stated: "For the population as a whole, the limit generally considered to be acceptable is 0.1 microcurie of strontium-90 per kilogram of calcium." Because the body of the average adult contains about one kilogram of calcium, this means that the maximum acceptable concentration is 0.1 microcurie for the average adult individual and correspondingly less on a weight-proportion basis for children and infants.

According to M. Eisenbud of the AEC, "the highest foreseeable skeletal burden in the United States," as the result of tests alone, is equivalent to one-fourth the maximum permissible concentration. Since this statement was made on November 15, 1956, and represented the projection of tests until that time but not afterward, the amount may now be too low. And it would be too low by a factor of at least 100 if so many as fifty 20-megaton bombs of the kind discussed in the July 23 example were dropped on the United States. In such an event, the strontium-90 uptake in the bones of survivors would amount to twenty-five times the maximum permissible concentration for a high percentage of individuals, so that the incidence of bone cancer would increase markedly.

The bone cancer threat is related to the manner of uptake of strontium-90 by bone tissue and to the effect upon the tissue of the emission of beta particles by the strontium. If strontium-90 was not taken up by plants, it would not be a serious hazard. As it is, plants take in the strontium, which is in turn concentrated still further by graz-

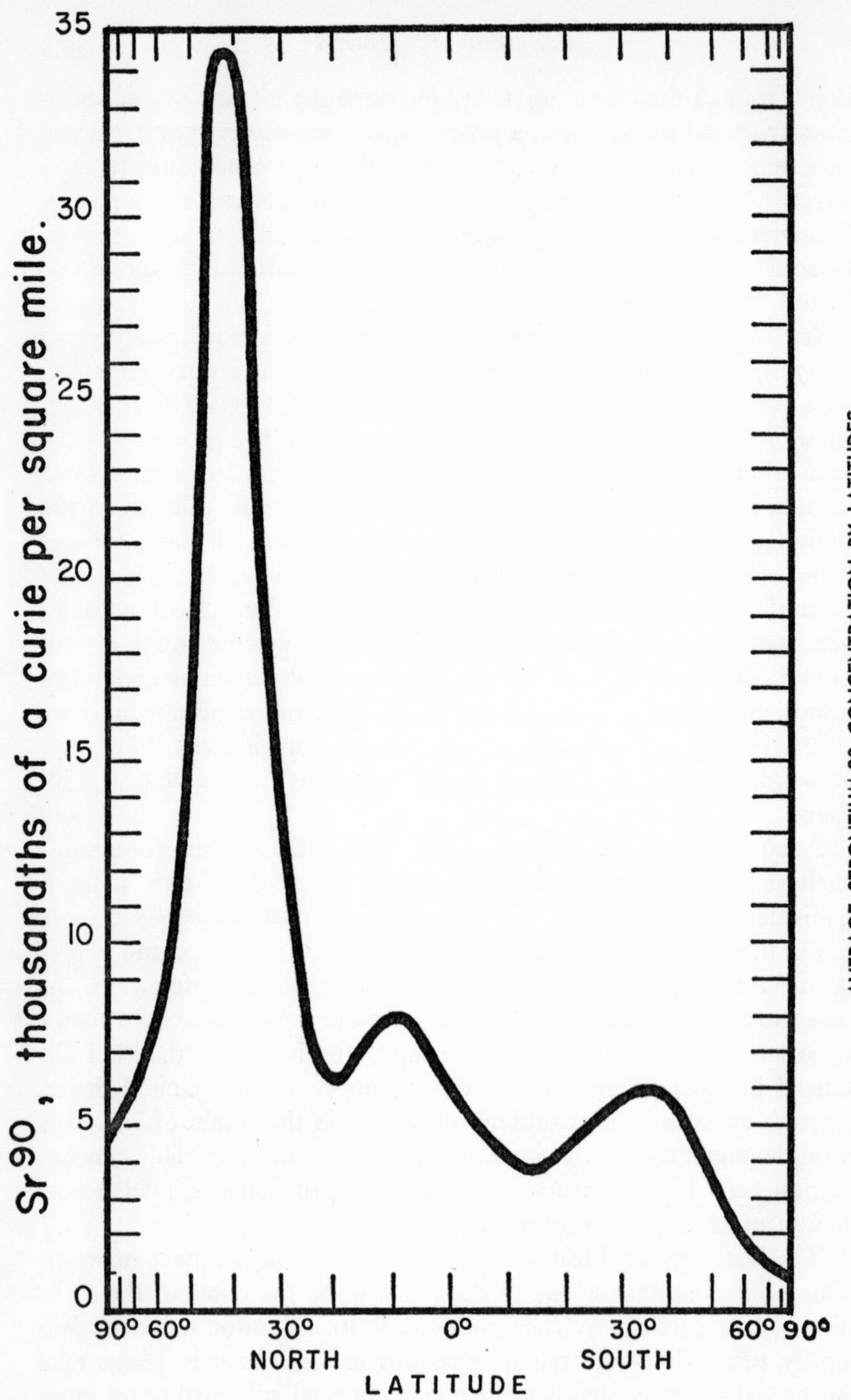

AVERAGE STRONTIUM-90 CONCENTRATION BY LATITUDES

ing animals. Thus the foods that people eat, both vegetable and animal, including milk, contain strontium which, being a close chemical relative of calcium, goes chiefly to newly forming bone tissues. Within the bone the strontium continues to emit beta particles and these emissions may produce cancer.

The causes of cancer are still not well understood. As Dr. Paul E. Steiner of the University of Chicago has stated, "Whether it be seen in the clinic or the experimental laboratory at its beginning or in the morgue at its end, a cancer can today be characterized in general terms of *what* happens, and *how*, but not *why*." All cancers consist of new tissues that are growing uncontrollably within the body and that serve no useful bodily function. Some grow rapidly, some slowly. Some spread to other parts of the body and there become established as growing tissues in a new site. So far as detailed morphology is concerned, some 300 kinds of cancer have been distinguished. In addition, cancer is classified in terms of sites, such as skin cancer, lung cancer, bone cancer, and the like.

From the viewpoint of the strontium-90 effect, it is especially unfortunate that bone cancer is often not detected until a cure is impossible. The earliest symptoms are easily confused with stiffness of the joints or, in children, "growing pains." By the time persistent pain has set in, it is often too late to save the patient, even through amputation of the afflicted member.

Through beta-particle emissions, strontium-90 induces bone cancer. To quote Dr. Furth of the Children's Cancer Research Foundation of Boston, "Radioisotopes localized in bones will induce cancers at sites of their deposition, and the tumor incidence is in direct relation to the dose." The exact dosage required to produce a malignant tumor (cancer) cannot be specified. Certainly it differs from individual to individual and from one specific bone site to another. Nonetheless, there is little doubt but that the danger is greater in children than in mature adults, whose bone tissues are not growing at such a rapid rate. Thus Furth states that "proliferating cells are more sensitive to acutely damaging effects of radiation than are resting cells."

If there is going to be any statistically significant increase in bone cancer merely as the result of weapons tests, the effects will be noted first among children and in the middle northern latitudes in rainy areas. If such an increase takes place, it will be so small that it will be difficult to isolate and establish statistically, even in these areas of greatest strontium deposition. Furthermore, the effect will become most pronounced only three to five years after the last weapons tests have taken place. This does not make the hazard less real; nor does it alter the fact that in the aftermath of a nuclear war, statistical proof of an increased incidence of bone cancer would be easy to come by.

In contrast with strontium-90, cesium-137 emits gamma rays. Like its close chemical relative, potassium, it is found chiefly in the muscles of the human body. "Based on one experiment with several human subjects, the current estimate of the time required for normal biological processes to reduce the amount of cesium in the body by one-half . . . is 140 days." Because of its short-term residence in the body, cesium is not as great a physiological threat as is strontium. However, because it is a gamma-ray emitter and because it is temporarily lodged in sites close to the gonads, it has a more pronounced genetic effect than does strontium. Its effects are therefore best considered in this connection.

Genetic Effects

In a major nuclear war the genetic effects upon succeeding generations would be heavy in some regions, moderate in others, and so slight in still others as to be perceptible only through precise scientific observations carried out over periods of many decades. Once more it would be the winds that would determine the pattern of destructiveness, this time in a genetic sense. The nature of the genetic damage that would be wrought by nuclear war and a notion of the wind-determined distribution of that damage will be better understood by consideration of a few of the fundamental facts that govern heredity in human populations.

The human body, like the bodies of all living organisms, is comprised of cells. These cells are of many kinds, depending in part upon their function and the tissues in which they occur. The cells of muscle tissues are different from those of the skin. Those of the skin differ from those of the bone or brain. Each vital organ contains many specialized kinds of cells, of distinctive character and with distinctive functions.

However, with few exceptions, all cells of the human body contain a nucleus within which there are bodies that can be stained and so observed under the microscope as colored organic particles. These are the chromosomes, which contain the determinants of heredity. For most persons, in virtually all the cells with nuclei there are forty-eight chromosomes, which appear as slightly bent or twisted rodlike bodies. These chromosomes occur in pairs, so that there are only twenty-four different kinds in any one cell. For some persons, the chromosome number varies slightly from forty-eight, but the principle of pairs still holds.

As the body grows, the cells multiply through division, a process that enables all body tissues to renew themselves and permits the organs to grow so that the individual matures and increases in weight and stature. Cell division of this kind invariably results in the replication of chromosomes in the new cells. Of critical significance from the viewpoint of heredity, and of the influence of radioactivity upon heredity, is what happens to the chromosomes within the germ cells of the male and the female.

In their earliest stages, the germ cells possess forty-eight chromosomes, just like other cells. However, as the germ cells mature, they undergo certain special cell divisions so as to yield not the usual forty-eight chromosomes in each newly formed germ cell, but only twenty-four unpaired chromosomes, one of each kind instead of two. Later, with union of a male and a female germ cell, the original forty-eight chromosomes are again established, twenty-four having been contributed by the male and twenty-four by the female cell. Thereafter, as the fetus grows within the womb of the female, there is cell duplication and cell differentiation, through cell division that once more takes place in the usual way, until a new individual has been formed with forty-eight chromosomes in each of his cells. And in each instance these forty-eight chromosomes are the lineal descendants of the initial set of forty-eight that was contributed half by the father and half by the mother upon conception.

Laboratory and field experiments carried out thousands of times with many different species of plants and animals have demonstrated beyond doubt that, though they cannot be seen, there are in each chromosome many different points or sectors that carry the specific elements of heredity. These parts of the chromosome are the genes, which have the hereditary determinant for such traits as eye color, mental ability, and so on. However, since the chromosomes occur in pairs, one set of which was derived from the father and one from the mother, it follows that each gene must also be present in duplicate, there being one from each parent. Accordingly, eye color or special factors relating to mental traits or stature are derived not from one parent but from both.

In considering this hereditary process from the viewpoint of the effects of radiation, it is essential to distinguish between dominant and recessive genetic traits. In eye color, brown is usually dominant and blue recessive. Because brown is dominant, brown eyes will nearly always result whenever one of two parental genes for eye-color determination carries brown. This will be true even if the other carries the recessive blue. In contrast, blue eyes will result only if both the parental genes carry blue. Two brown-eyed parents may produce a blue-eyed child, for both of the parents may carry not only the brown-eyed gene that dominated and gave him his eye color but also a blue-eyed gene, and it may happen that the child receives two blue-eyed genes.

The principle illustrated by this example is that if a genetic effect is recessive it may be carried on from generation to generation without being outwardly expressed in the individual until in the process of conception each parent happens to contribute the same recessive gene to a particular child. Only then will the recessive trait appear. This fact is particularly important in considering radiation effects, since many of the results of radiation are recessive and hence may not be expressed outwardly, in the body form, for two or three or several generations.

Had there never been any change in genetic constitution, there could never have been any evolution. Modern man would then be like such primitives as Pithecanthropus or Neanderthal, with a relatively small brain and far less acuity than the modern actually possesses. The changes that have occurred have resulted from the extremely slow process of changes in the genes. These seemingly spontaneous changes, or mutations, have in part been caused by the bombardment of chromosomes and genes by radiation from cosmic-ray showers and from radioactive rock. In part they have been caused by other means, such as unusual chemical conditions within the body.

Whatever its cause, each mutation produced offspring with altered characteristics, though these characteristics were seldom immediately and outwardly evident in the first mutant generation. In the majority of instances, the new characteristics have been deleterious and have resulted in the elimination of occasional individuals.

In prehistoric times, which occupied over 90 per cent of the time of man upon the earth, such elimination was produced through premature natural death, through the mutant individual becoming sterile, or through his inability to cope with his environment so that he was killed off before reproducing his kind. Where, for example, the mutation might have produced a tendency toward diabetes, the strain was usually eliminated through premature death. Where the mutation produced a nervous disorder that greatly retarded the muscular reaction time, the individual could be clubbed to death before he could defend himself.

In the modern world the cultural environment does not promote the elimination of the deleterious mutant forms, which among them represent the majority of total mutants. The diabetic is protected by insulin and so may and does procreate his kind. The individual with retarded muscular reaction time is seldom beaten to death.

This protective social environment has helped to increase what has been called the "genetic load" of modern man. Each person carries within his genes many traits that would have been eliminated long ago in a world of savagery, but that are now tolerated and even supported by modern medicine and modern social attitudes. A crucial question is whether mankind can withstand a further increase in his genetic load, such as the increase that would be engendered by the increased radiation resulting from fallout from winds carrying vast quantities of nuclear bomb debris.

Mutations may result from gamma rays, which can readily pierce the body and so reach the germ cells, or they may result from the bombardment of the germ cells by beta rays emitted by substances ingested by the body. Whatever the kind of radiation, it may smash a chromosome of the germ cell, causing it to break and thereafter to reform in an abnormal manner, so that the genes are no longer in proper linear sequence or are eliminated. More frequently, however, instead of such chromosome breakage, the damage will be of a second kind. Bombardment will alter one or more genes, thus changing their character as regards their influence upon inheritance. In either event, there is mutation and the inherited results are deleterious.

It is unfortunate that the atomic bomb was developed before genetics had advanced far enough to be certain of the degree of genetic damage that would be produced in the descendants of an individual who had been bombarded by a total of 1 or 10 or 100 roentgen units of radiation. However, all investigators are agreed that any dosage whatsoever is harmful and that the timing of the dosage is of no genetic consequence provided the individual conceives thereafter. If John Doe's gonads receive 5 r at the age of seven, 50 r at the age of twenty, and 45 r at age thirty, he has received a total of 100 r and is genetically in the same situation as Richard Roe, who receives the full 100 r within one hour at the age of two, provided only that Doe and Roe both conceive after receiving the full 100-r dosage.

In this respect, the genetic effects of radiation differ radically from other biological effects. Whether such other effects as burns or death through physiological shock are produced will depend in part upon the timing of the dosage, 100 r within an hour being fully as harmful as 200 r received over a period of days or weeks or months; but in the second instance, the genetic harm will be twice as great as in the first. This example underscores another relationship upon which all investigators are agreed: the harmful genetic effects will be proportional to the total dosage reaching the germinal tissue. Hence 10 r is ten times more harmful than 1 r, and 500 r is fifty times more harmful than 10 r.

Two critical questions now arise. What are the specific effects of mutation? How many roentgen units are required to create these effects in intolerable quantities?

At the present stage of genetic knowledge, it is impossible to state in precise terms what percentage of the mutants produced by radiation would suffer one general type of disability and what percentage another. Further, it is impossible to state just how much radiation would produce an effect of a certain stated intensity. This lack of precision in no way detracts from the scientific verity of the general conclusions arrived at by the geneticists. In this connection, the following remarks, which appeared in 1956 in the *Summary Report* of the Committee on Genetic Effects of Atomic Radiation, are especially apropos:

> Many people . . . suppose science to be definite—open or shut. Things are supposed to be so or not so. And therefore some persons

may, quite mistakenly, conclude that geneticists are unscientific because they do not completely agree on all details.

In relatively simple fields, where both theory and experiment have progressed far, a comforting kind of precision does often obtain. But it is characteristic of the present state of human genetics that one must carefully and painstakingly note a lot of qualifications, of special and sometimes very technical conditions, of cautious reservations. The public should recognize that the attitudes and statements of geneticists about this problem of radiation damage have resulted from deep concern and from attempts to exercise due caution in a situation that is in essence complicated and is of such great social importance.

Despite these qualifications, there is no doubt about the kinds of genetic effects that would be produced by increased mutations. An appreciable percentage would, like all mutations, yield tangible genetic effects, "such things as mental defects, epilepsy, congenital malformations, neuromuscular defects, hematological and endocrine defects, defects in vision or hearing, cutaneous and skeletal defects, or defects in the gastro-intestinal or genitourinary tracts," to quote again from the report of the committee. An appreciable percentage of the mutations would result in abortions or produce sterility that would prohibit reproduction. Finally, a high percentage, probably the highest of the three categories, would produce merely minor disabilities of the kinds described by Muller:

> . . . the impairment will usually be slight, or even unrecognizable, consisting of such traits as a slightly greater than average tendency to rheumatism or gastric ulcer, or high blood pressure, often not evident until the later years of life, or a higher requirement for some vitamin, or a slightly lowered I.Q. One reason for this lack of marked effects is that an offspring containing a mutant gene will almost always inherit from its other parent an undamaged gene of the original kind in question, and this normal gene will usually exert a much stronger effect than the mutant gene, being as we say "dominant." Yet, for all that, the mutant gene and the slight impairment caused by it will be inherited by a succession of generations, and it will hamper them to some small degree at least, even in the presence of the normal gene, until in the end some descendant finds himself in circumstances where just that disability happens to become the deciding factor in causing his death before maturity, or his failure to reproduce. Thus, the mutant will at long last be eliminated from the population, but only at the cost of the demise or frustration of some descendant, usually a re-

mote one, and the hampering, in some degree, of descendants belonging to the intermediate generations.

The degree to which succeeding generations would be handicapped both by extreme and mild genetic disabilities would depend upon the radiation dosage. One way of expressing the dosage factor is to attempt to estimate how many r would have to be delivered to the gonads to double the number of gene mutations that occur naturally in any population. As expressed in the report of the Committee on Genetic Effects:

> Each individual, on the average, inevitably experiences during his reproductive lifetime a certain number of harmful spontaneous mutations from natural causes. He would experience an additional *equal number* of harmful mutations if he received a certain dose of radiation during that same period. This is known as the "doubling dose." The actual value of the doubling dose is almost surely more than 5 r and less than 150 r. It may very well be from 30 r to 80 r.

Taking the middle value, a dosage of 55 r would double the natural mutation rate. Under the natural rate, about 2 per cent of the children presently born in the United States have genetic defects of the kinds already discussed. Fifty-five r would raise this value to 4 per cent; 110 r would raise it to 8 per cent, or almost one in twelve.

When these estimates are applied to the situation of July 21, 1953, as already discussed, their significance becomes clearer. Thus throughout more than 95 per cent of the area east of the Mississippi River and north of the Ohio River, and on the Atlantic Coast from Washington northward, the radiation dosage, *even outside the ovals of initial twenty-four-hour concentration*, would total more than 110 r during the first week after the attack because of continuing, cumulative dosages from dust on the ground, and throughout most of the area outside the ovals the weekly total would be in excess of 220 r. These are conservative estimates and they demonstrate that even those persons who escaped immediate death or were spared physiologically crippling radiation dosage would still suffer effects that would seriously handicap their future children.

In the succeeding discussion, which considers the basic weather aspects of the problems of weapons testing and nuclear warfare, reference will be made to the genetic effects of radiation dosages of even less than 55 r. It is pertinent to note that the Committee on Genetic

Effects set a level of only 10 r as the maximum reasonable cumulative dosage before serious genetic consequences would ensue. "Not *harmless*, mind you, but *reasonable*" are the words of the committee.

Basic Weather Problems in Nuclear Warfare

For the meteorologist concerned with radiation problems, there are three basic questions of a critical nature. How does the weather determine fallout distribution? Do nuclear explosions influence the weather? How accurately can the meteorologist predict what the winds, and hence the fallout pattern, will be?

Much has already been said about how the winds and rains influence fallout patterns. There is, however, the world-wide pattern that has already been established from studying the distribution of strontium-90 and other radioactive products of nuclear weapons tests, and this remains to be described as an entity. It is essentially the same pattern that would assert itself, but with vastly increased peaks and valleys of debris concentration, if there should be a nuclear war that involved the detonation of hundreds of bombs over the United States and Russia.

As of December, 1957, the total power of all test bombs detonated by the only experimenting countries—the United States, Russia, and Great Britain—was somewhat over 100 megatons. As of that date, these experiments had yielded an average deposition of radioactive debris that was greatest in the latitude zone of 35° to 55° N., a zone that embraces southern Canada and all but the southernmost part of the United States, from the Mediterranean to northern England, northern Germany, north-central Russia in Europe, and northern China, Korea, Japan, and much of the Soviet Union in Asia. For strontium-90 alone, the average fallout deposition in this zone, not including close-in fallout at or near test sites, was 15 to 35 thousandths of a curie per square mile. At the other extreme, not including Antarctica, where the fallout has certainly been least of all, in the latitude zone of southernmost South America and southernmost New Zealand (between 45° and 55° S.), the average deposition has been only about 2 to 4 thousandths of a curie per square mile, or about ten times less than in the maximum zone. The curve on page 374 is taken from Machta and List and gives the general relation between deposition and latitude. It does not show the present strontium-90 concentration, which would be significantly higher because of fallout from the extensive weapons tests held by Russia, the United States, and Great Britain since December, 1957, and because of continuing settling out of dust from tests prior to that date.

The great primary concentration of fallout in northern middle latitudes and the secondary concentration in low northern latitudes, as shown by Machta and List's curve, are explained by the locations of the major weapons testing sites and the behavior of the wind. The three major sites in terms of quantity of strontium-90 injected into the atmosphere are all in northern latitudes: around 58° in the Soviet Union, at 36° in Nevada, and at about 11° in the Pacific Proving Ground of the United States.

Dust from nuclear weapons blasts in Russia and Nevada was chiefly carried from west to east within the westerly winds of the troposphere. From the Pacific Proving Ground it was carried within the troposphere chiefly either from east to west in the trade winds or from west to east within the westerlies, high aloft within the troposphere above the trade winds. Therefore, the greatest bulk of the dust tended to be deposited at about the same latitude at which it originated, even though there was appreciable "spillover" into adjacent latitudes. The result was bands of maximum concentration between 35° and 55° N. and between the equator and 15° N.

These bands of maximum deposition were intensified by two other, supplementary, factors. The low-latitude band was fed not only by bombs exploded in the Pacific Proving Ground but also by British bombs exploded near Christmas Island, south of the equator. The higher-latitude band was reinforced by dust that was injected into the stratosphere as the result of the Pacific tests, transported northward by stratospheric wind, and then entered the troposphere chiefly around latitudes 35° to 45° N. through the sinking of air on the northern sides of the great anticyclones that drive the surface trade winds.

Before using Machta and List's findings to estimate the gross wind effects in a major nuclear war, one other aspect of their curve requires consideration. The slight hump centered at 36° S. is the result of the first British weapons tests, carried out in Australia. Had it not been for the strontium-90 from those tests, the curve would be smooth and fallout between 35° and 45° S. would have been almost as slight as between 45° and 55° S.

In an all-out nuclear war there might well be the equivalent of 1,000 20-megaton bombs exploded over Russia and the United States between latitudes 30° and 55° N. This may seem to be a preposterous bomb total, but it is of the right order of magnitude to conform with the kind of war referred to by General Gavin when he stated before a congressional committee that an all-out attack on Russia would yield heavy fatalities in Japan, the Philippines, and beyond.

One thousand 20-megaton bombs gives a total of 20,000 megatons, or 200 times the total already exploded in about one hundred nuclear weapons tests up to January 1, 1957. If these bombs were dropped only over the United States and the Soviet Union, the resulting strontium-90 curve, not including fallout at or near the points of bomb detonation, would show one enormous peak in the latitude zone of 30° to 55° N. and a rapid decrease in curve height southward to around 10° or 5° N., after which the curve would flatten out and taper off all the way to the South Pole. There would still be fallout everywhere, even at the South Pole, and it would be greatly augmented; but a far greater percentage would be in high middle latitudes.

Were it possible after such a hypothetical war to measure strontium concentration on the ground in France, England, Norway, and other areas well removed from the points of bomb detonation yet still between 30° and 55° N., it would be found that the mean strontium-90 fallout averaged at least 2 curies per square mile as compared with the December, 1957, average of 15 to 35 *thousandths* of a curie.

The exact value would depend on the precise fission yield of the weapons, the altitudes at which they were detonated, the exact places of detonation, the weather conditions at time of detonation, and other lesser factors. These variables can be altered in such a way as to give values of far more than 2 curies even in areas far removed from the bomb explosions. Of course, throughout most of the United States and the Soviet Union the values would be 10 to 20 curies and higher because of close-in fallout.

At the other end of the spectrum, in southernmost New Zealand and South America, the strontium-90 fallout would amount to around one-tenth of a curie per square mile, or about three times that shown in Machta and List's curve for the maximum zone as of December, 1957. This assumes, of course, that no bombs were detonated in the Southern Hemisphere.

This world-wide, wind-determined distribution of strontium-90 would have pathological repercussions whose severity can be estimated through reference to Eisenbud's statement, already mentioned. In northern middle latitudes, instead of having a maximum skeletal burden of strontium-90 equivalent to one-fourth the maximum permissible concentration, the burden would be twenty-five times the maximum in areas well removed from close-in fallout. In many parts of the United States and Russia the dose would be 1,000 times or more the maximum permissible. In southernmost New Zealand and South America the maximum dose would be just about the maximum. From about south-central Australia, southern Brazil, and South Africa northward all the way to the North Pole, the maximum permissible burden would at least be doubled.

Therefore, throughout nearly all of the inhabited world, wherever man continued to eat vegetable and animal food, the strontium-90 hazard would be extreme. Survivors of the war would not drop like flies, but many would suffer gravely. Even if steps were taken to decontaminate the soil in certain areas, it is at least highly questionable that the decontamination could be sufficiently thorough and at the same time extensive enough to save large percentages of populations either from starvation as one alternative or severe strontium-90 poisoning as the other.

In addition to strontium-90 effects, there would be genetic ones. The really heavy r dosages among survivors would be limited to the United States, the Soviet Union, and a few immediately adjacent areas, such as Japan and Canada. On the other hand, dosages somewhat above 10 r—the reasonable limit set by the Committee on Genetic Effects—would be exceeded here and there in northern middle latitudes outside these two countries and their immediate neighbors as the result of washout by rainfall. For example, with a particular weather situation, bomb drops over northern Russia might severely contaminate part of Denmark or Norway. Such remote areas as Australia or South Africa or Chile would, however, suffer only the most trivial genetic effects.

Except in a purely local sense and then only as regards small-scale features, nuclear weapons have had no effect on the weather. There is, however, the distinct probability that if enough nuclear bombs were exploded to place in the stratosphere as much dust as that produced by major volcanic eruptions, there would be weather changes on a world-wide scale. These would not be major climatic changes of a long-range nature, but they might well affect climates for at least a few years thereafter.

The Krakatoa volcanic eruption had weather effects that were felt for at least three years. These consisted chiefly in a lowering of summer temperatures. The equivalent of 1,000 20-megaton bombs would inject into the stratosphere at least five times more dust than did Krakatoa. Probably such an injection would lower summer temperatures for several years in higher latitudes, thus increasing local glaciation. Possibly also the effect would be to lower appreciably the amount of rainfall in the tropics. This would be expected because of the decrease in incoming sunlight and hence the corresponding decrease in rainfall caused by the heating of the earth's surface, a rainfall mechanism that is especially prominent in low latitudes. Thus widespread droughts might prevail in such normally rainy areas as northeastern Australia, the Amazon, and the Congo.

In an operational sense the most critical meteorological question is how accurately it is possible to forecast a day or six hours in advance what the winds will be and hence what the fallout pattern would be should Detroit, Los Angeles, New York, or any other point be hit by a nuclear bomb. Machta of the U.S. Weather Bureau has said that ". . . there is considerable uncertainty in the prediction of the winds." His statement is borne out by that of Lieutenant Colonel Spohn of the USAF Air Weather Service:

> . . . although both the fallout of radioactive debris and the path and dispersion of the radioactive cloud present potentially serious problems, no techniques are available which will provide more than very generalized answers on a forecast basis. Using observed wind data, usable forecast plots can be computed, valid for relatively short time periods (up to six to eight hours) beyond the time of observation. These computations show only the general sectors where fallout is likely to occur (allowing for short-period wind variability) but not fallout intensity.

Since Spohn, in the article just quoted, was concerned only with the meteorological aspect of the fallout forecast problem, he did not point out two sources of forecast errors far more radical than any inherent in the weather prediction problem itself.

Winds at various heights are now forecast at Weather Bureau stations throughout the United States on a routine basis. However, when these forecasts are applied to give predictions of fallout patterns, it is necessary to make certain fixed assumptions about the size of the anticipated bomb and the height at which it will be detonated. Even a perfect wind forecast could not compensate for the fact that a bomb of different size than that anticipated might be detonated at a different height. Thus, while the wind-fallout forecast could hardly be in error by 180°, calling for major fallout to the west of the target rather than the east, it could easily be off by as much as 45° or 60°, and the lethal effects might reach outward many miles beyond what the forecast called for.

The second, even more vital, source of error has to do with bombing accuracy. Even if those charged with making fallout predictions had available to them a perfect wind forecast, and even if their guess of bomb size and detonation height was correct, the bomb might well explode many miles from any reasonable "point zero" merely because of bombing error. If strong, deep west winds had caused everyone to be evacuated twenty miles upwind, to the west, and if then through error the bomb was detonated twenty miles to the west, the results would be worse than if no evacuation had occurred. This is, of course, an imponderable factor. Yet in civil defense planning it should be taken into account even though fallout predictions must continue to be employed to achieve the greatest chance of survival for the greatest number.

Weather forecasts will be helpful in a general sense in the event of nuclear attack provided there is ample warning, at least a few hours in advance, and provided that adequate shelters are available to the population. Forecasts cannot, however, define with any precision what the hazard will be or where it will be greatest. Thus it would appear that, both for actual attack conditions and for the conditions that linger afterward, the winds will play a decisive role that cannot be predicted certainly except in one sense. They will surely determine both the local and world-wide patterns of a lethal burden of radioactive debris.

Doctors and geneticists, within the Atomic Energy Commission and without, are continuing to study and analyze the effects of radiation upon human beings, both genetic and pathologic. Physicists and others are continuing to conduct a careful monitoring program to make certain that radiation intensities from bomb tests do not reach a level too far above the present low level of something like 3/1000 of one r per year in the United States. Meteorologists are working on problems of forecasting fallout patterns and on probability figures that can be used in civil defense planning.

These men and women approach their work in the hope that it will never have to be used in a wartime situation, for all know the magnitude of the dangers that would ride the winds if there should be a nuclear war. All would agree that under the present dangerous circumstances, with hundreds of nuclear weapons in Russia and the United States, the following words are hardly too dramatic: "Death stands at attention, obedient, expectant, ready to serve, ready to shear away the peoples *en masse;* ready, if called on, to pulverize without hope of repair what is left of civilization. He awaits only the word of command. He awaits it from a frail, bewildered being, long his victim, now–for one occasion–his Master."

The words are those of Sir Winston Churchill.

20 Weather in History

A Point of View

There have been great historians who virtually ignored the role of weather in history and those who exaggerated its importance. Thucydides, writing of the wars between Athens and Sparta, concentrated to such an extent upon strictly military and political events that he barely mentioned the weather, and then only in an incidental manner. Carlyle, obsessed with the notion that a few determined and inspired men determine the course of history, also ignored the influence of weather.

In extreme contrast, from many sources, including the Hippocratic writings of the ancient Greeks, the writings of Montesquieu in France, and Buckle's *History of Civilization in England*, the impression is created that far more often than not the weather and its composite counterpart, the climate, are between them the compass that points the primary direction in which history must move. Neither of these extreme viewpoints is correct.

The impact of weather upon mankind has frequently been expressed in different ways as the landscapes have changed and as man himself has changed, in his technological abilities, his attitudes, and his social organization. This is evident when comparisons are made between peoples of different cultures; and it becomes most clear when they are made between peoples of essentially the same culture, living in essentially the same natural habitat, but at two different periods of their history. Two examples underscore this point.

During the seventeenth century A.D., lightning storms played an insignificant role historically in the cultures of western Europe and among European-Americans in the New World. Except, perhaps, in isolated and extremely rustic communities, only a few superstitious souls viewed lightning as an omen of God or the devil, and nothing of historic importance resulted from their superstitious views. Lightning might start a fire in a forest or town, but this was rare compared with the frequency of fires set by other means. The Oslo fire of 1624, the great London fire of 1666, the Edinburgh fire of 1700, and the other great urban fires of the period were started inadvertently by man himself, rather than by lightning.

Completely different was the situation during the seventeenth century among the aborigines of Tasmania. Many of the tribes did not know how to make fire. Living in a habitat where there were no active volcanoes, they had initially obtained fire from forests or brushlands that had been set ablaze by lightning, and they cherished and carefully nourished this most critical possession. Yet sometimes they lost it, as in a local flood. When this occurred, unless they were close to friendly neighbors who would give them some fire, they either had to go without it until they finally could borrow or steal it or else hope for the coming of another lightning storm so located as to yield fire. For the Tasmanian aborigine of that time, a lightning storm was an event of importance.

The second example concerns the historically fateful change in the significance of a climatic fact: the existence of the Sahara Desert. The change cannot be ascribed to climatic shifts in the Sahara or to a change in the culture, except in a technologic sense. It was due solely to the revolutionary change in transport capabilities occasioned by the introduction of the camel.

In the sixth century B.C., northernmost Africa was under the control of three powers: Egypt, Cyrenaica, and Carthage. Egypt controlled the eastern segment of the North African coast in the region of the Delta of the Nile, as well as the Nile Valley itself as far south as the first cataract at Aswan. Carthage ruled the western segment of the coast, from Gibraltar eastward to what is now Tunisia. Much of the initiative for maritime trade in the Mediterranean world came from the Greeks, and by the sixth century B.C. the Greek colony of Cyrenaica governed a coastal segment between Egypt and Carthage, in what is now northeastern Libya, as well as a few nearby oases. All three were separated from one another by bleak desert regions that were seldom traversed.

So far as foreign trade was concerned, Egypt, Cyrenaica, and Carthage each faced outward, away from Africa. Theirs were maritime trade with the states and colonial settlement of the islands of the Mediterranean and the shores of Europe and the Near East. The

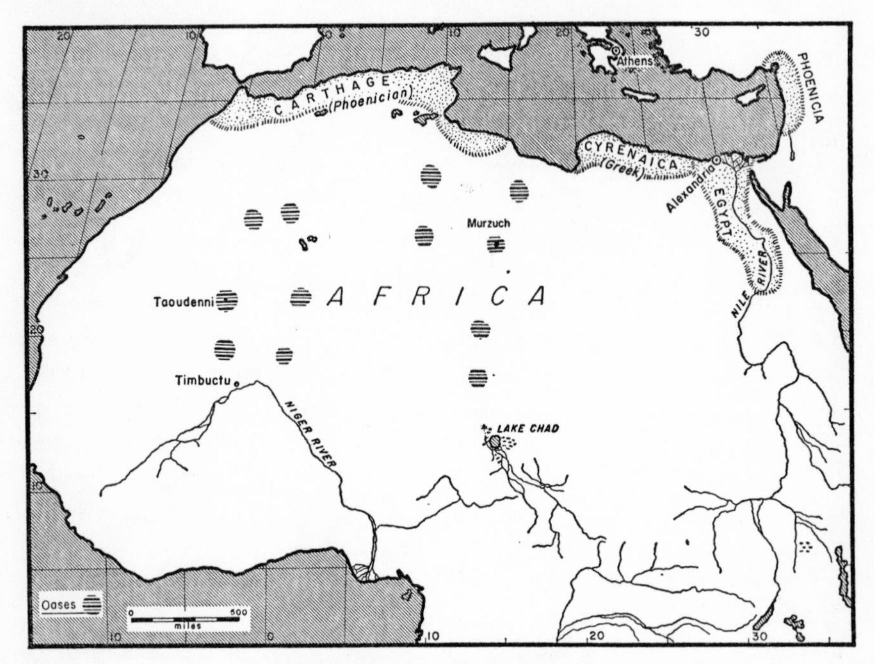

NORTH AFRICA ABOUT 550 B.C.
(Adapted from Shepherd's *Historical Atlas,* 8th ed., 1956)

contacts between these three powers and the rainy regions of central Africa, beyond the Sahara Desert, were so desultory as to be of no commercial consequence, even allowing for the occasional movement of goods and people along the Nile, between Egypt and Abyssinia. At that time the Sahara was all but an absolute barrier to trade between northern and central Africa. In the fifth century B.C. the Persians introduced the camel into Egypt. There it was adopted by the Berbers, who, with their new-found mobility, were able to spread westward across the Sahara, moving from oasis to oasis and along the semiarid fringe between the true desert to the south and the better-watered regions of advanced settlements in Cyrenaica and Carthage to the north.

Within a century the Berbers had spread across all of North Africa and had become established as the nation of the Tuareg. It was these Tuareg peoples who, with their camels, formed the caravan trains that as time went on moved with increasing frequency back and forth across the Sahara, from Lake Chad and Timbuktu on the south to the Carthaginian and Cyrenaican regions along the Mediterranean in the far north. They moved by the way of the great oases, like those of Murzuch and Taoudenni. They carried ivory and slaves northward from central Africa and salt from desert mines along the route, and grain and wool and oil to the south.

The trans-Sahara trade made possible by the introduction of the camel was well established by the third century B.C. and has continued ever since. It contributed substantially, and in turn, to the economic might of Carthage, Rome, the Saracen Caliphates, and the French colonial empire. As recently as fifty years ago slaves were still moving across the Sahara, and today Saharan caravans still carry grain, wool, salt, and ivory as well as other, more strictly modern, commodities.

Historically, the outstanding fact is that in the Sahara, as also in Arabia and other parts of the Dry World, the camel permitted the establishment of trade routes that were the first well-developed corridors for the movement of goods and peoples and ideas between regions separated by great desert areas. Never again was the desert quite the effective barrier that it was before, even though it still remained a semipermeable obstacle of great historical importance.

The camel caused a lowering of the desert barriers to trade. Lightning meant little to the advanced European and much to the Tasmanian aborigine. These instances demonstrate that the significance of weather and climate to mankind varies from time to time and from one culture to another. They might, however, be interpreted to indicate that with technologic advance weather and climate become less and less important in the affairs of men. That this is not so is evident from the following examples.

When man lived by gathering fruits and by hunting, a severe drought might force him to flee with the animals to nearby lake or river regions where there was still some moisture; but in those times each small tribal group had ample living room and each was highly mobile, so that absolute famine was rare. Later, when men had learned to cultivate plants, had lost their mobility, and had come to populate the earth far more densely, famines born of drought often killed them by the hundreds of thousands.

As recently as fifty years ago the winds of the high upper air were of historical concern only insofar as they promoted the spread of insects, plant spores, or dust that affected man's health or his crops. With the coming of high-flying aircraft, those winds assumed a new meaning for the first time in 10,000 years. Later, with the coming of nuclear weapons, they assumed still another new meaning.

These and other examples lead to the formulation of a point of view regarding the role of weather in history: *Though weather does not determine history, its historical influence is often profound. Though the influence of weather varies from culture to culture and from time to time within one culture, weather has been historically important at all stages of man's history. Though man may, through his technologic advance, free himself of particular weather influences, in doing so he becomes just as entangled with the weather in other ways.*

There remains the task of reviewing how this point of view has been exemplified in the past both through the seemingly random intervention of weather events and through the recurrence of major themes that relate history to the weather.

Weather Episodes

A weather episode is a single brief event, such as a storm, a shift in the wind, or a sudden freeze. It commands the immediate attention of the historical participants, who often regard it as of crucial consequence. Yet in retrospect, its true historic importance is exceptionally difficult to evaluate.

On October 5, 1519, when Magellan's ships were south of Cape Verde, having just begun their voyage around the world, the crew, already uncertain and grumbling about their fate and the storms just past, were greatly heartened by an auspicious omen: the play of static electricity known as St. Elmo's fire. "During those storms the holy body, that is to say St. Elmo, appeared to us many times, in light . . . among other times on an exceedingly dark night, on the maintop, where he stayed for about two hours or more, to our consolation; for we were weeping. When that blessed light was about to leave us . . . we all [called] for mercy. And truly, when we thought we were dead men, the sea suddenly grew calm."

At Princeton, in January, 1777, Washington's army fought a superb delaying action against the troops of Cornwallis. In this he was greatly aided by the fact that early in the morning, on the day of battle, "the wind veered to the north-west; the weather suddenly became cold; and the by-road, lately difficult for artillery, was soon frozen hard." Thus the American field pieces could be brought into line in time for the engagement.

In 1609, Sir George Somers, bound for Virginia, encountered a storm that threw his ship off course and cast it up upon the islands of the Bermudas. Thereafter the English settled Bermuda, and from that date onward British sovereignty was maintained.

According to Bancroft, in 1773 there would have been a "Boston Tea Party" at New York had it not been for sudden contrary winds which held the English tea-bearing ships away from New York Harbor.

History has frequently been colored by weather episodes of these kinds, some more substantial and others less. Each has been so thoroughly enmeshed in the event of which it was a part that in many instances it has been difficult for the historians who came afterward to determine whether the weather episode was critical, important, or merely incidental to the historical action. In the examples cited, two of Magellan's ships would probably still have circumnavigated the globe. Washington's holding action might still have been successful. And it is even possible that the English might still have come, through other circumstances, to obtain and hold the Bermudas. Nor is it certain that, had there been a "New York Tea Party," the result would have been of historic consequence.

The historical influence of a particular isolated weather episode can seldom be evaluated. Nevertheless, in the aggregate these episodes have had a marked historic weight. Though they cannot be granted the same status as the more unified major weather themes of history, they are nonetheless a vital part of its fiber. They are not mere weather episodes, but historical episodes of notable importance.

Climate and Race

Long before the dawn of written history, the human species, Homo sapiens, had become sorted out into biological varieties, or races. These races were distinguishable by differences in their color, their body size, the shapes of their heads, the amount and character of their body hair, the appearance of their eyes both in color and shape, and by other, less obvious, differences. Because of biological admixture, there were many individuals who did not clearly belong to any particular family; but the great majority could at least be identified as belonging to one of the three major races: Negroid, Caucasoid, or Mongoloid. Without the benefit of anthropometric measurements, these and other racial distinctions were already being made at the beginning of written history.

Race has been a potent factor in history because of the powerful attitudes and beliefs that racial differences have evoked. The "outlander," the member of another society, is always suspect. He is suspect because he is different. If his differences include his being black instead of white, dwarfed instead of tall, or so-called slant-eyed, he is so utterly different as to be triply suspect. Few people have considered racial differences simply and without emotion. They have usually viewed the members of distinctly different races with slight suspicion or with pity, and often with contempt or untempered hatred. Such racial attitudes have been molded and used effectively to help justify all kinds of social practices and wars.

For over 2,500 years the Nubians have been a slave and servant class throughout North Africa and the Near East; this is a status they initially received as black-skinned outlanders of the Egyptian Empire.

At Clermont, just prior to the First Crusade, Pope Urban addressed his fellow Christians as follows: ". . . a race from the kingdom of the Persians, an accursed race, a race wholly alienated from God . . . has violently invaded the lands of those Christians [of Palestine]. . . . Enter upon the road to the Holy Sepulcher; wrest that land from the wicked race, and subject it to yourselves."

The Japanese look down upon their fellow islanders, the Ainu, in part because the Ainu are of a different race, being hairy like the Caucasoids.

During the First World War, millions of Americans thought and spoke and acted as if the Germans were a subhuman race of "dirty Huns," and in the Second World War many Americans fought not so much against the Japanese as against "a bunch of yellow ginks."

The dominant members of a society have virtually always been proud of their blood line, whether it was really pure or not, and have abhorred the thought that their line might be racially contaminated through admixture with members of a totally different race. Shakespeare's Brabantio speaks for the proud fathers of many ages when he refuses to believe that his daughter could have married the black Moor, Othello, unless she had been drugged by him: "To fall in love with what she feared to look on. It is a judgment maimed and most imperfect, that will confess perfection so could err against all rules of nature. . . ."

Certainly race attitudes have had powerful historical repercussions at every level of historic action and in all ages since those early times when man lived in tribal groups that were too isolated to establish contact with peoples of markedly different race. For these reasons it is pertinent to examine the controversial proposition that climate has been a major determinant of race.

Charles Darwin believed that many of the major racial differences, including differences of skin color, were the result of the races having developed under different climatic conditions. By the early part of this century, this view had been largely discarded and most physical anthropologists believed that race was completely independent of climate. Now there is a modern view, exemplified by the writings of Carleton Coon, that may see a return to Darwin's belief, but with a far greater marshaling of supporting evidence than Darwin, living when he did, could possibly have commanded.

Coon chiefly considers the relations between climate and three racial traits: skin color, body size as indicated by weight, and the size and shape of the extremities, especially the forearms and hands. As for skin color:

> Speaking very broadly, human beings have three kinds of skin. One is the pinkish white variety which burns badly on exposure to the sun, and fails to tan. Such skin is found in a minority of the individuals in the cloudy region of northwest Europe, also among descendants of

> the inhabitants of this area who have migrated elsewhere, and among albinos everywhere. . . .
>
> At the opposite extreme is black or chocolate-brown skin, familiar as the integumental garb of the full-blooded Negro. Persons who wear skin of this type are the same color all over, except for their palms and soles. . . .
>
> In between is the range of integumental color possessed by the majority of mankind, belonging to skins which, although appearing as white, olive, yellowish, reddish, or brown, have one feature in common. The skin that is covered by clothing, if any, is relatively light. Exposed areas, if the light is strong enough, tan. . . . However, skin that can tan can also bleach. Peoples who live in mid-latitude regions where the air is dry and the sky cloudless in summer, while in winter dampness and clouds are the rule, can shift their skin color with the seasons.

Coon's logic is convincing. He points out that unalterably dark skin is correlated not with the high temperature of the tropics, as was once supposed, but with continuous exposure to sunlight in the unshaded tropical grassland regions. Thus he solves the problem of many former proponents of the race-climate theme by explaining why the Indians of the densely forested regions of the Amazon have skins that are changeable in color. Further, from archaeological evidence, he concludes that the permanently dark-skinned inhabitants of forested Africa are relatively new arrivals who formerly inhabited the grasslands, where their skin color was a biologic advantage just as is the dark skin color of the hairless plains animals, such as the elephant, rhinoceros, and African buffalo.

When it comes to body weight, there is an advantage to being heavy in cool climates and light in hot ones. The large, heavy body, characteristic of peoples of high latitudes, has relatively little skin surface for each pound of body matter. Accordingly, there are relatively few pores to permit perspiration and the ready loss of body heat. In contrast, the pigmy, the Negrito, and most of the other inhabitants of the hot tropics have small bodies with an ample skin surface per pound of body matter, thus facilitating heat loss.

Temperature is also the regulator of the size and shape of the extremities. Long, thin forearms and long, thin fingers promote loss of heat; accordingly, they are dominant features among the races native to the warm climates. Thick, stocky forearms and fingers are found chiefly in races whose initial habitat was the colder climatic areas.

Coon's theory of race and climate implies that man lived such a highly precarious existence for thousands of generations that there was time for such racial traits as skin color to become fixed through mutation and selection. For unless there is merit in the Lamarckian notion of the inheritance of acquired characteristics, the Negroids, for example, must have developed and persisted as a favored type in the ultrasunny lands where their skin pigmentation was an advantage. It is, however, remotely possible, as Coon points out, that each of the major races developed from different animal forebears that by mutation and selection were already destined to yield modern human descendants with different racial characteristics.

Future research will demonstrate whether or not climate has had as profound an effect upon race as Coon supposes. Meanwhile, the presumption remains that it is not coincidental that the Negroids are associated archaeologically and historically with the sunny tropical regions, the majority of the Caucasoids and Mongoloids with cool climatic realms that are partly sunny and partly cloudy, and a few fair-skinned Caucasoids, who cannot acquire a tan in the sun, with a realm of cold and cloudy climate. It is almost, though not absolutely, certain that one of the major roles of climate in history has been expressed through racial differentiation.

The Age of Primitive Man

The human story began approximately one million years ago. Then the first truly manlike creatures appeared on earth, most likely within the warm climatic realm of Central Africa. They probably emerged in many different localities within this realm at about the same period. The descendants of most of these new groups could not withstand the environment and the competition with the other beasts, so that they persisted for only a few thousand years. Several of the groups gave rise to descendants who lived on for hundreds of thousands of years, only to meet extinction during the coming ice ages of the Pleistocene period. A few were destined to become the direct ancestors of modern man. It is pertinent to speculate how this may have come about.

The forebears of primitive man were almost certainly apelike creatures, primarily arboreal. They descended to the ground quite frequently, as do the anthropoid apes of today; and when upon the ground they probably walked in a semierect manner like the gorilla rather than on all fours like the chimpanzee. They were herbivorous, depending for their food upon the fruits and tender sprouts that grew in abundance in the tropical forests that were their home.

Then something began to happen. It happened so slowly and extended over so many thousands of years that it could not have been perceived by the apelike creatures even if they had had the intelligence of modern man. One year there was a severe drought. Many young saplings were killed and some of the older trees, in hill and slope locations where the soil moisture was seldom high, failed to bring forth their usual crop of fresh buds. On many trees also the fruits were shriveled and stunted. Because of the drought the apelike creatures were forced to migrate to locations along the well-watered lowlands, where there were still fresh shoots and where the fruits were still tasty and almost as large as during normal times.

For the next four years the weather was normal, with copious rains at all seasons. Then there were two severe droughts in a single year. Once more the forest suffered and once more the ape creatures had to migrate temporarily. Over the next decades and centuries the droughts became more and more severe and more and more frequent. Now the changing climate was exacting a heavy toll among the forest trees and shrubs. The species whose water requirements were the greatest were now to be found only in a few limited areas. Trees were less abundant and were smaller. Grassy glades were larger and more numerous than before. Many of the foods that were once common had become scarce. Some had disappeared.

Meanwhile the descendants of the original bands had through successive short migrations, generation after generation, moved hundreds of miles from their original location. They moved from site to site, following the original forest, which was itself retreating toward the rainier margins of its tropical habitat.

In their wanderings some of the bands were trapped in a shrinking pocket of thinly forested land along the margins of the ocean and others along the edges of great open grasslands. Most of the bands caught in this way were exterminated: they died of hunger in the worst drought periods or were the victims of marauding carnivores.

A few, however, began to adapt themselves to the changing conditions. For protection they still slept in the trees, but during the daytime they ranged across the ground looking for grubs to eat as supplement to their meager vegetable diet. Occasionally they discovered a nest of rodents to devour. In time they began to hunt full-fledged game.

All this happened throughout hundreds of generations, so that again and again those best fitted for survival on the ground lived to maturity and gave birth to descendants, while those least fitted died young. Through biologic evolution the ape creatures began to become primitive men, and by imitation, the older creatures teaching the children through example, they began to become more manlike in behavior. What had started as a single, unusual drought thousands of years before ended with the appearance of the first primitive men.

The foregoing is, of course, hypothetical. But if the first pre-man was arboreal, there appears to be no mechanism other than climatic change that could possibly have driven him from the trees to the ground. Animals are conservative in habit. Their chief concerns are food, water, evading or eliminating their enemies, and procreation of their kind. As Coon has pointed out, the ape creatures who were man's forebears had an easy time of it. So long as they stayed in the trees, their only enemy was the snake. They certainly would never have left the trees to face a wide diversity of predators upon the ground unless they had been forced to do so.

By all standards, these men who started history were primitive, but they nonetheless were distinctly more advanced than their tree-living ancestors. They walked erect. Their brains were unusually large and well developed. Their eyes could focus with a new keenness upon objects held in the hand. The thumbs of either hand could move so as to oppose any one of the other four fingers directly; but the feet were primarily for walking rather than grasping, so the big toes were not opposable. Almost from the start their reasoning brains led them to search out sharp-edged rocks that could be grasped firmly in the hand and used to slash and cut the hide of a wild horse or an antelope.

During his long history, primitive man withstood the vicissitudes of tremendous swings of climatic conditions. He lived, or at least barely existed, during four major glacial periods. Four times, and for tens of thousands of years in each instance, he was barred from the regions of central and northern Eurasia by vast ice sheets that topped the Himalayas and spread into northern India, capped the Caucausus Mountains between the Black Sea and the Caspian, spread outward from the Alps, and reached out from Scandinavia to engulf much of Europe and from the scattered mountains of northern Asia to cover large regions of the Siberian plains. There was also glaciation on a small scale in Africa and on a large scale in North America, to which man came toward the end of the Primitive Age.

The climatic changes were by no means confined to the regions of glacial ice. Humid forests were converted to subhumid plains, and plains were converted to arid deserts. Hot lands changed to warm lands, and warm ones to cold. Then the process was reversed and re-reversed, not in a regular, consistent manner, but so as to yield a climatic pattern of great complexity.

During the exceedingly long Primitive Age, climate was a crucial factor in four ways. At the outset a change in climate may have driven the forebears of man down from the trees and forced them to develop biologically or to perish. Thereafter, other changes led to further biologic evolution, probably including the development of races, as has already been noted. Third, the spread of man was immutably related to the expansion and shrinkage of the glaciers and of the various climatic regions with their associated natural vegetations. Finally, the changing climatic conditions were related to major technologic advances, especially toward the end of the Age of Primitive Man.

Once he had come into being, most-primitive man continued to develop biologically. He walked more and more erectly. His brain size increased and the brain itself became more complex. Changes of these kinds were also stimulated by stress situations of climatic origin. The stress was not always owing to increasing aridity. With glaciation there was also increasing cold; in some regions there was excessive heat and sunshine, while in others there was a superabundance of rain and cloudy skies. Whenever a stress situation developed and persisted for many generations, the biologic forces of mutation and selection worked with maximum effectiveness. In many such instances, at the end of such a period of stress primitive man was a slightly more advanced biological specimen than he was at the beginning.

During all this time men were spreading across the earth. Before they captured fire, their spread was sharply limited by temperature conditions. Afterward, they were able to move to colder lands, as in northern China. Primarily, however, their movements were related to the climatic pattern not so much in direct terms as in the sense that they spread across lands that were climatically favorable for the kinds of plants and animals that were their customary food.

For example, the men of Aurignacian culture who inhabited Europe toward the end of the Pleistocene period specialized in hunting cave bears and in fishing. Therefore they spread across the humid forest lands, rather than the plains. In contrast the Gravettians, of about the same period, appear to have followed the plains regions from Asia into Europe, for they "were plainsmen specializing in the pursuit of mammoth and the various gregarious herbivores that grazed on open steppes and tundras." Among them, the forest men and the plainsmen had, by the end of the Age of Primitive Man, come to inhabit all of the earth outside of the true desert areas and the regions of glacial ice.

The technologic changes that marked the advance of primitive man throughout this entire period were also closely intertwined with the climatic conditions. During the period from about 7000 to 1000 B.C., northern Europe was subjected to unusually abrupt climatic changes as the glaciers retreated at a rapid rate and as the melting of the heavy ice sheets permitted the upward rebound of the land, so that the seas were in many places cast from off the lands and in other places the rise of sea level permitted water to replace the regions of former ice. Culturally, the result of these rapid changes in environment was the development of new economies involving new skills and techniques. V. Gordon Childe describes these changes as follows:

> The new conditions completely upset the Upper Paleolithic economy based on the pursuit of gregarious game on open steppe and tundra and salmon fishing. . . . The forests now isolated bands of hunters so that a confusing multiplicity of distinct cultures arose as adaptations to varying conditions. Some innovations are common to most if not all. In the food quest the collection of nuts, snails and shellfish generally made important contributions to the food supply. Everywhere remains of dogs suggest that some sort of wolf or jackal had been making himself useful to man in the pursuit of new types of game. And nearly everywhere the bow was now used for hunting. . . .

Among the innovations described by Childe for particular cultures during this period was the appearance of "handled axes or wedges of reindeer antler," of "a special type of conical bone arrow head, perhaps for killing fur bearing animals with minimum damage to the pelts," and of new types of harpoons, nets, and floats to which fishnets were attached. Culturally, the climatic stresses of this period clearly had an exhilarating effect, and there is little doubt but that similar periods at much earlier times in man's history were equally animating.

The thesis that climatic stress has often been associated with technologic advance agrees with Toynbee's major theme that adversity of any kind has always tended to stimulate creativity on the part of man. Toynbee sees in such adversity the requirement for a fructifying upheaval brought about through crisis.

It is certain, however, that primitive man in a situation of climatic stress had only three paths to follow. He could perish beneath the rigors of the bitter climates of the last glaciation. He could migrate to regions where the climate was more congenial. Or he could improvise and invent new modes of living, including especially the development of new and specialized technologies. Because he had often done the latter, man emerged from the Primitive Age with a variety of cultures that were remarkably advanced considering his dependence upon nondomesticated supplies of food.

The Dawn of Agriculture and the Rise of Civilizations

Man has never achieved a more far-reaching technologic advance than when he first domesticated plants and animals. By those acts he changed the basis of his economic life radically and forever. He made possible the rise of civilization and also an extravagant growth of population in the millennia to come. And through discovering in his new-found agriculture the means of such extravagant population increase, almost at once he became dependent upon the weather in a different and imperative manner.

In the Old World, the domestication of plants and animals and the subsequent rise of several different civilizations probably took place within 8,000 years, between 10,000 and 2000 B.C. In the New World, this critical transition was somewhat delayed but occupied an even smaller interval of time: perhaps from 3000 or 2000 B.C. to around the time of the birth of Christ. Both in the Old World and the New the climatic circumstances that attended the acts of domestication and the rise of civilizations were decisive in helping to determine where, how, and when the pivotal events of this period of notable advances took place.

Around 8000 B.C. the Pleistocene ice sheets of the fourth glaciation still covered large regions of Eurasia, even though the ice had been slowly retreating for several thousand years. Large regions of the Sahara, of Arabia, and of other parts of what is now the Dry World were receiving a good quota of rainfall, so that they were grasslands rather than arid deserts as they are today.

Beyond the margins of the ice, throughout all of southern Eurasia and virtually all of Africa, there were scattered groups of primitive men, living by hunting, fishing, and gathering. Most of these groups were migratory. There is, however, evidence that some were sedentary, having settled down along the banks of major rivers that could assure an abundant supply of fish at all times of the year. Groups already accustomed to such sedentary living appear to have arrived in northern Europe from Asia between about 4000 and 3000 B.C.

The early history of domestication cannot be reconstructed with assurance. It seems likely, though, that with the exception of the dog, which was an early camp follower of man rather than a true domesticate, animal domestication came after plant domestication and was actually carried on by sedentary agriculturalists, some of whom then became nomadic herders or passed on to neighboring tribes the animals first used in nomadic herding.

In any event, plant domestication first took place, both in the Old World and in the New, toward the edges of the forests, in warm, humid lands. Climatically, and in terms of their vegetation and soils, such sites were especially suitable for the first plant domestications. The climatic environment was varied, especially in hilly lands, and this helped to create a great diversity of environmental niches, leading to a corresponding diversity of plant species and subspecies that were available for domestication. Moisture and warmth were assured the first domesticates. There was ample room for planting among the trees and shrubs, and the soil was far easier to cultivate than were the tough soils of the grassland regions.

On this basis, in the Old World the centers of plant domestication were adjacent to the subhumid grasslands that stretched from the

Atlantic Ocean to northwestern India across much of what is now the southern sector of the Dry World. One center—the oldest of all, according to Sauer—was in southeast Asia, generally from Burma eastward. Here the banana, taro, and yam were among the earliest domesticates, with rice a somewhat later one. China, to the north, contributed the soybean and the millets; southwestern Asia, from Afghanistan to Anatolia, wheat and barley; and Ethiopia the sorghums, coffee, and, possibly, also cotton. These earliest domestications may well have been carried out by peoples who were already sedentary, being fisher folk, like the groups that arrived in northern Europe from Asia around 4000 B.C.

The list of plant domesticates at this early time includes such important plants as the coconut palm, the date palm, and the olive tree, as well as those already mentioned. The essential feature, however, was the broad pattern, which followed climatic lines. At the center were the subhumid grasslands, which already held patches of semiarid and desert regions and which were shrinking in size as conditions became more and more arid. Around this centerpiece, whose size was measured in millions of square miles, there lay the regions of plant domestication, at the edges of the humid forests. Even by 6000 B.C., climatic conditions were still too harsh in the north to permit the poleward spread of agriculture, but they were favorable to its spread into many localities within the subhumid central lands. And this is precisely what happened. During the period 6000 to 3000 B.C., agriculture came to be practiced on a greatly intensified scale in the riverine locations of Egypt, the Tigris-Euphrates, the Indus, and China.

In the New World the situation was the same except that, since plant domestication occurred at a later date, there was not the rapid pace of climatic change that marked the era of domestication in the Old World. The initial centers of domestication were the hilly forest regions in the humid zone extending from Central America southward to Peru. Maize, the potato, and manioc were among the chief domesticates. And in Mexico and Peru, agriculture was greatly intensified under conditions of irrigation, just as in the Old World.

This intensification of agriculture, with the practice of irrigation in a subhumid to arid region, is characteristic of five of the seven earliest high civilizations of the Old World and the New and is partially characteristic of a sixth one. Egypt, the Tigris-Euphrates, the

Indus Valley, Mexico, and Peru all follow this formula. China does not fit it so precisely because the climate is humid rather than subhumid, but winter drought is a factor of great practical concern, so that the Chinese situation is somewhat the same.

Only in the Mayan civilization of Central America was there no irrigation. Agricultural intensification through irrigation within a region that lacks abundant rainfall, at least at certain seasons of the year, appears to have been especially favorable for the rise of the first true civilizations. In this it is likely, as Wittfogel has pointed out, that the practice of large-scale irrigation demanded a high level of social organization which led to the rise of civilization.

The climatic situation alone did not determine the location of the high civilizations. If this were true, then, as Toynbee points out, high civilizations should have developed in many other places as well, as along the Jordan River. But the climatic situation was, with only one exception, a necessary but not sufficient cause, which became operative in those particular instances in which the technologic level of the peoples concerned permitted them to capitalize on their situation through development of irrigation techniques.

As time went on and the climates became milder in the high-latitude lands, agriculture spread poleward from its first central zones of origin and intensification. In its form of animal husbandry, it also spread into drier lands through the domestication of animals and the coming of nomadism. In both its crop form and its animal-husbandry form, this new agriculture was highly vulnerable to weather fluctuations, especially in marginal climate areas. Even today there is this vulnerability. As Morison and Commager have expressed it: "In spite of all that has been 'done for the farmer' no one has been able to industrialize the weather."

From the time of the first domestications down to the present, the impact of the weather upon agriculture has had major historical repercussions. Among these there have been occasional agricultural crises on such a major scale as to produce great migrations.

The Great Migrations

The upheavals of great sectors of human populations and their migration to new homelands have been among the most dramatic and important events in the history of mankind. Such migrations have included the mass movement of nomadic peoples across the dry lands of the Old World at many different times in the past, the displacement of large populations in Europe during the Middle Ages, and the flow of peoples from Europe to the Americas in vast numbers during the nineteenth century. Many of the migrations were largely or wholly the result of major swings in weather conditions. There is considerable doubt over the role the weather played in many others.

The theme that weather has been a principal factor in inducing migration is an ancient one, dating back at least to the time of the classical Greeks. It found its greatest elaboration in the writings of Ellsworth Huntington. Huntington carried the theme to an absurd extreme, for in time he came to assume that all great migrations were the result of climatic change and to use migrations as an index of climatic conditions. Nonetheless, his many unsound deductions by no means detract from his real contributions in defining the role of climate and weather in the great historical migrations. Despite his many critics, he has been vindicated in many instances by the inquiries of archaeologists, geographers, and historians who came afterward, including such people as Childe, Coon, Clark, Thompson, and Toynbee.

A balanced view of the role of climate in the migrations across the dry lands of the Old World is well presented by Myres:

> It might be an accident—if it stood alone—that when Egypt, under the Nineteenth Dynasty, was harassed by one wave after another of exodus from the Libyan Desert, Palestine was enduring the raids of Semitic nomads beyond Jordan; the Aegean was in the throes of a conquest by northern invaders; and Italy, too, was experiencing a calamity which seems to have cut off the Terramare Culture of the Po Valley with simultaneous fire and sword. . . . But it can hardly be an accident that on the next great occasion when Arabia emptied itself of its men [there was also a great simultaneity of invasions from the dry lands]. . . . When in addition we find that an earlier Semitic exodus approximately corresponds with earlier Libyan aggression west of the Nile, and apparently also with the establishment of a new and original regime in the heart of Asia Minor . . . it almost seems as if we were confronted with large cosmic occurrences of which these regional migrations were local symptoms.
>
> I venture to suggest that this cosmic occurrence was the periodical drying up of the great belt of grassland and desert which runs from Cape Verde to the Altai; that this desiccation forced the nomad pastoral peoples of the steppe to strike outwards . . . and that the peri-

ods of quiescence which intervened were phases of more copious moisture. . . .

For the Middle Ages, the historian James Westfall Thompson writes as follows:

> Beyond all doubt the worst privation of the medieval peasant was famine. This, if of a widespread and general nature, was almost always due to adverse weather conditions . . . the eleventh century [for example] was a time of terrible and widely prevalent famine which indubitably was responsible for the remarkable restlessness of the population, group movements and religious exaltation extending sometimes to sheer mania.

To these might be added many other examples: the floods in Flanders in 839, when, "partly owing to the ravages of the Norsemen, but more on account of inundations of the low coast by the sea, we find record of the exodus of masses of people"; the drought-induced Irish famines of the 1840's that contributed to an unprecedented emigration to America; and the conditions in the Great Plains of the United States in the early 1930's, when thousands lost their homes and trekked hopefully westward to California.

Weather is by no means the single cause of great migrations. Wars, persecutions, population growth, and the sheer economics of better opportunities elsewhere are also major factors. But swings in the weather have frequently been the primary, immediate, and absolute factors that wrested peoples from their accustomed homes and caused them to migrate to new regions that in many instances were far removed from their original familiar surroundings.

Corridors and Barriers

In his movements across the lands and waters of the earth, man has followed the routes of easiest travel whenever possible. He has shunned such cultural barriers as regions inhabited by hostile peoples, such physiographic barriers as rugged mountains, and such climatic barriers as icecap regions and deserts. Until the coming of the airplane man rarely breached the icecap barriers. Even with the camel he traveled the desert only along relatively easy, well-planned routes, which were discovered by explorers who in their own way were just as daring as Columbus. An oasis is not a new continent, but it is a mooring point for trade routes that in a land of constant drought must be tied to at least a few dependable sources of water supplies.

Outside the icecap regions and the deserts, the traveled corridors have with one exception always tended to follow the river valleys. The exception has been the tundra lands of winter, which were at first impenetrable but which by 1500 B.C. were being readily traversed in almost any desired direction by sled. In contrast, upon the tundra in the summer the river valleys became the traveled routes just as they were at all seasons of the year in the well-watered forest regions and upon the steppe. Yet there have been major changes in the historical significance of these corridors as man's technologies have changed and as the climates themselves have shifted. A few illustrations will underscore the historical weight of these concepts.

For thousands of years prior to 3000 B.C., the steppeland zone that stretches from Dzungaria in central Asia all the way westward into the eastern edge of the Danubian lands of central Europe had been a corridor for wandering hunters who followed the mammoth and other grassland game on foot.

Hunting and fighting parties must have been forced to use the watered areas along the river as their bases and to sally out upon the much drier plains only for short distances. Whole tribes on the move must have clung to the rivers or to the moister fringe of the steppe near the edge of the forest zones to the north. They could have made only small portages from one watered area to another.

About 3000 B.C., the domesticated horse first appeared upon the steppes of Asia. Within 500 years the steppes became a corridor of vastly increased importance and one of much greater effective width. It did not become, as some writers have implied, a corridor thronged with horsemen and chariots dashing to and fro. But with horses used as draft animals, household goods and implements as well as people could now easily be moved across wide reaches of the plains. When riding was learned, hunters and fighters could cover 100 miles a day if necessary and could readily carry with them food, water, and heavy stone battleaxes.

With the coming of the horse, the steppe corridor, though it still tended to follow the rivers in many areas, was greatly widened toward its drier, southern border, and the distance between its eastern and western edges was effectively diminished by a factor of something like ten. It was along this new corridor that the Aryans and their horses moved into Europe from out of the East. Later many other horsemen traveled the same corridor, such as the Goths, Huns, and Mongols.

Among the Mongol armies that used the steppes as a pathway for the invasion of Europe was that of Botha, who in 1241 suddenly appeared before the city of Pest, on the Danube, and, after quickly routing the defending Hungarians, burned the city to the ground. That he did not sweep farther west was partly owing to the forests that now blocked his way; for although the Mongol horsemen could and did move into regions of open forest, they thereby lost much of their mobility and often did not fare as well as upon the plains.

In America, the arrival of the horse, brought by the first Europeans, similarly changed the significance of the plains as a corridor for the movement of peoples. Within a few decades the Plains Indians learned to capture and to utilize the horses that had escaped from early European exploring parties, and almost at once these Indians ceased to move almost exclusively along the rivers and the moist, forested edges of the plains and began instead to use the open plains as a broadened corridor for the travels of hunters and warriors and the large-scale migration of whole tribes.

In the moist forest lands the importance of river valleys for travel has remained remarkably constant despite great technologic changes. The Mohawk Valley was successively a much-traveled route for the Iroquois Indians, who traveled both by canoe and along trails that paralleled the river. It was used for travel by boat, trail, and road in colonial times. Next came the Erie Canal; then, finally, the railroads and the New York State Thruway.

As for the effects of shifts of climates upon the importance of corridors, Huntington gives a good example of a corridor that has almost disappeared:

> Observant travelers in the more arid parts of Iran have almost without exception been much impressed with the unmistakable evidences that a change of some sort has overwhelmed the country. Ruins are incredibly numerous. . . . Those who have followed the track of Alexander declare that today it would be utterly impossible to travel as the conqueror did with a huge army in regions where now a small caravan of twenty or thirty camels can scarcely find water and forage.

> . . . Many of the Kariz have probably been abandoned because of wars, but that does not explain how Alexander procured water for an army [of 110,000] where there are now merely salt pools: nor how he procured forage for all his baggage animals where today a few score can barely subsist.

Since earliest times the seas have also had their corridors of travel whose locations have changed with advances in navigation and the character of ships. These have nearly always been established along those seaways that were the best weatherwise.

Through proper respect for the storms of the Mediterranean the Greek or Phoenician navigator of the fifth century B.C. kept his galley, with its single square-rigged supplementary sail, close to shore. For reasons of safety, the sea routes zigzagged from island to island, with the all-important historic consequence that in island-filled seas, such as the Aegean, even the smallest islands held settlements that were bound together by trade.

Upon the oceans, the reliable winds, especially the trade winds and the monsoons, defined the corridors of earliest travel. Even today, with steamships commonly making 15 knots and more, the transocean routes shift poleward in summer so that ships may sail the shortest possible path, and they shift equatorward in the winter to avoid the ice and storms of higher latitudes. This seasonal shift of trade routes amounts to about ten degrees of latitude in the North Atlantic and the North Pacific Oceans.

The preferential location of the routes of human movements overland and on the seas has exerted influence upon the history of exploration. In this realm, however, the corridors of easy travel must be considered in conjunction with the barriers to movement.

For one hundred years Australia remained undiscovered by Europeans largely because it remained shielded by the patterns of the winds and storms of the sea. From before 1500 to after 1600, da Gama, Houtman, Middleton, and many other navigators rounded the Cape of Good Hope, then traveled north and east to pick up the monsoon winds and so head into India. They knew that they could continue eastward with strong westerlies to whip their ships along, but they feared the storms of the westerly zone and so failed to discover Australia. Finally the Dutchman, Hartog, took a more southerly route and reached the western Australian coast.

During the same period Magellan's, Drake's, and other expeditions sailed westward across the Pacific; but always, being fearful of the calms of the doldrum regions, they held to the trade-wind belt of the Northern Hemisphere and so at most they barely saw the shores of northern Australia. Finally, 1642–43, Tasman, who was specifically bent on exploring the unknown ocean of the Australian regions, completely circumnavigated the Australian continent.

For somewhat different reasons, but for reasons also closely bound to the weather, both the northwest coast of North America and the Bering Sea were closed to the view of Europeans for more than two centuries after the time of Columbus.

In 1579, Drake had sailed northward along the west coast of North America to 48° N., but he decided to turn southward again when the weather proved too cold. In 1728, Bering, having traveled first overland across Siberia and then by ship from Kamchatka, proved for the first time that Asia and North America were not connected. Finally, in 1778 James Cook sailed up the northwest coast and through Bering Strait to 70° N. Until then the ice and cold that had defeated Hudson and many others had kept alive the myth that there might be a Northwest Passage, in reasonably low latitudes, from the Atlantic to the Pacific.

By land there are weather barriers that continue to shield large sectors of the continents from exploration even to this day. Antarctica and Greenland are still but little known. The driest sectors of the tropical deserts have not been traveled by modern man. The Amazon Basin is but poorly known, as much because of the difficulties of travel away from the rivers as of the hostility of the tribes in many areas. Even today land areas that among them total twice the size of the United States have at best been seen in part only from aircraft.

Only in the last half century of his million years has man traveled regularly through the air. At first, largely because of icing conditions, air travel in polar regions was too hazardous to be practical on a scheduled basis. Now there are regular flights across almost all regions of the world, including the North Polar Sea. There are, however, still serious weather problems associated with the establishment of terminals in many localities, and the efficiency of flight services varies widely from one route to another depending on the weather probabilities. Through the efficiency factor, often expressed in economic terms, the weather will always help to determine the location of the commercial airways no matter what course the development of aircraft may take in the future.

Patterns in Space and Time

The themes that relate weather and history are almost endless in number. Yet all of them have found expression in two ways: they have influenced where certain critical events have taken place and when they have taken place. They have helped determine the geographic patterns that give history its spatial reality and the patterns in time that are the substance of history.

The themes already treated are a part of these patterns. There are patterns of "where" and "when" to the spread of mankind across the earth, and to man's racial differentiation or his domestication of plants or the rise of his civilizations. To these must be added many other themes that fall within the same framework.

Climate is a resource, sometimes rich, sometimes poor. For at least twenty centuries there have been many broad regions that consistently have been the primary granaries of civilizations. Again and again these granaries have been located upon the same kinds of climatic lands, the lands that yield abundant harvests of rice or wheat or other staple grains. They have included what Myres called "the lands of habitual colonization," the outlands. In Greece and Rome they included the wheat-climate lands of the shores of the Black Sea and the Mediterranean. Today they include as well the subhumid lands of the plains regions of the Americas, Russia, and the Argentine; and the warm, humid rice lands of many areas of southeastern Asia.

Climate is more than a resource for agriculture; it is a resource for all of human activities. There are mineral deposits of great richness that have not been exploited because of the adversity of weather. Many other deposits are not even known because the climate shields them from discovery. There are regions that because of their "climatic location" lie beyond the reach of many other forms of industry, and of commerce as well.

Yesterday these relations still held in a fundamental sense; but with different technologies and outlooks, in those earlier times the areas that were forbidden climatically were of different outlines and locations. They were different, too, because of changes in the climates themselves. In this single theme there is a major aspect of changing history, one in which the climatic factor is prominent beyond all question.

As for patterns whose chief dimension is time, the weather has had an equally important role. Whole modes of living have been geared to the weather, like the periodic, seasonal movements of nomads, of migratory agricultural workers, or of fishing folk who go down to the sea with the end of winter and then, at last, turn homeward as the autumn months come on. The weather has changed whole patterns of living, as it did among the farming peoples who first settled the Great Plains of the United States:

> The farmers who crossed the ninety-eighth meridian could look at the horizon and see that they had left log cabins and rail fences behind them, but they could not understand that they had left much else, including their methods of handling land and water. Their accustomed methods of farming, so well integrated with forty inches of annual precipitation, were to prove disastrous in a land where rainfall averaged twenty inches, and in years of drought fell to ten or twelve. The suffering that resulted from efforts to farm in the traditional manner they knew, is a tragic story of broken fortunes, broken men and broken women. In the good wet years the migrating homeseekers moved out like a tidal wave on the ocean shore, but the wave broke on the hard dry years, receded, and left behind the wreckage of the high hopes and illusions. But not all went back; some stay-behinds remained . . . and kept experimenting, adapting, and adopting until something of a solution was found.

In addition, the weather has affected the timing of great historical events. The defeat of Athens by Sparta was not caused by the weather, but the timing of that defeat was certainly determined in part by the drought that afflicted the plains of Attica in the last few years of the war. On a broader scale, the time of entry of man into the Americas was certainly related to the climatic oscillations of the glacial periods, even though his entry was not determined by these events.

From the history of war other examples may be adduced. How long would World War II have been prolonged had it not been for the period of clear skies in February, 1944, which permitted the bombing out of the German Luftwaffe? How would Napoleon have fared, how much longer might he have lingered, had he not encountered an unusually early winter in Russia during the year of 1812? The answers are imponderable, but the questions illustrate how history, in its vital time dimension, is geared to the succession of weather events.

Without geographic and time co-ordinates, history is meaningless. Within this essential co-ordinate system, weather is a factor that helps determine the quantitative values of the "where" and "when" co-ordinates. Weather is a force that cannot be deleted from the historical equation without forfeiting all chance of having that equation produce so much as a crude model of reality.

Past, Present, and Future

Man is born into the midst of an environmental scene. He is born with a certain biologic inheritance. By the quick process of learning and the slow process of new discoveries and inventions, he changes his relations with his physical environment. Among the elements of man's environment, none stands higher on the list than weather and climate.

The ocean of air and its weather have not forced man here or there, now or then, to follow one course or another, regardless of his own resources. But again and again the weather has stacked the odds in such a way that it would have been a miracle had particular men not reacted in certain ways.

If man refrains from extinguishing himself with the help of nuclear weapons and the winds, the coming ages will witness wonderful events. They will see new technologies that bring with them new kinds of relations between man and weather at great altitudes as well as in the lower air. In time, there will be either a return of the glaciers or the onset of an era when the polar lands will be regions bearing mild and hospitable weathers. But whatever the future may bring, if man persists his fate will always be related to weather. For man does not live with man alone. He lives upon the planet, earth, in a world of weather that is forever embodied in the ocean of air.

Notes

In general, the notes identify the sources on which I have relied most heavily and present occasional elaborative comments. More specifically, they give the sources of quotations, present the bases for those quantitative values that are not well known or generally agreed upon, and acknowledge the sources of anecdotal material. The notes pertaining to the illustrations appear separately at the end of this section.

Introduction

Page

3 The Plato quotation is from the Jowett translation of the *Phaedo*.

4 My 18,000-mile height for the atmosphere is greater than that commonly given. It is a matter of definition. I am defining the uppermost surface of the atmosphere as the surface below which the atmospheric particles, however rare and whatever their composition, have at least a slightly greater chance of following the earth as it moves around the sun than of being left behind in space. And since the recently discovered electron belts (high radiation belts) appear to move with the earth and to extend to at least 18,000 miles, my height value is about right under my definition.

5 In the quotation from Father Joseph de Acosta, I have modernized the spelling of the English translation (Hakluyt Society, 1880).

8 The quotation from Captain Scott's journal is taken from *Scott's Last Expedition* (Dodd, Mead, 1923).

10 The statement that the Krakatoa dust spread throughout the

Page

world and remained in the atmosphere for several years is based upon the work of Herbert H. Kimball. See "An Examination of the Dust Content of the Atmosphere," *Transactions of the American Geophysical Union*, IV (1923), 99–100.

CHAPTER 1

15 The low temperature of 125° F. below zero was observed at Sovietskaya (78° 24′ S., 87° 45′ E.) in Antarctica, on August 9, 1958. See *Monthly Weather Review*, LXXXVI (1958), 308.

17 The material on Rumford is based chiefly on George E. Ellis, *Memoir of Sir Benjamin Thompson, Count Rumford* (Estes and Lauriat, 1871), and Sir Benjamin Thompson Rumford, *Essays, Political, Economical, and Philosophical* (D. West, 1798–1804), 3 vols.

CHAPTER 2

28 The quotation is from Shklovsky, *In Far Northeast Siberia* (Macmillan, 1916).

29 The extreme low temperatures for Tromsö, Kiev, Ketchikan, and Omaha are from U.S. Department of Agriculture, *Climate and Man* (Yearbook of Agriculture, 1941).

33 The description of the weather situation of January 7–12, 1937, is based on stories in *The New York Times* and the *San Francisco Chronicle*. Temperature values are from *Climatological Data* for the various states (U.S. Weather Bureau, January, 1937).

34 The temperature values for Delhi and Eagle Pass are from *Climate and Man.*

36 The quotation describing the winds off Antarctica is from Alan Villiers, *By Way of Cape Horn* (Garden City, 1930).

37 The estimate by E. F. Gautier is from his *Sahara* (Columbia University Press, 1935).

39 The quoted description of sunrise on the desert is from L. March Phillipps, *In the Desert* (Arnold, 1905).

40 The temperature values for the sirocco are from W. G. Kendrew, *The Climates of the Continents* (Oxford University Press, 1953), and from Julius von Hann, *Klimatologie* (J. Engelhorns, 1932).

41 The description of the heat wave of July, 1936, is based primarily upon accounts in the *Detroit Free Press.*

Page

42 The Tulagi temperature is from *Climate and Man.*

45 The Eiffel Tower temperature data are from W. G. Kendrew, *Climatology* (Oxford University Press, 1949). Sven Hedin's account is from his *Southern Tibet (1906–1908)*, Chap. IV, "Kara-Korum and Chang-Tang" (Brockhaus, 1922).

46 The account of the occurrences at Rapid City are based on reports in *The New York Times* and the *Washington Star*, and upon the article by Roland R. Hamann, "The Remarkable Temperature Fluctuations in the Black Hills Region, January 1943," *Monthly Weather Review*, LXXI (1943), 29–32.

Chapter 3

48 The Biblical quotation is from John 3:8.

The examples of how primitive peoples viewed the wind are chiefly from Sir James George Frazer's *The Golden Bough.*

49 I have somewhat simplified the synoptic weather situation that existed at the time of the wave and swell forecasts for the North African invasion. However, the facts as given are essentially correct and are based on discussions that were held shortly afterward in the AAF Weather Service, for which I was working at the time.

52 The discussion of the discovery of the barometer and its early use is based chiefly on Sir Napier Shaw, *Manual in Meteorology* (Cambridge University Press, 1926), I.

Chapter 4

57 The quotation is from Melville's *Omoo* (Constable, 1922).

59 My statement that on an earth covered with water there would be only two major wind belts in each hemisphere disagrees with most authorities, who believe there would be three belts: low-latitude easterlies (trade winds), middle-latitude westerlies, and high-latitude (polar) easterlies. I believe there would be no polar easterlies of any consequence. The fundamental question is whether a dynamic HIGH could be maintained in the polar areas without the enormous radiational cooling that takes place over the snow and icecap regions of Baffinland, Greenland, and Antarctica. I believe that without such land effects the polar HIGHS and the accompanying polar easterlies that are actually observed would be wholly insignificant or nonexistent.

Page

61 My values for wave heights are from Vaughan Cornish, *Ocean Waves and Kindred Geophysical Phenomena* (Cambridge University Press, 1934), and from H. U. Sverdrup, Martin W. Johnson, and Richard H. Fleming, *The Oceans* (Prentice-Hall, 1942). As regards the rise and decline of Charleston as a major port, I have followed L. Rodwell Jones and P. W. Bryan, *North America* (Methuen, 1950).

63 The famous loop hurricane of 1910 is described by Ivan Ray Tannehill, *Hurricanes* (Princeton University Press, 1952). My description of the effect of the typhoon upon Halsey's fleet is based upon the account given me by Robert S. Ingram, who was the aerologist aboard the U.S.S. *Rudyard Bay* (CVE–81) during the storm.

64 The account of the typhoon strike upon Jaluit atoll is from my own observations and those of members of the field party of which I was a member. See David I. Blumenstock, "Typhoon Effects at Jaluit Atoll in the Marshall Islands," *Nature*, CLXXXII (1958), 1267–69.

66–67 The damage and loss figures for the New England hurricane of 1938 are from Tannehill, *Hurricanes*. Tannehill also states that as many as 300,000 may have perished in the Hooghly storm surge of 1737. So far as I have been able to determine, the only natural disasters that produced greater loss of life were the earthquake in Shensi, China, in 1556 and the flood on the Hwang Ho in 1887. The Calcutta earthquake of 1737 may have produced about the same number of deaths as the Hooghly storm.

69 My description of the growth habit of vegetation on Marin Peninsula is based chiefly on Robert W. Richardson, "Summer Air Transport Along the Coast of Central California," 1943 (MS. on file, University of California Library, Berkeley).

72 The quotation by Conrad is from *Lord Jim* (Random House, 1931).

73 My description of the monsoon flow and of forecasting its onset is greatly generalized. The flow is not perfectly uniform, but involves eddies, surges, and other variations in detail. And the relation between surface air pressures and the onset of the monsoon is far from simple, as is noted by Sir Charles Normand, "Monsoon Seasonal Forecasting," *Quarterly Journal of the Royal Meteorological Society*, LXXIX (1953), 463–73.

Chapter 5

Page

76 The quotations and information concerning the winds of Seistan are from the article by Colonel Sir Henry McMahon, *Geographical Journal*, XXVIII (1906), 209–28.

81 Margaret Bourke-White's description is from her article in *The Nation*, May 22, 1935.

82–85 The definition of smog according to California law and the description of the smog situation in the New York area are from a series of articles in *The New York Times* during the period November 16–23, 1953. In discussing the chemistry of smog formation, I have relied chiefly on A. J. Haagen-Smit, "The Control of Air Pollution in Los Angeles," *Engineering and Science*, XVIII (1954), 11–16.

86 Sir Samuel Baker's description of the winds in Ceylon is from his *Eight Years' Wanderings in Ceylon* (Longman, Brown, Green, and Longmans, 1855). I was led to this book through the discussion by William Marriott, "Report on the Helm Wind Inquiry," *Quarterly Journal of the Royal Meteorological Society*, XV (1889), 103–16; and I have relied greatly upon Marriott in my own discussion of this kind of wind situation.

88 A discussion of the extreme winds on Mount Washington is given by Salvatore Pagliuca, "The Strongest Wind Ever Measured," *Appalachia*, XX (1934), 150–51.

89 Will Keller's description of the Kansas tornado is from Alonzo A. Justice, "Seeing the Inside of a Tornado," *Monthly Weather Review*, LVIII, 5 (1939), 205–6. I was led to this article by Snowden D. Flora, *Tornadoes* (University of Oklahoma Press, 1953).

The examples of freak occurrences during tornadoes are from Flora, *Tornadoes;* from the tornado article in the U.S. Yearbook of Agriculture, 1930; and from James P. Espy, *Philosophy of Storms* (Little & Brown, 1841).

92 The tornado frequency values for different parts of the United States are from Flora, *Tornadoes*. Probably the true frequencies are even higher, for many tornadoes are so short-lived or cause so little damage (as over croplands) that they are not reported, and others occur in uninhabited areas and so are not observed.

Chapter 6

Page

97 The wonderful nature of financial accounting sheets was suggested to me by A. A. Milne's essay, "Certain Financial Matters," *By Way of Introduction* (Dutton, 1929).

99 My description of the Vermilion Basin is based on my own memory of it, on the U.S. Geological Survey topographic sheets for the basin, and on the Federal Writers' Project book, *Illinois* (McClurg, 1947). My figures on crops are from John C. Weaver, "Crop-Combination Regions in the Middle West," *Geographical Review*, XLIV (1954), 175–200. My discussion of the water budget in the Vermilion Basin is based on data in Illinois State Water Survey, *Proceedings of the Conference on Water Resources October 1–3, 1951* (Urbana, 1952), and on Illinois State Planning Commission, *Report on the Upper Illinois River Basin in Illinois* (Chicago: State of Illinois, 1939).

102 Pierre Perrault's work appears in part in Kirtley F. Mather and Shirley L. Mason, *A Source Book in Geology* (McGraw-Hill, 1939).

Chapter 7

104 My estimates of the depths of water in a world-wide sea that would be derived from different sources were arrived at as follows:

The depth of water derived from the oceans and adjacent seas and gulfs is based on Erwin Kossinna, "Die Tiefen des Weltmeeres," Berlin University, Institut für Meereskunde, Veröff., N.F., A., *Geogr.-naturwiss.*, Series IX (1921).

For the depth of water tied up in glaciers I have taken the generally accepted value of 180 feet rise in sea level, were all glaciers to melt (see, for example, J. K. Charlesworth, *The Quaternary Era* [Arnold, 1957], II, or Richard Foster Flint, *Glacial Geology and the Pleistocene Epoch* [Wiley, 1949]), and have increased this value to 200 feet on the basis of very recent findings of the great thickness of Antarctic ice (discussions with Harry Wexler). I have then spread this water over an earth of uniform surface.

My estimates for the depths attributable to ground water, on the one hand, and surface waters of the lands, on the other, are fairly crude. They rest on an educated guess, with my reasoning

Page

in this manner. For ground water beneath the lands I took the uppermost thousand feet of the land surface and assumed a mean porosity of 15 per cent and one-third of saturation on the average. For waters on the lands, I took the surface areas of the forty-five largest lakes and inland seas in the world, assumed they had a mean depth of 100 feet, and further assumed that they contained 50–60 per cent of the water upon the lands.

The one-inch depth for atmospheric moisture has become a standard estimate. See, for example, W. J. Humphreys, *Physics of the Air* (McGraw-Hill, 1940).

105 I have followed Shaw, *Manual in Meteorology*, in surmising that it was probably Hutton who invented the wet-bulb thermometer.

107 The Karachi situation of January, 1943, was described to me by my former colleague, Iven Bennett. Mr. Bennett was a weather observer with the AAF Weather Service in Karachi at the time.

110 "A sky without clouds . . ." is from Thoreau's *Journal* (Houghton Mifflin, 1949), IV. The phrases from Aristophanes are from his *Clouds*, and follow the Athenian Society translation (1912). The description of clouds over the tropical ocean is from H. M. Tomlinson, *The Sea and the Jungle* (Duckworth, 1912). The incident of planes flying through the intertropical front near New Guinea during the war is from *Military Uses of Weather Information*, a wartime publication of which I was the senior author.

112 The description of changes in the height of West Coast stratus is chiefly based on Morris Neiburger, "Temperature Changes during Formation and Dissipation of West Coast Stratus," *Journal of Meteorology*, I (1944), 29–41.

114 In preferred locations, fog drip equivalent to ten or twenty inches of rainfall per month is not at all unusual. Twomey gives an extreme value of seven inches of fog drip in slightly less than twenty-four hours. S. Twomey, "The Collection of Cloud Water by a Vertical Mesh Wire," *Bulletin de L'Observatoire du Puy-de Dôme*, III, (1956), 65–70.

115 My discussion of ice-crystal formation in clouds and of other aspects of cloud physics is based on the papers by G. M. B. Dobson, B. J. Mason, and H. Dessens in *Centenary Proceedings of the Royal Meteorological Society 1950*, pp. 34–36, 51–61.

117 Shortly after its inception, I visited the thunderstorm project

Page

at Orlando, Florida. Thus my description is partly based on my own observations. My principal source, however, is Horace R. Byers and Roscoe R. Braham, Jr., *The Thunderstorm* (U.S. Weather Bureau, 1949).

Chapter 8

124 The term Dry World is from Richard Joel Russell and Fred Bowerman Kniffen, *Culture Worlds* (Macmillan, 1951), and I have, for the most part, followed their geographic definition of this area.

125 In my description of the Dry World, I have relied heavily on Carleton S. Coon, *Caravan* (Holt, 1951), and to a somewhat lesser extent on Augustin Bernard, "Sahara-Afrique Occidentale," *Geographie Universelle* (Armand Colin, 1939), XI, and E. F. Gautier, *Sahara.* The quotations are from Coon.

130 There is considerable disagreement over where and when the plants that came to Egypt were first domesticated. I have followed John L. Myres, "Neolithic and Bronze Age Cultures," *The Cambridge Ancient History* (Cambridge University Press, 1923), I, 68 ff.; N. I. Vavilov, *The Origin, Variation, Immunity and Breeding of Cultivated Plants,* tr. K. Starr Chester (Chronica Botanica, XIII, 1949/50); and Carl O. Sauer, *Agricultural Origins and Dispersals* (American Geographical Society, 1952), in stating that domestication occurred at the edges of the forest. On the other hand, my date for entry of agriculture into Egypt is later than some of these gentlemen would say; and in this I follow Coon (personal correspondence). My hypothetical remarks about the coming of civilization in Egypt incorporate some of the points made by Karl A. Wittfogel, "The Hydraulic Civilizations," *Man's Role in Changing the Face of the Earth* (University of Chicago Press, 1956), pp. 152–64.

131 In describing the Amazon Basin on this and the following pages, I have relied to a marked extent upon Tomlinson, *The Sea and the Jungle;* Henry Walter Bates, *The Naturalist on the River Amazon* (Murray, 1892); Professor and Mrs. Louis Agassiz, *A Journey in Brazil* (Houghton Mifflin, 1909); Richard Spruce, *Notes of a Botanist on the Amazon and Andes* (Macmillan, 1908), I, II; P. W. Richards, *The Tropical Rain Forest* (Cambridge University Press, 1952); and Marston Bates, *Where Winter Never Comes* (Scribner, 1952). For the extent of the

Page

tropical rain forest I have followed Lúcio de Castro Soares, *Limites Meridionais e Orientais de Ocorrência da Floresta Amazônica em Território Brasileiro* (Institutu Brasileiro de Geografia e Estatística, 1953), as well as Spruce and Richards.

My statement that the Amazon discharges more water than the Mississippi and Congo combined is based on my own estimate. My value for the Mississippi was from H. K. Barrows, *Floods* (McGraw-Hill, 1948). The Mississippi has an annual discharge of about 170 cubic miles of water. The Congo Basin has a discharge of about 660 cubic miles, assuming a mean annual rainfall throughout the basin of eighty inches (probably too high) and one-third runoff. Thus together, the Mississippi and Congo have an annual discharge that probably does not exceed 830 cubic miles of water. In contrast, if just an eighty-inch mean annual rainfall is assumed for the Amazon—a value that is certainly too low—and if only 30 per cent runoff is assumed, the Amazon total is 900 cubic miles of water per year.

133 The expression "a forest planted upon another forest" is from Alexander von Humboldt and Aimé Bonpland, *Personal Narrative of Travels to the Equinoctial Regions of America during the Years 1799–1804* (George Bell & Sons, 1900), II, 255. The quotation "a greater gap would be made . . ." is from Spruce, *Notes of a Botanist.*

134 Richards, *Tropical Rain Forest,* gives J. Mildbraed as the source of the metaphor that a man in the rain forest is a prisoner upon the forest floor.

135 The description of the Murderer Liana is from Bates, *Naturalist on the Amazon.*

135 The climatic boundaries that I give for the tropical rain forest are generalized and follow a broad interpretation of what constitutes a rain forest. What I did was to rely on Richards, *Tropical Rain Forest,* for the general distribution of the tropical rain forest and then to check against rainfall maps.

136 For my statement on the influence of soils on vegetative formations in New Guinea, I am indebted to Louis Peltier, who was there during the war and who described these razorlike dividing lines to me.

137 My notion of the unobtrusiveness of the natives of the rain forest is after Bates, *Where Winter Never Comes.* As regards stability of the tropical rain forest throughout millions of years, I do not mean to imply that there were not shifts in its size and

Page

location. On the contrary, I am convinced that because of climatic changes the rain-forest areas have not been stable geographically and were at times reduced markedly in area.

Chapter 9

139 My remarks about Robert Horton, for whom I had the greatest admiration, are based on my own memory of him. I knew him only slightly, but the few times I met him made a great impression upon me.

141 The description of the flood on the Kansas River is based on accounts in *The New York Times;* on U.S. Geological Survey, *Kansas-Missouri Floods of July 1951* (Water Supply Paper 1139, 1952); and on U.S. Weather Bureau, *Kansas-Missouri Floods of June–July 1951* (Technical Paper No. 17, 1952).

147 For the anecdote of the Catholic fathers and their mission house I am indebted to C. Warren Thornthwaite.

149 The quotation about the well of Akita is from A. H. Sayce, *Records of the Past* (Samuel Bagster, 1891), V.

150 My statement that the population density of the Pueblo Indians was greater than that of any other cultural group north of the Rio Grande is taken from A. L. Kroeber, "Cultural and Natural Areas of Native North America," *University of California Publications in Archeology and Ethnology*, XXXVIII (1939).

150–51 The brief description of the Gold Rush and the Mormons, including the prices paid for various items, was obtained from Ray Allen Billington, *Westward Expansion* (Macmillan, 1949).

153 The official U.S. Agricultural Census of 1951 is the source of my figures for the extent of western irrigation and for the comparative yields of irrigated versus nonirrigated fields.

154–57 My discussion of the water allocation problems of the Delaware River is largely derived from a series of articles by John M. McCullough in the *Philadelphia Inquirer*, November 30 to December 8, 1952.

157 The statements about the early Boston waterworks are from *The Physical Basis of Water Supply and Its Principal Uses* (U.S. Congress, House of Representatives, Interior and Insular Affairs Committee, 1952).

158 For the comment that Philadelphians have without ill effect long drunk their own sewage water, I am indebted to my former

Page

colleague at Rutgers University, Thurlow C. Nelson. My remarks concerning ground water as against surface water sources of supply for various cities are derived from John R. Borchert, "The Surface Water Supply of American Municipalities," *Annals of the Association of American Geographers*, XLIV (1954), 15–32.

158–61 My remarks regarding early wells are based on C. E. V. Bromehead, "The Early History of Water Supply," *Geographical Journal*, LXXXXIX (1942), 142–51, 183–93, who also cites the Pliny quotation on switching. The quotation from Tompkins is taken from F. W. Robins, *The Story of Water Supply* (Oxford University Press, 1946). In remarking on the signs that indicate the presence of ground water, I have largely followed O. E. Meinzer, *Plants as Indicators of Ground Water* (U.S. Geological Survey *Water Supply Paper* 577, 1927). My comments on ground water largely follow C. F. Tolman, *Ground Water* (McGraw-Hill, 1937), and Harold E. Thomas, *The Conservation of Ground Water* (McGraw-Hill, 1951).

Chapter 10

163 The quotation from Halley is from his paper in *Philosophical Transactions of the Royal Society of London*, XXIX (1714).

164 My division of the atmosphere into four regions follows G. Grimminger, *Analysis of Temperature, Pressure and Density of the Atmosphere Extending to Extreme Altitudes* (Rand Corporation, 1948). This four-region nomenclature is still widely used, but its system is undergoing change. Among the newer terms are *chemosphere*, corresponding to my middle and upper stratosphere and lower ionosphere, and *thermosphere*, corresponding to my ionosphere and lower exosphere. See G. W. Wares, "Model Atmospheres," *Handbook of Geophysics* (USAF, 1957).

164–65 My reasoning in assigning an 18,000-mile height to the atmosphere is stated in the note for p. 4. In describing the general structure and nature of the atmosphere here and in the pages that follow, I have with one exception relied principally on Grimminger, *Analysis;* Sydney Chapman and Julius Bartels, *Geomagnetism* (Oxford, 1940); I. S. K. Mitra, *The Upper Atmosphere* (Asiatic Society, 1952); and Wares, "Model Atmospheres." The exception is in describing the radiation belts. (See

Page

the note for page 167.) For the very high atmosphere I have relied especially on Grimminger, and thus far very high altitude rocket and satellite data indicate that his density and temperature values are of the right order. See I. Harris and R. Jastrow, "An Interim Atmosphere Derived from Rocket and Satellite Data," *Planetary Space Science*, I (1959), 20–26, and G. F. Schilling and T. E. Sterne, "Densities and Temperatures of the Upper Atmosphere Inferred from Satellite Observations," *Journal of Geophysical Research*, LXIV (1959), 1–4.

166 My statement of the number of particles striking a square-inch surface at sea level and at the top of the ionosphere follows my own calculations, based on normal sea-level densities and temperatures and on Grimminger's temperature and density estimates for his Model II atmosphere at the height at which he assumes the atmospheric particles can be considered as free-moving bodies in a gravitational field.

167 The statement that Sputnik II encountered only one-third ounce of air in a single revolution is derived by direct computation from H. S. W. Massey and R. L. F. Boyd, "Scientific Observations of the Artificial Earth Satellites and Their Analysis," *Nature*, CLXXXI (January 11, 1958), 78–80. My discussion of the radiation belts is based largely on James A. Van Allen, Carl E. McIlwain, and George H. Ludwig, "Radiation Observations with Satellite 1958ε," *Journal of Geophysical Research*, LXIV (1959), 271–86, and on James A. Van Allen, "Radiation Belts around the Earth," *Scientific American*, CC, No. 3 (1959), 39–47.

168 I have relied chiefly on F. L. Whipple, in U.S. School of Aviation Medicine, *Physics and Medicine of the Upper Atmosphere* (University of New Mexico Press, 1952), in my discussion of meteors and meteorites. It is possible, however, that the danger of a meteor strike upon a space ship may not be quite as great as is generally thought. This is indicated by G. F. Schilling, "Soviet Orbit Information for Satellites 1957α2 and β1," *Smithsonian Contributions to Astrophysics*, II (1958), 281–84.

169 Lindemann and Dobson's theory is given in their paper, "A Theory of Meteors, and the Density and Temperature of the Outer Atmosphere to Which It Leads," *Proceedings of the Royal Society*, CII (1922), 411–37.

171 My discussion of the earth's magnetic field is based chiefly on J. A. Fleming, "Terrestrial Magnetism and Electricity," *Physics*

Page

of the Earth (McGraw-Hill, 1939), and on Chapman and Bartels, *Geomagnetism.*

175 Two general papers have served me especially well in providing the major bases of my remarks on cosmic rays. These are Serge A. Korff, "The Origin and Implications of Cosmic Rays," *American Scientist*, XLV (1957), 281–300, and J. A. Simpson, "The Cosmic Radiation and Solar-Terrestrial Relationships," *Annales de Géophysique*, XI (1955), 305–29. My statement that a man as energetic as a cosmic ray, mass for mass, could lift the earth a mile follows proportionally from the statement in Korff, "Cosmic Rays," that a proton as energetic as a cosmic ray could lift one kilogram one meter.

Chapter 11

182–84 My account of the early history of weather observations follows Shaw, *Manual in Meteorology*, quite closely.

184 The quotation from William Dampier is from *A New Voyage around the World* (James Knapton, 1703).

187 Toricelli's statement about the *horror vacui* is from Martha Ornstein, *Rôle of Scientific Societies in the Seventeenth Century* (University of Chicago Press, 1938), p. 33.

189 The statement that "the anemometer did not take to the seas" is correct historically, but much more recently anemometers have been installed on some ships. For example, when the Russian oceanographic vessel *Vityaz* put into Honolulu early in 1959, I noticed on going aboard that she had two anemometers, one on the port and one on the starboard side. We were told by the meteorologist that between them these anemometers gave a reasonable estimate of wind conditions, whether the ship was barely making headway, as at an oceanographic observation point, or whether she was well under way. In the latter instance, of course, great allowance had to be made for the ship's speed.

190 The quotations regarding the Beaufort scale are after Shaw, *Manual in Meteorology*.

192 In describing the automatic weather station in the Coral Sea during the war, I am relying on my own memory of the matter. I was stationed in New Caledonia at the time (1944), and we used reports from this station regularly.

195 The description of Alexander Wilson's kite experiments is

Page

based on Patrick Wilson, "Biographical Account of Alexander Wilson, M.D., Late Professor of Practical Astronomy in Glasgow," *Transactions of the Royal Society of Edinburgh*, X (1826), 279–97.

196 Benjamin Franklin's letter to Peter Collinson of October 1, 1752, appeared in the *Transactions of the Royal Society of London*.

200 In my discussion of observations from rockets and satellites I have relied chiefly on L. V. Berkner (ed.), "Manual on Rockets and Satellites," *Annals of the International Geophysical Year*, VI (1958).

The reference to the release of aluminum confetti to measure winds is from a note in *Science*, CXXVII (1958), 1037.

CHAPTER 12

210 The "Jones" anecdote is true. He himself told me about it, and later a fellow forecaster verified it.

212–16 The anecdotes of the Funafuti forecast and the forecast at the Massachusetts Institute of Technology follow my own memory of the matters, since in both instances I was present.

217 L. F. Richardson's classic study was his *Weather Prediction by Numerical Process* (Cambridge University Press, 1922).

223 The quotations from Namias are from his "General Aspects of Extended-Range Forecasting," *Compendium of Meteorology* (American Meteorological Society, 1951).

225 Regarding the Multanowski forecasting scheme, a recent comment indicates that while some success was achieved, the level has remained low: "In spite of persistent and painstaking work . . . the quality of long range weather forecasting remains, unfortunately, low and for the last ten years it has not notably improved." Ivan Grigor'evich Pchelko, "Twenty Years of Scientific Research Work of the Institute in the Field of Exploration of Methods of Short-and-Long Range Weather Forecasting," *Trudy Tsentral'nogo Instituta Prognozov*, LV (1957), 12–22 (tr. U.S. Joint Publications Research Service).

226 My description of the D-day forecast is based on the accounts given me by two of the participating forecasters.

Chapter 13

Page

229 Richard Foster Flint, *Glacial Geology and the Pleistocene Epoch* (Wiley, 1949), gives 32 per cent as the maximum proportion of the lands covered by glaciation. There is wide variation in the estimates of rise of sea level since the peak of the last widespread glaciation; but 100 meters, or around 300 feet, seems to be the general consensus. J. K. Charlesworth, *The Quaternary Era* (Arnold, 1957), II; C. E. P. Brooks, *Climate Through the Ages* (McGraw-Hill, 1949); Frederick E. Zeuner, *The Pleistocene Period* (Ray Society, 1945). For the rise in sea level that would be produced by melting of the present glaciers, see the note for p. 104.

231 The chronology follows Cesare Emiliani, "Pleistocene Temperatures," *Journal of Geology*, LXIII (1955), 538–78. Emiliani's chronology is not generally accepted, but then neither is any other so far as I know. I have followed Emiliani's because I believe it has a better physical basis than others.

231–32 The idea of comparing a geologic period with a calendar year is derived from Richard Joel Russell, "Climatic Change through the Ages," in *Climate and Man*, pp. 67–97. Russell, however, applied this idea to the entire geologic period, not just the Pleistocene.

232 My statement that the Tertiary lasted fifty to one hundred million years is after Charlesworth, *Quaternary Era*.

234 The quotation from C. E. P. Brooks is from his *Climate Through the Ages* (McGraw-Hill, 1949), p. 296. I have, however, inserted modified dates in this quotation (shown in brackets) to bring the dates more in line with the chronology that I follow.

236–37 The discussion of radioactive dating is based largely on J. Laurence Kulp, "Geological Chronometry by Radioactive Methods," *Advances in Geophysics* (Academic Press, 1955), II, 179–219.

238 The C-14 dates are from H. de Vries and H. T. Waterbolk, "Groningen Radiocarbon Dates III," *Science*, CXXVIII (1958), 1550–56. Kulp is my authority for stating that glacial ice was still in Wisconsin 11,000 years ago.

239–40 My discussion of chemical thermometers is based on Harold C. Urey, "The Measurement of Paleotemperatures," *Proceedings of the Conference on Nuclear Processes in Geologic Settings* (1953), pp. 71–72, and on Emiliani, "Pleistocene Temperatures."

Page

240 The Ewing-Donn theory is presented in Maurice Ewing and William L. Donn, "A Theory of the Ice Ages," *Science*, CXXIII (1956), 1061–66, and in "A Theory of Ice Ages II," *Science*, CXXVII (1958), 1159–62.

241 The Charlesworth quotation is from his *Quarternary Era.*

241 The discussion of the early work on solar-weather relations is partly based on Walter Orr Roberts, "Does Solar Activity Affect the Weather?" *Proceedings of the American Petroleum Institute*, Parts 6/7 (1956), 76–81.

242 The sunspot observed on February 7, 1946, is described by Harlan True Stetson, *Sunspots in Action* (Ronald, 1947).

243 The work by Harry Wexler that is specifically discussed is his paper, "Radiation Balance of the Earth as a Factor in Climatic Change," *Climatic Change* (Harvard University Press, 1953), pp. 73–106.

244 Solar activity may trigger warming of the kind observed over Berlin, but cannot produce it directly. This point is discussed by Sidney Teweles, "Anomalous Warming of the Stratosphere over North America in Early 1957," *Monthly Weather Review*, LXXXVI (1958), 377–96. Roberts also discusses this point in "Does Solar Activity Affect the Weather?" He states: ". . . temperature effects over large areas of the earth are controlled by the fluctuations of the large-scale circulation of the atmosphere, and not by brute-force heating effects."

Chapter 14

247–49 My account of General Dyrenforth's experiments at San Antonio is based on reports in the New Orleans *Picayune*, November 25–December 2, 1892. The quotation on Dyrenforth's experiments is in S. Newcomb, "Government Rain-making," *The Nation*, LIII (1891), 309–10.

The quotations from the witnesses' testimony are from the report of the Subcommittee on Weather Control and Augmented Potable Water Supply, Committee on Interior and Insular Affairs, U.S. Senate, 82nd Congress, March, 1951.

251 The committee appointed to study modern rain making was titled the Advisory Committee on Weather Control. Vannevar Bush's statement appears in *Final Report of the Advisory Committee on Weather Control* (Report to the President of the U.S., December 31, 1957), II, 289. The point that from an energy view-

Page

point it is and almost certainly always will be impractical to make it rain or otherwise alter the climate to any significant extent has been made by a great many scientists, including R. C. Sutcliffe, "Water Balance and the General Circulation of the Atmosphere," *Quarterly Journal of the Royal Meteorological Society*, LXXXII (1956), and Charles Galton Darwin, *The Next Million Years* (Doubleday, 1953).

CHAPTER 15

259 The quotation about the sensitivity of mammals to temperature changes is from Anton J. Carlson and Victor Johnson, *The Machinery of the Body* (University of Chicago Press, 1944). In my discussion of the physiology of heat control I have relied especially on Carlson and Johnson, and on Richard Day, *The Effect of Cold on Man* (Josiah Macy Jr. Foundation, 1943).

261 My figure of 1,200 hospitalized in two months on Attu for cold injury is from a letter sent to me by the Office of the Surgeon General, January 5, 1955. The same letter stated that there was no official follow-up information whether there had been any amputations.

262 The quoted account of Blagden's experiment is from Douglas H. K. Lee, *Physiological Climatology* (Class Notes, Johns Hopkins University, 1948). My description of the desert experiments is from E. F. Adolph, *Physiology of Man in the Desert* (Interscience Publications, 1947).

264 I have simplified matters somewhat in referring to comfort in terms of a range in temperature (68°–83°) and, separately, a range in relative humidity (70–40 per cent). In practice the two must be coupled. Thus from a comfort viewpoint 68° at 70 per cent is equivalent to 72° at 40 per cent relative humidity, and 75° at 70 per cent is equivalent to 78° at 40 per cent. These kinds of relations have been worked out in detail and made available in standard guides issued by the American Society of Heating and Ventilating Engineers (*ASHVE Guides*).

The magnitude of the effect of wind upon comfort is evident from the fact that when the relative humidity is 90 per cent and there is a very light wind (about 2 m.p.h.), a temperature of 84° is equivalent in comfort terms to a temperature of 79° with no wind. C. P. Mom, "Determination of the Influence of

Page

Air Velocity on the Feeling of Comfort of Man," *Chronica Naturae*, CIII (1947), 147–64.

264 The study by Ellsworth Huntington is *Civilization and Climate* (Yale University Press, 1915), pp. 144 ff.

266 My remarks on Carlos Monge refer to his *Acclimatization in the Andes* (Johns Hopkins Press, 1948).

269 The studies of the effects of exposure upon the incidence of common colds were reported in *Time*, LIV (1949), 99.

270 The adverse effect upon the ill of sudden changes in the weather is well documented by William F. Petersen, *The Patient and the Weather* (Edwards Bros., 1936).

Chapter 16

273 My description of the corn crop and its progress in relation to the weather is based on the actual weather and crop conditions in eastern Nebraska in 1945. It is, however, a generalized example in that it represents the typical (composite) sequence of events during that year rather than the sequence on one particular farm.

275 I am indebted to J. C. Ellickson of the U.S. Department of Agriculture for the example of the twenty-four-bushel yield of spring wheat with virtually no rain after planting.

285 The episode of the professor who recommended turning the eroded canyon into a national monument occurred in 1938, when I was with the Soil Conservation Service.

288 The yield figures for the intensive production of vegetables by means of artificial heating are cited in David B. Greenberg and Charles Corbin, *So You're Going to Buy a Farm* (Greenberg, 1944).

289 For much of the information on weather and cranberry culture I am indebted to Philleo Nash, a Wisconsin cranberry grower.

Chapter 17

296 The description of the Tillamook fire is based on Stewart H. Holbrook, *Burning an Empire* (Macmillan, 1943).

299 In describing some of the difficulties encountered in building the Alcan Highway, I have relied largely on Herbert C. Lanks, *Highway to Alaska* (Appleton-Century, 1944).

300 Tomlinson, *The Sea and the Jungle*, is the source of the quota-

Page

tion regarding the building of the railroad around the rapids of the Madeira River and also of my information on this subject.

306–8 The information on the Smith-Putnam turbine follows Palmer Crosslett Putnam, *Power from the Wind* (Van Nostrand, 1948).

309–10 The quotation from Eugene Ayres and Charles A. Scarlott is from their book, *Energy Sources: The Wealth of the World* (McGraw-Hill, 1952). In my discussion of solar energy as a power source I have relied chiefly on this work and on the series of papers that appeared in the *Transactions of the Conference on the Use of Solar Energy*, Tucson, 1955 (University of Arizona, 1958), I–V.

312 The statement concerning the amount of energy required to heat homes is from Eugene Ayres, "Power from the Sun," *Scientific American*, CLXXXIII, No. 2 (1950), 16–21.

Chapter 18

321 The quotation from Herodotus is from George Rawlinson (tr.), *The History of Herodotus* (Appleton, 1885).

321–22 The quotation from General Dwight D. Eisenhower is from *Crusade in Europe* (Doubleday, 1948). Ernie Pyle's statement is from his *Brave Men* (Holt, 1944).

326 Napoleon's remark about the desert as an obstacle is from Conrad H. Lanze (tr.), *Napoleon and Modern War* (Military Services Publishing Co., 1943).

329 Churchill's words regarding the wide range of activities that are involved in waging war will be found in *Their Finest Hour* (Houghton Mifflin, 1949), p. 18. The use of ice bridges by the Russian engineers is one of several highly specialized techniques developed during the last war to cope with particular weather circumstances. The practice is among those mentioned briefly in the wartime manual, *Military Uses of Weather Information.*

330–32 My account of Operations Overlord and Coronet, including the quotations, are from W. C. Jacobs, "Wartime Developments in Applied Climatology," *Meteorological Monographs* (American Meteorological Society, 1947), I.

334 The quotation from Warren Amster is from "Design for Deterrence," *Bulletin of the Atomic Scientists,* XII, No. 5 (1956), 164–65.

337 Baldwin's statement concerning the intercontinental ballistic

Page

missile is from "The New Face of War," *Bulletin of the Atomic Scientists*, XII, No. 5 (May, 1956), 153–58.

338 The words by General D. N. Yates are from a speech delivered at an Industrial Luncheon of the American Meteorological Society in New York, March 21, 1946.

342–46 My description of the organization of the Soviet weather service is based on an account given me by a former member of that organization. The Troitsky Plan was a subject of discussion in the Pentagon in Washington during 1943, shortly after Colonel Pagava and other Soviet meteorologists visited the United States. Much more recently, a former Soviet meteorologist verified Phases I and II of this plan. This individual could not, however, verify Phase III, perhaps because he was not stationed in Moscow, where it is said to have been carried out.

Chapter 19

347 My account of *Lucky Dragon* is based on Jack Schubert and Ralph E. Lapp, *Radiation: What It Is and How It Affects You* (Viking, 1957).

348–49 The remarks by Murray are from Ralph E. Lapp, "Radioactive Fall-out III," *Bulletin of the Atomic Scientists*, XI, No. 6 (June, 1955). General Gavin's testimony is from a dispatch from Washington by Rowland Evans, Jr., who was reporting on hearings before a special Senate subcommittee investigating air power. See also James M. Gavin, *War and Peace in the Space Age: A New Approach* (Harper, 1958).

349 The Mogens Westergaard quotation is from his article, "Man's Responsibility to His Genetic Heritage," in *Bulletin of the Atomic Scientists*, XI, No. 9 (1955). The blast and flash-burn areas for a 20-megaton bomb are based on the figures for the Hiroshima bomb, applying the cube-root and square-root laws.

353 The krypton-90 chain is after Edward Teller and Mary Langs Argo, "Nucleus," *Encyclopaedia Britannica*, XVI (1956). The molybdenum-99 chain is after Samuel Glasstone, *Sourcebook on Atomic Energy* (Van Nostrand, 1950).

355 The passage by Robert F. Bacher is from his article, "The Hydrogen Bomb: III," *Scientific American*, CLXXXII, No. 5 (1950).

356 My remarks about C-14 are based on O. I. Leipunsky, "The Radiation Hazards of Explosions of Pure Hydrogen and Ordi-

Page

nary Atomic Bombs" (undated translation from the Russian, mimeographed), and on John R. Totter, M. R. Zelle, and H. Hollister, "Hazard to Man of Carbon-14," *Science*, CXXVIII (1958), 1490–95.

357 In my discussion of bomb sizes, the reference to Libby is to the U.S. Atomic Energy Commission, mimeographed press release, June 3, 1955, 9:30 P.M.

360 The publication *Meteorology and Atomic Energy* was issued by the Atomic Energy Commission, dated 1955.

360–64 My analysis of the effects of a fifty-bomb attack on the evening of July 21, 1953, is based on my own analysis, using wind data from the *Northern Hemisphere Map Series* (U.S. Weather Bureau) and applying the vector technique given in *Meteorology and Atomic Energy*. I assumed a particle density of 3 and a range in particle size of from 50 to 150 microns. Winds were used from five heights: 500 meters, 2 km., 4 km., 6 km., and 8 km. Population densities in the afflicted areas were estimated from the 1950 U.S. Census values. Fallout patterns were plotted on a map (scale of 1:5,000,000) and the individual fallout areas were estimated to the closest 500 sq. mi.

368 My discussion of the protection afforded by shelters is chiefly based on Ralph E. Lapp, "Radioactive Fall-out," *Bulletin of the Atomic Scientists*, XI, No. 2 (1955), 45–51.

370 My statements about winds over the Soviet Union are based on my own analyses of data from the *Northern Hemisphere Map Series* and from various papers by Russian meteorologists (summarized in English for me by Olga Ph. Prozorowski). See, for example, David I. Blumenstock and Olga Ph. Prozorowski, *Synoptic Climatology of the Moscow Basin* (USAF, Cambridge Research Center, 1956), and Kh. Pogosjan and E. I. Savchenkova, "The Quantitative Representation of an Atmospheric Circulation Type," *Meteorologiia i Gidrologiia*, III (November, 1950), 5–13.

372–73 The quotations concerning AEC estimates of strontium-90 in the atmosphere are from Schubert and Lapp, *Radiation*, and the discussion that follows is chiefly from this source, including the statement by Merrill Eisenbud.

375 The quotations on cancer are from Paul E. Steiner, "The Nature of Cancer," *Canadian Cancer Conference* (Academic Press, 1955), I, 74–90, and Jacob Furth, "Problems of Carcinogenesis in Relation to Ionizing Irradiations," *ibid.*, I, 404–418.

Page

377 The number of chromosomes in man may range from forty-six to forty-nine. See, for example, C. E. Ford and J. L. Hamerton, "The Chromosomes of Man," *Nature*, CLXXVIII (1956), 1020–23.

378 Eye color does not strictly follow the simple genetic rule, with brown dominant and blue recessive. If it did, two blue-eyed parents could not produce a brown-eyed child; yet they sometimes do.

379 In my discussion of the genetic effects of radiation, I have relied to a large extent on the report, "Genetic Effects of Atomic Radiation," *The Biological Effects of Atomic Radiation* (National Academy of Sciences, 1956).

381 The quotation from H. J. Muller is from his article, "Race Poisoning by Radiation," *Saturday Review*, XXXIX (1956).

383 The strontium-90 values for concentrations on the ground as of December, 1957, are from L. Machta and R. J. List, "Meteorological Interpretation of Sr^{90} Fallout," *Environmental Contamination from Weapon Tests* (U.S. Atomic Energy Commission, October, 1958).

387 Machta's statement about the uncertainty of predicting winds that spread nuclear debris is from his paper, "Discussion of Meteorological Factors and Fallout Distribution," in *Environmental Contamination.* The quotation from Spohn is in "Meteorological Problems in Estimating Radioactive Dispersion and Fallout," *Bulletin of the American Meteorological Society*, XXXIX (1958), 152–53.

389 The statement by Sir Winston Churchill is from *Bulletin of the Atomic Scientists*, XI, No. 2 (1955).

Chapter 20

392 My discussion of the introduction of the camel follows the viewpoint of Carleton S. Coon, *The Story of Man* (Knopf, 1954), also personal correspondence.

394–95 The quotation about Magellan is from Antonio Pigafetta, *Magellan's Voyage Around the World* (A. H. Clark, 1906); that about Washington's army is from George Bancroft, *History of the United States* (Little, Brown, 1875), IX.

396 Pope Urban's address is from Frederic Austin Ogg, *A Source Book of Mediaeval History* (American Book, 1907).

397–99 The quotation by Carleton Stevens Coon and my discussion

Page

of his ideas on race and climate are from his "Climate and Race," in *Climatic Change*. Coon's ideas on climate and skin color, at least in general, accord with the views of many other physical anthropologists. As for his thoughts on climate as related to body weight and the shape of extremities, I have not seen views of this kind expressed by any other anthropologist; and I have been told that most would disagree with them.

400 Some anthropologists believe that the forebears of man may not have lived in trees at all, but rather may have dwelt along the edges of the grasslands.

401 Coon's point about the easy life of the ape creatures who were man's forebears is from his *Story of Man.*

403–4 My discussion of ancient man in northwestern Europe toward the end of the Pleistocene is based chiefly on V. Gordon Childe, *Prehistoric Migrations in Europe* (Aschehoug, 1950), and on J. G. D. Clark, *Prehistoric Europe* (Methuen, 1952). The quotations are from Childe.

405–6 For a brief comment on the controversial nature of the question of time and place of plant domestication, see my note for p. 130. The reference to Carl O. Sauer is to his *Agricultural Origins.*

407 The quotation regarding the farmer and weather is from Samuel Eliot Morison and Henry Steele Commager, *The Growth of the American Republic* (Oxford University Press, 1930).

408–9 Ellsworth Huntington's viewpoint on climate and migration is best expressed in his book, *The Pulse of Asia* (Houghton Mifflin, 1907). The quotation about migrations into the Mediterranean area is from John L. Myres, *Geographical History in Greek Lands* (Oxford University Press, 1953). James Westfall Thompson's remarks are from *An Economic and Social History of the Middle Ages* (Century, 1928).

411–12 The Huntington quotation is from his *Pulse of Asia.*

414 Myres's phrase is from his *Geographical History.*

415 The quotation about the Great Plains is from Walter Prescott Webb, *The Great Frontier* (Houghton Mifflin, 1952).

Illustrations

38 The hot desert areas follow Koeppen, in somewhat generalized form. W. Koeppen, *Grundriss der Klimakunde* (De Gruyter, 1931).

Page

71 The arrows showing the general flow of monsoon winds are based on the wind-constancy arrows in Willard F. McDonald, *Atlas of Climatic Charts of the Oceans* (U.S. Weather Bureau, 1938).

126 The boundary of the Dry World as shown in this figure is adapted from that shown by Richard Joel Russell and Fred Bowerman Kniffen, *Culture Worlds* (Macmillan, 1951).

277 The generalized crop distribution for the Ganges-Indus plains area is based on information in L. Dudley Stamp, *Asia* (Methuen, 1952).

299 The underdeveloped lands are drawn to show the areas that are virtually uninhabited (roughly less than one person for each five square miles). Only the larger blocks of uninhabited lands are shown, however, and small population inclusions, as along the Amazon River or in oases of the Sahara, are not distinguished from the surrounding uninhabited region.

362 See the note, above, for pp. 360–64, for an explanation of how the fallout patterns were arrived at.

374 The strontium-90 curve is from Machta and List, "Meteorological Interpretation of Sr^{90} Fallout."

Index